THAMES BRIDGES

By the same author
The United Kingdom Patent System: A brief history (Havant: Kenneth Mason, 1979)
James Watt and the Patent System (London: The British Library, 1989)
Days of Steam: Two generations of railway photography (Sparkford: Patrick Stephens, 1991)

United Kingdom Copyright & Design Protection: A brief history (Emsworth: Kenneth Mason, 1993)
Classic Steam: A family railway album (Wadenhoe: Silver Link, 1995; reprinted as *The Heritage of Steam*, Great Addington: Silver Link, 2002)

THAMES BRIDGES

From Dartford to the source

A survey of every public river crossing,
past and present

NEIL DAVENPORT

Silver Link Publishing Ltd

I dedicate this book to
Brian Coe,
photographer, scientist and lecturer;
author of books on cameras, the history of photography,
and stained glass in England;
Curator of the Kodak Museum
when at the Kodak Works, Wealdstone;
and an excellent friend

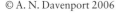

Half title Tower Bridge, 21 January 1969.
Title page London Bridge on 21 January 1969, during the transition from the 1831 and 1973 bridges.
Right The bridges at Godstow. *Hall*
Opposite page The original rustic upper footbridge at Upper Mill Farm, 13 May 1974.

First published in 2006

The right of Arthur Neil Davenport to be identified as the author of this work has been asserted in accordance with sections 77 and 78 of the Copyright, Designs and Patents Act 1988.

British Library Cataloguing in Publication Data
A catalogue record for this book is available from the British Library.

ISBN 1 85794 229 9
ISBN 978 1 85794 229 3

Silver Link Publishing Ltd
The Trundle
Ringstead Road
Great Addington
Kettering
Northants NN14 4BW

Tel/Fax: 01536 330588
email: sales@nostalgiacollection.com
Website: www.nostalgiacollection.com

Printed and bound in Great Britain

All photographs are by the author or from the author's collection.
Other illustrations are credited as follows:
'Dalton': *The New and Complete English Traveller* by W. H. Dalton (1794)
'Dredge': *Thames Bridges from the Tower to the Source* by J. Dredge (1896-98)
'Hall': *Book of the Thames* by Mr & Mrs S. C. Hall (1886)
'Ireland': *Picturesque Views on the River Thames* by S. Ireland (1792)
'Leyland': *The Thames Illustrated* by J. Leyland (1897)
'Murray': *Picturesque Tour of the River Thames* by J. F. Murray (1845)
'Elmes (Shepherd)': *Metropolitan Improvements* (1830), with drawings by Thomas Shepherd
'Tombleson': *The Thames and Medway* (1865)

CONTENTS

PREFACE

This book has a long history. It was on Boxing Day 1964, a day of brilliant winter sunshine, that I took my first pictures of Thames bridges. The one of Richmond Bridge (reproduced on page 91) gave me most pleasure and engendered the idea of photographing all the bridges across the river. I started on this pleasant and never-ending task in 1967, and also began collecting books about the Thames, and early illustrations of its bridges.

One day I was taken by Brian Coe, a Kodak colleague and friend, to the antiquarian book and print dealer Stanley Crowe. He thought he had a copy of an illustrated complete Thames bridges book lurking somewhere in his unusual premises, the basement of a bombed building near the crossing of New Oxford and Bloomsbury Streets. Sadly, he never found it. In the summer of 1975 I obtained a reader's ticket for the British Library Reading Room (then in the British Museum), and, with help, established that the book could only have been James Dredge's *Thames Bridges – from the Tower to the Source*. This work had been published, in parts, in the years 1896-98 by the Journal *Engineering*, of which Dredge was editor. There was an evident need for a new book of similar scope, and I decided to use my growing collection of pictures and information as the basis for one.

I started research, initially by making notes from Dredge, and by 1977 had written more than half the projected book. I then tried for several years, without success, to find a publisher. It later transpired that two publishers I had approached as seeming likely to be interested in producing Thames bridge books had been in the process of doing just that. In 1981 David & Charles published *Thames Crossings*, by Geoffrey Phillips, which became a standard work; and in 1983 Blandford Press published *Bridges over the Thames*, by Ruth and Jonathan Mindell, which, with its colour illustrations, was an attractive addition to the literature. Following the appearance of Phillips's book, I stopped work on mine and wrote books on intellectual property and railways instead. The last of these appeared in 1995.

After a five-year rest from writing, my unease at discontinuing a project on which I and many kind helpers had expended so much effort, and about which my friends, including the vital Arna Davis, had heard so much, led me to resume work. By then, a number of new Thames bridges had been built and there was a greater need for a further book. After surprisingly large amounts of additional effort and help, and the good fortune of being able to interest Silver Link Publishing (publisher of my second railway book) in the present work, I enjoy the satisfaction of seeing the book in print. I hope it pleases my fellow Thames enthusiasts.

1. INTRODUCTION

The River Thames

The Thames is the longest river wholly in England. The word 'wholly' is needed because the Severn is 5 miles longer overall, but more than 5 miles of its course lies in Wales.

It is 215 miles from the source of the Thames in Gloucestershire to the Nore, at the entrance to the Thames Estuary. The Source, dry for most of the year, is in Trewsbury Mead, at Thames Head, 3½ miles south-west of Cirencester. For many years it was argued that the true source was not there but at Seven Springs, 3 miles south of Cheltenham, and, accordingly, that the River Churn constitutes the upper reaches of the Thames. The attractions of this argument were that it made the Thames a longer river and provided it with a source higher above sea level. However, the junction of the two rivers, just north of Cricklade, does not support this theory. The river flowing from the south-west is clearly more important than that arriving from the north, and there is no case for challenging the accuracy of historians and map-makers.

On its journey from the Source to the North Sea, the Thames now flows through or beside the counties of Gloucestershire, Wiltshire, Oxfordshire, West Berkshire, Buckinghamshire, Surrey, Kent and Essex; the unitary authorities of Swindon, Reading, Wokingham and Windsor & Maidenhead; Greater London; and the City of London. In the course of that journey it passes through Cricklade, Lechlade, Oxford, Abingdon, Wallingford, Reading, Henley, Marlow, Maidenhead, Windsor, Staines, Kingston and Richmond.

There used to be fewer main administrative areas bordering the Thames. Before the administrative County of London was formed on 1 April 1889 by the Local Government Act, 1888 (51 & 52 Victoria, c. 41), the river flowed through London between Essex, the City of London and Middlesex to the north, and between Kent and Surrey to the south. Thereafter it flowed through the London County Council area between Metropolitan Boroughs formed by the London Government Act, 1899 (62 & 63 Victoria, c. 14), and later through Greater London between London Boroughs formed by the London Government Act 1963 (c. 33). Outside London, boundary changes resulted from the passing of the Local Government Act 1972 (c. 70), which created Metropolitan and Non-Metropolitan County and District Councils. A big change affecting the Thames was the transfer to Oxfordshire of the Berkshire territory, which extended to north of Oxford. Later big changes resulted from the formation of the unitary authorities noted above, using powers obtained under provisions of the Local Government Act 1992 (c. 19).

It has been suggested by the famous Thames photographer and author Henry Taunt (1842-1922), and other writers, that the river was once navigable as far upstream as Waterhay Bridge, just below the village of Ashton Keynes in Wiltshire. However, there seems to be no documentary support for this suggestion and it is safer to consider Cricklade as the former upper limit. The present-day limit for holiday cruising is at Inglesham, a little above Lechlade, near the entrance to the former Thames & Severn Canal.

The Thames bridges

At the beginning of the 18th century there were only 17 road bridges across the Thames from Old London Bridge to St John's Bridge, Lechlade; these were all mediaeval because none had been built in the 16th and 17th centuries.

In the year 1700 Old London Bridge, with its 19 stone arches and single navigation opening, still had buildings at each side. There were

eight more bridges of stone, these being (in upstream order) at Wallingford, Abingdon, Oxford (Folly and Osney Bridges), Godstow, Newbridge, Radcot and Lechlade (St Johns). The northern part of Abingdon Bridge and the bridges at Godstow, Newbridge and Radcot still retain their beautiful original appearance. The eight other bridges were of timber: the first was at Kingston, 20 miles above London Bridge, and the remainder were at Chertsey, Staines, Windsor, Maidenhead, Marlow, Henley and Caversham.

During the 18th century there was a revival of bridge-building and alteration. Old London Bridge was altered in both structure and appearance by the removal of the buildings from it and the replacement of the ninth and tenth arches (counting from the south end) with a great central arch. The changes in water flow caused by this arch were to lead to the failure not only of London Bridge but also of bridges further upstream. Of bridges built, 15 provided new

crossings and 11 replaced earlier structures. The new crossings included, in London, Blackfriars and Westminster (of stone) and Battersea and Putney (of timber), and outside London the stone bridges at Richmond, Swinford and Lechlade. The replacements included the elegant stone bridges still to be seen at Chertsey, Maidenhead and Henley.

The 19th century saw construction of 14 new road crossings. Of these Tower Bridge (opened in 1894) is so well known that its silhouette has come to symbolise London. Of 24 replacement bridges built, those of stone at Kingston and Shillingford are notable. The century also saw construction of 22 bridges for a new mode of transport – the railway. In central London bridges were built to carry trains from the South of England across the Thames to termini at Cannon Street, Blackfriars, Charing Cross and Victoria. Further upstream, bridges were built for suburban lines, as at Barnes, Richmond and Kingston; for above-ground extensions of the Underground system, as at Fulham and Kew; for Great Western Railway main lines, including the fine brick bridges at Maidenhead, Basildon and Moulsford; and for GWR branch lines to Windsor, Henley and Marlow.

In the 20th century there were five main activities for Thames bridge engineers: (1) replacement of important road bridges in London, including London, Waterloo and Vauxhall bridges; (2) replacement or reconstruction of railway bridges, including those to the London termini and wrought iron bridges on the Oxford main line; (3) the building of motorway bridges, in particular those for the M3 at Chertsey, the M4 at Maidenhead and the M25 at Runnymede and Dartford; (4) the building of bypass bridges, as at Windsor, Marlow and Oxford; and (5) the construction of footbridges, including the Millennium Bridge and the two Golden Jubilee (Hungerford) suspension bridges in London (all opened in the 21st century). New footbridges were also built for the Thames Path, including those near Temple Lock and St John's Bridge, Lechlade. In the present century, two new road bridges are due to be built: the Thames Gateway Bridge,

Dalton

View of the Town and Bridge of KEW, in Surrey.

below Tower Bridge (see Appendix 4), and a bridge to replace the temporary one at Walton on Thames.

If Thames bridges feature in a conversation, someone is likely to ask, 'How many bridges are there?' This apparently simple question cannot be given a simple answer because the Thames separates into more than one stream over several parts of its course. Accordingly, a count of the bridges passed under in sailing – and later paddling! – along the most direct route from sea to source misses bridges across additional channels. Those bridges include the oldest, and arguably the most beautiful, Thames bridge, which crosses the former main stream at Radcot.

The accompanying table, compiled to help in deciding which bridges to include in this book, summarises the numbers of Thames bridges according to type, ownership and situation for the whole river. It shows that there are almost 400 bridges under which Thames water flows, but only 173 [sub-totals (1)+(4)] across the main channel up to the Source. The term 'main channel' is used to mean the navigable portion from Dartford to Inglesham and the remainder from there to the Source, at Ashton Keynes, where the river is divided into three streams, following the middle stream through the centre of the village. If the bridge count is made only for the navigable portion up to Inglesham, just above Lechlade, the total of 173 is reduced by 62 (18 public road bridges, 11 public footbridges, 20 private drive bridges and 13 private footbridges) to 111.

In selecting the bridges to be included in this book, I first decided to follow Dredge (*Thames Bridges from the Tower to the Source*, 1896-98) by considering the whole length of the river and including footbridges, as well as road and railway bridges. I then decided to limit the number by:

(a) including only public bridges and thereby excluding bridges to or on private properties;
(b) including (with the exception of the bridges in (c) below) only bridges across the main stream; and
(c) including, at crossings with two or more successive bridges, only those across subsidiary channels that I thought were of particular interest.

Numbers of Thames Bridges

		Rail	Road	Foot	Sub-total	Total
Public bridges across:						
(1)	the main channel	23	82	35	140	140
(2)	a second channel	1	8	10	19	159
(3)	a third channel	0	4	2	6	165
Private bridges across:						
(4)	the main channel	0	20	13	33	198
Public and private bridges:						
(5)	to islands	0	5	37	42	240
(6)	to locks: 1st part	-	2	17	19	259
(7)	2nd part	-	0	8	8	267
(8)	3rd part	-	0	3	3	270
Public and private bridges across subsidiary channels:						
(9)	Jubilee River	2	11	6	19	289
(10)	Abingdon	0	7	5	12	301
(11)	Oxford	3	21	19	43	344
(12)	Ashton Keynes	0	10	4	14	358
(13)	elsewhere	0	11	14	25	383

Doing this retained a number of important bridges, including the ancient ones at Culham, Godstow and Radcot.

This selection process resulted in descriptions and illustrations of all 140 public bridges over the main channel, 14 descriptions and eight illustrations of bridges across second channels, and four descriptions and two illustrations of bridges across third channels.

The Thames Path

The idea of a public path based on the old towpath was first discussed in the 19th century. In the 20th it was supported by the Council for the Protection of Rural England (in 1929), the River Thames Walk Committee of the Thames Conservancy (in 1946) and the Ramblers' Association (in 1977) and others. In 1984 the Countryside Commission recommended a route from the Thames Barrier (which had been completed in 1982) to the Source that was officially designated a National Trail by the Secretary of State for the Environment in 1989. It may be noted that, in 1993, the Countryside Commission became the Countryside Agency.

The creation of a path entirely along the river bank is the ultimate aim and is progressively being achieved. The old horse towpath, completion of which was a stated aim of an Act of 1795 (25 George 3, c. 106), changed banks along its course, so, where this occurred, the river had to be crossed by ferry or bridge. Because almost all the ferries have by now been closed, several footbridges have been built for the Thames Path, and others are planned. Because of the changing route of the Path, its length is altered from time to time – a recent official figure is 184 miles (294km).

A joint National Trails Management Group manages the Thames Path and the Ridgeway. It is composed of senior officers of each of the relevant highway authorities, the Countryside Agency, the Environment Agency, and Tourism South East. The Management Group receives information and advice from a Thames Path Forum, having members from organisations interested in the use and protection of the river.

The 1993 Thames Path footbridge attached to Bourne End Railway Bridge.

2. BRIDGE DESIGNS

Bridge materials

Timber

Timber has been used for bridge building over thousands of years. However, its advantages of cheapness, lightness and ease of working, as compared with stone or metal, have often been outweighed in the long term by the difficulty of preventing its decay. This problem was overcome, to some extent, by the Romans and later builders when they erected wooden superstructures on stone abutments and piers.

Stone

Techniques for quarrying and shaping stone were developed to an amazing extent by ancient peoples. Stone has the great advantages for bridge construction of having a potential life of centuries and of being able to resist compression to an extent that allows it to be used in making virtually indestructible arches. These virtues, together with its beauty and the ease with which it can be ornamented by carving, have been responsible for its use in the construction of numerous elegant bridges, including several 18th-century bridges across the River Thames.

Bricks

Building-bricks, which are made by heating moulded clay to a high temperature in a kiln, have been used extensively in bridge construction. Clay is a hydrated form of aluminium and silicon oxides, but the material used for brick-making is dug from natural deposits and contains impurities, notably iron oxide, the amount of which determines the redness of the bricks, and chalk, which is present in yellow bricks.

Mortar and cement

Until the introduction of Portland cement, bricks were bonded in buildings with lime mortar, which is made by heating calcium carbonate, in the form of chalk or limestone, to redness to drive off carbon dioxide gas and produce calcium oxide. This product is called 'quicklime' and, when wetted with water, reacts with it violently, with the evolution of much heat, to form calcium hydroxide ('slaked lime') as a fine white power. Lime mortar is a thick paste of slaked lime and sand, which sets by loss of the moisture by evaporation or absorption by bricks, and slow conversion by carbon dioxide from the atmosphere to calcium carbonate.

The Romans discovered that if a lime mortar was made using volcanic dust from the Bay of Naples region, near Pozzuoli, instead of sand, it set and hardened more quickly and would set under water. This 'hydraulic mortar' was of great importance for bridge-building because it enabled production of concrete, for foundations, which would set under the surface of a river or the sea.

The art of making pozzolanic mortar may have survived locally on the continent of Europe, but was largely forgotten until translated writings of the Roman author Vitruvius were published in the 15th century. When John Smeaton (1724-94) was recommended to the Commissioners responsible for rebuilding the Eddystone lighthouse (achieved between 1757 and 1759), he finally chose a mortar consisting of equal amounts of blue Lias hydraulic lime and pozzolana for the foundation stones.

Smeaton had stated that limes owed their hydraulic properties to clayey constituents of the limestones from which they were prepared. James Parker found that limestone nodules from Northfleet, on the Thames Estuary, could be ground and burned to produce a good cement, and he successfully marketed this as

'Roman Cement' from 1796 on. It was not superseded until about 1850 when artificial cements of controlled composition and properties became available.

In 1811 Joseph Aspdin (1778-1855) set up a plant for burning a mixture of lime and clay in 1811 at Wakefield. He patented his process in 1824. As a young man, Isaac Charles Johnson (b1801) tried unsuccessfully to discover the secret of Aspdin's 1811 process and, after experiments of his own, patented in 1844 a process for making 'Portland Cement' by sintering a ground, carefully controlled, mixture of lime and clay at a temperature of 2,550°F (1,400°C). The composition and temperature are substantially those used today.

A mixture Portland cement and sand is cement mortar, which sets, after mixing with water, more quickly than lime mortar and gives a harder reaction product. Cement mortar is now almost always used for bonding bricks, an exception being in the repair of old brickwork made with lime mortar.

The manufacture of Portland cement in very large quantity followed the invention of rotary kilns, patented in 1877 by Thomas Russell Crampton (1816-88), and improvements to those patented in 1885 by Frederick Ransom (1818-93).

Concrete

Concrete is a mixture of cement mortar and gravel or crushed stone, which sets to a hard mass after wetting with water. Like stone, it has a poor tensile strength so that a slab of it is likely to break if an attempt is made to bend it. Nevertheless, concrete has become of enormous importance in bridge-building because it can be greatly strengthened by reinforcement with steel.

Reinforced concrete was suggested as early as 1808 by Ralph Dodd (c1756-1822), using wrought iron bars, but his concrete was too poor to give good results. By 1854 the availability of reliable cement produced by Johnson's process made it worthwhile for Wilkinson to patent a method of making floor slabs according to

Dodd's suggestion. Nowadays, steel bars are used for reinforcing concrete, these being positioned in a mould before wet concrete is poured into it.

The French engineer Eugène Freyssinet (1879-1962) realised as early as 1903 that if concrete could be compressed to neutralise any tensile forces that might occur in service, it could be used for making stronger and lighter bridges. Known as **pre-stressed concrete**, it had been suggested earlier by P. H. Jackson in a United States patent of 1886, but it was Freyssinet who overcame the theoretical and practical problems of using the technique and devised the two methods for pre-stressing – 'pre-tensioning' and 'post-tensioning'. In pre-tensioning, steel strands are held in tension across a mould before concrete is poured in and allowed to set; the strands are gripped firmly enough by the set concrete for the tension in them to be retained. In post-tensioning, a cable of high-tensile steel wires is passed through a duct in the concrete unit, or units, to be stressed, tensioned (by tightening nuts on threads at the cable ends or by using jacks), then anchored firmly in the duct. One method of anchorage is to drive a conical wedge home between the cable and the wall of a cavity formed at the end of the duct.

Iron and steel

Three main types of iron have been used for bridge building: 'cast iron', which contains a high concentration of carbon; 'wrought iron', which contains very little carbon but does contain a minutely and uniformly distributed quantity of slag; and 'steel', which contains a carbon concentration between those of wrought iron and cast iron. This order of use was the order in which the three types of iron became available in quantity, not the historical order of their invention.

Cast iron was first made in England in the late 15th century following the introduction of the blast furnace from the Continent, in which iron ore was heated with charcoal and a flux to a temperature high enough to melt the iron and allow it to be cast in a mould. The charcoal needed was produced by 'charcoal-burning', a process in which wood, in a carefully arranged heap covered with turfs, is burned in a limited flow of air regulated by the size and number of holes made in the sides of the heap.

In the 18th and early 19th centuries, during the English Industrial Revolution, iron came to be needed in ever-increasing quantities, but in that same period the supply of wood for charcoal-burning was running out. A process for extracting ('smelting') iron from its ores without using charcoal became urgently needed.

The first satisfactory process was devised in about 1710 by Abraham Darby I (1678-1717) at his ironworks at Coalbrookdale, on the River Severn in Shropshire. He heated coal in a closed retort to form coke, then heated the coke with iron ore in a blast furnace to produce **pig iron**, metal named after the piglet-like row of small ingots produced by the mould in which it was cast. In about 1730 his son Abraham Darby II (1711-63) improved the method by adding limestone to the mixture in the furnace to act as a flux. Pig iron is an impure form of cast iron, and contains from 2½ to 4½% carbon. This amount makes the iron hard and brittle, so that beams cast from it are liable to break under load. For bridge-making, a less brittle and more malleable form of iron is desirable and such a metal is wrought iron.

Iron was probably first extracted from its ores, as **wrought iron**, in India, in about 1400BC. That date marks the beginning of the 'iron age' when iron came to be used, instead of the comparatively rare bronze, in making many commonplace articles.

Wrought iron was originally made in small quantities by heating iron ore with charcoal, marl (clay) and lime on an open hearth subjected to an air blast from a bellows, to produce a pasty form of pure iron; this paste was then beaten and hammered to squeeze out most of the slag and obtain a bloom of solid metal. It did not become readily available until after 1784 when Henry Cort (1740-1800) devised the first large-scale process for its manufacture. In his process, pig iron was refined over a coke fire and, after mixing with clinkers rich in iron oxides, put on the hearth of a 'reverberatory furnace', one

in which flames were passed over the surface of the material to be heated. When the iron had melted, it was stirred with a 'clinker bar', whereupon carbon burned from the metal and pure metal gradually formed a spongy loop. This loop was gathered up, hammered to expel slag, and rolled between cylinders to produce 'wrought iron' bars or plates. In wrought iron, residual slag is minutely and uniformly distributed throughout the metal but is not alloyed with it.

Steel had been made in small quantities since ancient times by working wrought iron in a manner leading to the absorption of more carbon. The amount of carbon in steel is from 0.1 to 1.5% by weight, a low-carbon steel containing less than 0.25%, a medium-carbon steel containing from 0.25 to 0.7%, and a high-carbon steel containing more than 0.7%.

Large-scale manufacture was made possible by the converter invented by Henry Bessemer (1813-98) and patented by him in 1856. This is a pivoted steel vessel with a refractory lining in which air can be blown through molten pig iron, run from a blast furnace, to burn out all the carbon, together with impurities. The amount of carbon needed for the steel is then provided by dissolving an iron-carbon-manganese alloy in the molten metal, which can then be poured out of the converter by pivoting it. Originally the refractory lining was of silica bricks, which are acidic and allow removal of silicon impurities. Thomas and Gilchrist (1847-1917) found that a basic lining of lime and magnesia additionally allowed removal of sulphur and phosphorus impurities and enabled better steel to be made from pig iron obtained from a wider variety of ores. They patented their process in 1877.

The other 19th-century large-scale process of steel-making was the open-hearth process patented by William Siemens (1823-83) in 1866. In this, pig iron, nowadays mixed with steel scrap, is melted on an open hearth by directing flames from pre-heated flows of coal gas and air across it. As in a Bessemer converter, a basic lining of dolomite allows phosphorus to be removed from the pig iron.

In the 20th century two more important methods of producing steel were developed. The first uses an electric furnace in which an arc is struck between an electrode and the metal to be fused. In the second, developed in Austria after the Second World War, oxygen is blown through molten metal from a tube dipped into it.

Bridge types

The beam bridge

The simplest type of bridge is obtained when a beam, which may be as elementary as a wooden plank or as complicated as a steel deck stiffened with a girder framework, is positioned across some feature with its ends resting on supports at either side.

When a beam is loaded, it is compressed at the top and stretched at the bottom; to be able to support a heavy load, a beam must therefore be made to have good compressive and tensile strengths. Suitable materials for beams are timber, wrought iron or steel, and reinforced or pre-stressed concrete.

In past centuries there were a number of timber road bridges across the Thames, including those at Kingston, Staines and Windsor, which had numerous spans and piers consisting of piles driven into the river bed. Now the only timber bridges are footbridges, for instance Tenfoot and Old Man's Bridges.

In the 19th century, during the earlier years of railway building, bridges were made using cast iron beams. Spans of 20 to 30 feet only required single beams, but larger spans required compound beams in which two or more beams were joined together. In May 1847 a three-span railway bridge across the River Dee at Chester collapsed under the weight of a train, killing five people and injuring 30. Each span was 108 feet long and each girder consisted of three cast iron beams bolted together and strengthened with wrought iron bars.

In August 1847 a Royal Commission was appointed to 'Inquire into the Application of Iron to Railway Structures'. Its Report of July 1849 resulted in legislation banning the use of compound (but not single) cast iron beams in bridges for new lines. Those were not banned until after an accident at Inverythan in 1882. Existing bridges continued to fail and, in 1891, after an accident at Norwood Junction, the task of replacing all cast iron girders in railway bridges was begun.

Wrought iron girder bridges were built over the Thames in the 19th century by the railway companies, and some of these, for instance those at Cannon Street, Staines and Windsor, are still in use. On the Great Western Railway line from Didcot to Oxford, temporary bridges of timber were provided at Appleford and Nuneham, which were soon replaced with simple wrought iron girder bridges. Those were, in turn, replaced with steel bridges in which the sides of the deck were supported and stiffened by bow-and-string lattice girders of the kind proposed in 1847 by Squire Whipple in the United States of America.

Reinforced concrete was used in London for the Waterloo Bridge built in the years 1939 to 1944 to replace John Rennie's famous structure of 1817. Despite its appearance, it is in essence a beam, not an arched, bridge.

Pre-stressed concrete has been used for deck beams in a number of smaller post-Second World War road bridges, including Waterhay Bridge and the bridge carrying the Somerford Keynes bypass.

The cantilever bridge

A cantilever is a beam fixed at one end to a support so as to project horizontally from it. In a cantilever bridge it is usual to provide cantilevers that project towards each other with their free ends either close enough to be joined, or spaced apart to produce a gap which is filled with a suspended span. It is also usual for a pair of cantilevers to share a support so that they balance each other.

The most famous British cantilever bridge is the steel railway bridge across the Firth of Forth, opened in 1890, which has three pairs of balanced cantilevers between which are two suspended spans. Examples of cantilever bridges across the Thames are at Wandsworth (opened in 1940), which is of steel, and Marlow Bypass (opened in 1972), which has cantilevers of reinforced concrete.

The arched bridge

A true masonry arch is an arc of wedge-shaped stones, called 'voussoirs', which support each other by mutual pressure resulting from their weight. It is an ideal element for a bridge because it can only be distorted or broken by a load if the voussoirs are forced out of their normal positions, and this cannot happen if the arch is strongly built between unyielding supports, which may be abutments or stonework of adjacent arches.

The earliest large bridges that survive are masonry ones with semi-circular arches built by the Romans about 2,000 years ago. Famous examples are the Pons Fabricius, which crosses to an island in the River Tiber in Rome and was built in 62BC; the Ponte di Augusto, which crosses the River Marecchia at Rimini and was built in 20AD; and the Puente de Alcántara (Arabic for 'the bridge'), which crosses the River Tagus at Caceres, in Spain near the Portuguese border, built in 105AD.

A masonry arch is made by positioning all the voussoirs, other than that for the crown of the arch, on a strong temporary wooden arch (known as the 'centring') built between the supports at each side of the gap the arch is to span. The voussoir for the crown, known as the 'keystone', is then forced into the gap left for it to make the arch self-supporting. If bricks, instead of wedge-shaped stones, are to be used for an arch, they can be laid, and the gaps between them filled with mortar, on the centring. For a sizeable arch, it is usual to lay two or more concentric layers of bricks. The space between the outer surface of a brick or masonry arch and the surface used by traffic, known as the 'spandrel', is usually filled to strengthen the arch and spread the weight of traffic more uniformly throughout the structure.

The principal changes in the design of masonry arched bridges since Roman times were in the use of different arch shapes. Pointed arches, some internally ribbed, were introduced in mediaeval times as may be seen in the Thames bridges at Radcot (c1154) and Newbridge (c1250). Tudor four-centred arches then became fashionable and were used later (in 1865) for Clifton Hampden Bridge across the Thames. Those were followed by shallower arches, more suitable for wide spans, shaped as a segment of a circle or portion of an ellipse. As an arch is made shallower, a greater sideways thrust is produced by its own weight and any load put upon it, and the abutments have to be strong enough to resist this.

French engineers pioneered the construction of masonry bridges with shallow arches of wide span supported by narrow piers in the second half of the 18th century. A Corps des Ponts et Chaussées had been established in 1716 and founded an École des Ponts et Chaussées in 1764 with Jean-Rodolphe Perronet (1708-94) as Director. In 1772 his masterpiece, a five-arch bridge across the Seine at Neuilly, just north of Paris, was completed. This had elliptical arches of 128-foot span supported by piers only 13 feet thick. The design produced by John Rennie (1761-1821) for the first Waterloo Bridge across the Thames owed something to the design of the Neuilly Bridge but had a span-to-pier-width ratio of 6.1 instead of 9.3.

The River Thames has several fine examples of brick arched bridges including Maidenhead Railway Bridge (1838), and Basildon and Moulsford Railway Bridges (both 1840), all designed by Brunel (1806-59) for the Great Western Railway.

In the 20th century, arched bridges came to be made using reinforced concrete and, later, pre-stressed concrete. There are reinforced concrete bridges across the Thames at Reading (1923) and Caversham (1926), both built according to the system devised by the French engineer Francois Hennebique (1842-1921). Frames that support the deck of the bridge at Runnymede (1986), which carries anticlockwise M25 traffic, include arched portions of pre-stressed concrete.

The first iron bridge to be built anywhere in the world is the arched bridge that still spans the River Severn at Ironbridge (originally Coalbrookdale) in Shropshire. It was built in the years 1776 to 1779 by Abraham Darby III (1750-89) to the design of T. F. Prichard. He chose to use an arch because cast iron, like stone, has excellent compressive strength. The arch has a span of 100 feet and is formed of sections held together by mortise joints and pegged dovetails.

Numerous bridges across the Thames having a deck supported by cast iron arched ribs were built during the 19th century. Road bridges that retain these ribs include those at Battersea, Windsor and Oxford (Osney Bridge). Railway bridges, including those at Barnes (1849), Richmond (1848) and Kingston (1863), were also built with cast iron ribs but were rebuilt with wrought iron ones in 1895, 1908 and 1907 respectively.

Steel was used in London during the 20th century in building replacements for earlier iron road bridges, including Southwark (built 1819 of cast iron and replaced in 1921) and Vauxhall (built 1816 of wrought iron and replaced in 1906).

A number of modern road bridges, including the Chertsey Motorway (M3) and Winterbrook (Wallingford Bypass) Bridges, have a deck carried by steel girders arched at their lower edges to give greater rigidity. These bridges therefore have characteristics of both beam and arched structures.

The suspension bridge

In a modern suspension bridge, a stiffened deck is suspended with vertical hangers of varying lengths from cables that hang in curves from vertical supports and are anchored at each end of the bridge.

Although suspension bridges with flexible decks had been known for centuries, the first with a stiffened deck was built by James Finlay (1756-1828) in the United States of America at about the end of the 18th century.

The first suspension bridges across the Thames were at Hammersmith (1827) and Marlow (1832), both designed by William Tierney Clark (1783-1852). There followed bridges at Chelsea (1858) and, just upstream, the Albert Bridge (1873). The Marlow and Albert Bridges were strengthened in 1966 and 1973 respectively, and the Chelsea and Hammersmith Bridges were replaced in 1937 and 1887.

The cable-stayed bridge

In a cable-stayed bridge, a stiffened deck is supported by a straight tie, usually a cable or rod, inclined between it and the top of a vertical support. Usually, there is more than one vertical support, each with a number of ties fanning from the top. Each tie forms a triangle with the support to which it is attached and part of the bridge deck to produce a rigid structure.

The only cable-stayed bridges across the Thames are the Queen Elizabeth II Bridge (1991) from Dartford to Thurrock, which carries southbound M25 traffic, and the elegant Golden Jubilee footbridges (2002) at either side of the Charing Cross Railway Bridges (1863 and 1887).

Bridge foundations

A bridge of any type is only as strong as its foundations, and it is possible that more bridges have needed replacement through failure of the foundations than through failure of the superstructure. Foundations have to transfer the weight of the bridge, and anything upon it, to an area of a firm stratum at the crossing site sufficiently large to prevent subsidence. For the River Thames, the firm stratum is likely to be of earth, clay, gravel or chalk, because bedrock, of limestone or granite for instance, is not present.

The load produced by a bridge is distributed between its supports, which normally include an abutment at each end and, for a long bridge, one or more piers. Each support needs a foundation individually designed to suit the stratum on which it is built, which may vary even within the site of a single crossing. For example, where the Chertsey M3 Motorway Bridge crosses the Thames, a surface gravel layer is thicker at the eastern than at the western bank, and foundations of different design were required at opposite sides of the river.

A bridge across water requires excellent foundations because the flow of the water can, in time, erode the river bed around them (an effect known as 'scour') and lead to their exposure and eventual failure. Several Thames bridges in London, including John Rennie's (1761-1821) famous Waterloo Bridge of 1817, had to be replaced because of scour.

Water hinders construction of a river bridge. Occasionally it is possible re-route a river past a construction site so that the foundations and bridge can be built on dry land. In 1978 this was done at two sites on the Upper Thames: for a footbridge over a subsidiary channel near Buscot Lock (not included in this book) and for a bypass bridge at Somerford Keynes. In most places it is impractical to divert a river, and therefore necessary to build foundations on the river bed. The main methods of doing this involve the use cofferdams and caissons, and are described later.

Driven piles

Piles, which originally were stakes of wood but later were also made of iron, steel or reinforced concrete, have always been important in bridge-building. They have been driven into the beds and banks of rivers both as foundations in their own right and as parts of temporary structures (notably 'cofferdams') in which foundations were built.

Piles are sometimes divided into three classes according to their function, projecting piles, bearing piles and sheeting piles.

Projecting piles, as the name indicates, are piles long enough to project above a land or water surface after being driven securely. They can form trestles or piers for supporting bridge decks and are then commonly braced together above the water level. The piers of Tenfoot and Old Man's Bridges, attractive footbridges across the Upper Thames, were provided in this manner.

Bearing piles are driven deeply into a river bank or bed to provide (after any necessary cutting) a firm, level support on which timber, masonry or concrete can be laid during the construction of a bridge abutment or pier. A bearing pile is held by skin friction, and more firmly still if its tip is driven into contact with a hard substratum.

Sheeting piles are driven closely together to enclose a foundation, during or after its construction. They can be left in place, possibly after being reducing in height, to protect the foundation against scour. This was done in the case of Twickenham Bridge.

Screwed piles

Screwed piles are provided with a large thread at the tip and are pulled into the bank or river bed by rotation of the upper end. They were used in the construction of Cookham Bridge, where they support cylindrical iron piers.

Cofferdams

A cofferdam is an enclosure built around the position where an underwater foundation is to be constructed. If it is leak-proof, the water can be pumped out of it to allow men to work on the river (or other) bed, and some authors use the word 'cofferdam' to cover only a structure of this kind.

It was the Romans who, more than 2,000 thousand years ago, perfected the art of building masonry bridges, and the cofferdam was one of several inventions they made that were responsible for their mastery. The Roman engineers made cofferdams by driving two concentric rings of wooden stakes into the riverbed and packing the gap between the rings with wicker baskets filled with clay. They then either (a) pumped the water out of the cofferdam, prepared the river bed and built the foundation, or (b) dredged inside the cofferdam to remove loose material from the bottom, then poured in concrete that could set under water to form a secure platform for a stone foundation.

In mediaeval and more recent times, cofferdams have been made by driving into the river bed single or double rings of piles of various types. For example, during the building of Old London Bridge in the years 1176 to 1209, the foundations were made by making a boat-shaped cofferdam (called a 'starling') for each stone pier by driving close-fitting elm piles into the river bed, then driving larch piles over a smaller central area to support a platform of wood covered with pitch on which the masonry was built. The spaces beneath the wooden platform and between the larch piles and the cofferdam were filled with large stones.

At present, a single ring of interlocking sheet-steel piles is commonly used as a cofferdam. This can be removed after foundations have been built inside it, or left in place, possibly after being cut lower, to reinforce the foundations or provide, after filling with concrete, a stable foundation by itself.

Thames bridges at which cofferdams were left in place included the old (1856) Chelsea Bridge.

Open caissons and cylinders

Strictly speaking, a caisson is a prefabricated, watertight cofferdam that is sunk into position in a river, pumped dry to allow foundations to be built on the riverbed, then removed. However, the word has come additionally to cover a caisson that is not removed after use, and also a foundation made using a caisson.

Charing Cross Railway Bridge, showing an altered brick pier from Hungerford Suspension Bridge and iron piers formed of tubes sunk in open caissons. The picture also shows the temporary footbridge provided when the bridge was given a new deck in 1979.

In the building of piers for the first Westminster Bridge during the years 1738-46, heavy timber caissons in the form of open boxes with removable sides were used. Once a pier had been built on the timber bottom of the box, which served as a platform for masonry, the sides were removed and re-used in a further caisson.

A caisson can be made to sink deeper into a river bed by excavation near its lower edges and, if necessary, weighting the top. To keep the top above water, the caisson can be heightened by adding one or more extensions.

The iron cylinders used as piers for a number of 19th-century girder railway bridges (including those at Cannon Street, Charing Cross and Staines) functioned as caissons but were left to form part of the structures after at least partial filling with brickwork and concrete.

Pneumatic caissons

If it is necessary to sink a caisson a long way to reach a firm stratum, such as rock, a pneumatic caisson may be have to be used to allow dry working at the river bed. A 'pneumatic caisson' is a caisson having a working chamber at the bottom to which compressed air can be admitted to prevent water entering. The ceiling of the working chamber is provided with an air lock through which men and materials can enter and leave.

As in the case of deep-sea divers, those working in a pneumatic caisson have to go through a decompression procedure on leaving to avoid suffering from the 'bends'. Pneumatic caissons were used during the widening of Blackfriars Bridge in the years 1907-09.

Bored piles ('caisson piles')

It is possible to make a pile in situ by boring a cylindrical shaft in land or a river bed and filling it with concrete. It is usual to line the shaft with steel and position reinforcement bars inside before filling it with the concrete. If the bottom of the shaft is widened towards its lower end, a pile can be made that is flared at the base to spread the load over a larger area of substrate.

A concrete bored-pile cast in a steel-lined shaft is closely similar to a concrete-filled cylindrical caisson – hence the second name in the heading.

Pile caps and bank seats

It is becoming usual to cast a reinforced concrete block around the tops of adjacent bearing piles (driven or bored) to unite them and produce what is known as a 'pile cap', which provides a very stable foundation. This was done during the making of piers for the Millennium and Golden Jubilee footbridges.

A small block cast at a river-bank around one or two piles for one end of a footbridge is often called a 'bank seat'. Examples are at the ends of the new Shifford Island and Bloomer's Hole footbridges, which were completed in the years 1994 and 2000 respectively, to carry the Thames Path.

3. HIGHWAY AND BRIDGE AUTHORITIES

Building or rebuilding a bridge across the Thames has usually required action or approval by some authority. Initially the authority was the Crown, but as Parliament evolved in the Middle Ages that assembly won increasing influence over the content of new laws. After the Civil War of 1649-60, England became a constitutional monarchy and Parliament continued to become more responsible for the substance of new legislation, and the Crown now merely provides the Royal Assent.

Parts of the history of the Crown and Parliament explain the origins of the many successive authorities that have been concerned with roads and bridges. The church was also responsible for building bridges. Because Christianity was introduced into Britain in 597, before the birth of England, a note on its arrival is given first.

The Church
In about the year 585, Ethelbert, the Anglo-Saxon King of Wessex, married Bertha, great-granddaughter of Clovis of Francia. She was a Christian, and some years after the marriage Ethelbert decided that he wished to be baptised. Pope Gregory was informed that the people of Britain wished to be converted, so he sent Augustine from Rome to do this. He landed in Kent in 597 and succeeded in his mission. This success led to the formation of monasteries and other religious houses, and some of these later became associated with bridges, and also with the division of the land into parishes. Centuries later, the inhabitants of these became, for a time, responsible for the upkeep of roads and bridges.

A religious society called 'The Brethren of the Bridge' originated in France in the 12th century. Peter of Colechurch, who directed the building of the last timber bridge across the Thames in London and supervised the building of its stone replacement from the year 1176

until his death in 1205, was probably a member of this or an equivalent English society; the bridge was completed in 1209. Other Thames bridges associated with religious foundations, and paid for by benefactions were those at Chertsey, Henley, Caversham, Streatley, Abingdon, Oxford (Osney Bridge), Godstow and Lechlade (St John's Bridge).

The Crown
England was formed from seven kingdoms, including Wessex, established by the Anglo-Saxons after their conquest of Britain from 495AD onwards. This successful invasion had been carried out by Angles, Saxons and Jutes from what is now Germany, and they elected kings to rule the regions in which they settled. This was both surprising, because these tribes had not been ruled by kings in their regions of origin, and important, because it introduced into Britain both the Anglo-Saxon language (Old English) and a form of monarchy that led to the law and government of England becoming, and remaining, fundamentally different from those of countries in mainland Europe. The Kingdom of Wessex (which, as it happened, included almost the whole course of the Thames) was divided into five shires and contained centres known as 'burhs'. These were precursors of the shires and boroughs that became, and still are, such important administrative areas for local government.

The process of forming England from the seven Anglo-Saxon kingdoms was begun by Alfred the Great, King of Wessex (871-899) and completed by his son, Edward the Elder (899-924). Viking raids on England had become regular from the year 835 onwards and, in the years 865 to 878, they conquered all but the kingdom of Wessex. During the latter year King Alfred was at first defeated by them, but he escaped captivity and, after raising an army from the shires, defeated the Vikings later that same year at the battle of Edington. In 886 Alfred recaptured the 'burh' of London from the Vikings and, by moving the population back into the Roman walls, became the second founder of the City. In a treaty following the recapture, those on King Alfred's side were described as 'the counsellors of the English nation' and those on Guthrum's as 'the people who dwell in East Anglia'. Thus Alfred was described as king of the whole nation, even though he did not control the whole of England. In the ensuing years of peace he built 30 new burhs and a strong navy so that in the third Viking war of 892-896 the invaders were once more defeated.

After succeeding his father to the throne, Edward the Elder defeated Viking kingdoms elsewhere in Britain and was acknowledged as King of England at Bakewell, in Derbyshire, in the year 920. He then created new shires and burhs to achieve administrative unity throughout his kingdom.

Despite the Danish conquest of 1013 and the more famous conquest by William of Normandy in 1066, the Anglo-Saxon forms of kingship and government were not completely swept away. William I and his successors developed the old law into the common law and modified and augmented the old courts, establishing a legal system with many features that survive.

The Roman bridges in England had been of timber and for centuries after Britain had ceased to be part of the Roman empire were allowed to decay. It was not until the mid-8th century that successive kings of England tackled the problems caused by their loss, promulgating charters and laws to make the public responsible for improving river crossings. Over a period lasting until about 1250, many bridges were built as replacements for fords and ferries. In fact, these bridges were so numerous that few more were needed between then and the onset of the Industrial Revolution in the 18th century. Of those few, notable survivals across the Thames are Culham and Abingdon Bridges, constructed in the years 1415-22 during the reign of Henry V (see Harrison (2004)).

Parliament

Parliament, consisting of the House of Lords and House of Commons, evolved between the beginning of the 13th and the end of the 14th century. The evolution of the House of Lords began with the king inviting prelates and magnates to his court to join his advisers to produce a feudal assembly, or Great Council, which became known in the mid-13th century as a Parliament. The evolution of the House of Commons began with the king summoning, on other occasions, knights and burgesses, representing shires and towns, to treat with him about taxes and other matters. It ended when conflicts between the king and the magnates, and the need to raise taxes to pay for the Hundred Years War, led to the presence of the local representatives becoming an essential feature of a Parliament.

Statutes, Rules and Orders, and their citation

It became accepted in Edward I's reign (1272-1307) that a statute (or Act of Parliament) was a law enacted by the King in Parliament and could only be repealed (cancelled) by Parliament. The main features of the present system of making statute law had been devised by the end of the 15th century. In 1539 a distinction was made (which still exists) between Public Acts, which affected the law of the land, and Private Acts, which did not, and had to be proved in litigation.

In the 17th century the practice evolved of adding a clause to a Private Bill concerning a public utility, such as a road, canal or (much later) railway, that the Act was to be treated as a Public Act. In 1798 Public Acts produced in this way were numbered in their own sequence and published as 'Local and Personal Acts' to distinguish them from the Public General Acts.

An Act can be cited in two ways: (i) by giving its short title and the year in which the session of Parliament in which it was passed commenced, or (ii) by giving the regnal year or years of the session in which it was passed and the chapter number. From 1963 (under the Acts of Parliament Numbering and Citations Act, 1962, 10 & 11

Elizabeth 2, c. 34) Acts were numbered serially each calendar year. For Acts passed before 1963 cited using method (i), a comma is provided between the short title and the year, whereas for Acts passed from 1963 onwards, no comma is provided. The type of an Act cited by method (ii) is now indicated by the type used in printing the chapter number, which is Arabic for a Public and General Act, lower case Roman for a Local or Personal Act, or italic Arabic for a Private Act. Because italic numbers are not highly distinctive, an ordinary Arabic numeral followed by '(Private)' is alternatively used in the latter case.

Many details concerning Acts (such as the date of their coming into force) have been specified in Rules made under them. Before 1891 there was no systematic record of these, but in that year all the public and general orders, rules and regulations made in 1890 were published in what became the first volume in a series that still continues. Publication was initially regulated by the Rules Publication Act, 1893 (56 & 57 Victoria, c. 66), and from the 1894 Volume onwards the rules were printed with Statutory Rules & Orders numbers (eg S. R. & O. 1894/1). The 1893 Act was replaced by the Statutory Instruments Act, 1946 (9 & 10 George 6, c. 36) so that from 1 January 1948 Rules and Orders were published with Statutory Instrument numbers (eg S. I. 1948/1).

Acts and Rules for building bridges

For centuries an individual or body wishing to build a public bridge, or a public highway containing one or more bridges, has had to obtain an Act of Parliament authorising construction. The Act has many possible functions, including formation of a company or trust; empowering the purchase of land; specifying how money can be raised by the issue of shares; defining the tolls that users of the bridge, or the road it carries, can be charged; and imposing design limitations so that the bridge will not impede navigation. Acts relating to individual bridges and stretches of road have normally been Local and Personal Acts, whereas Acts relating to bridges and roads in general have normally been Public and General Acts. Sometimes authority to build a bridge is given with a Statutory Instrument obtained under a general Highways Act.

Successive authorities

Counties and Justices of the Peace (1530)

The first Act of Parliament about bridges in general was the 'Statute of Bridges' of 1530 (22 Henry 8, c. 5). This was a statement of the relevant common law and laid down that the repair of bridges in corporate towns was to be a charge on the citizens and that bridges elsewhere were to be maintained by the counties in which they stood, under the authority of the Justices of the Peace in Quarter Sessions. These requirements did not apply to those bridges that had, by custom, been repaired by parishes or private bodies. Repair of a bridge had to include repair, for a short distance, of the approaches to it.

The Bridge Act of 1740 (14 George 2, c. 40) made Justices in Quarter Sessions responsible for building or repairing bridges and buying any land required. The Bridges Act, 1803 (43 George 3, c. 59) made a county not liable to repair a bridge built privately to an unsatisfactory standard.

Parishes and Surveyors of Highways (1555)

The common law regarding the maintenance of roads was embodied in the Highways Act, 1555 (2 & 3 Philip & Mary, c. 8). Roads were to be maintained by parishes and each year the parishioners were to elect a Surveyor of Highways who, during four (later six) days a year, was to oversee repair of the roads by parishioners themselves or paid substitutes.

The power of electing Surveyors was given to the quarter sessions by The Highways, etc, Act, 1691 (3 William & 4 Mary, c. 12). That Act gave parishes the power to levy rates as necessary to pay for repairs. The Highway Act, 1773 (13 George 3, c. 78) enabled parishes to demand appointment of a salaried surveyor. It also fixed the sums to be paid by those wishing to avoid 'statute labour' under the 1555 Act.

Turnpike trusts (1706)

The idea of levying tolls from travellers along a section of road to pay for its construction or maintenance was first tried out in England on the Great North Road between Wadeshill, in Hertfordshire, and Shilton, in Huntingdon, a distance of almost 70 miles. An Act of Parliament was obtained in 1663 (15 Charles 2, c. 1) allowing gates, which became known as 'turnpikes', to be erected across the road at which tolls could be charged. Many travellers managed to evade payment and the experiment failed.

A second attempt to establish a turnpike road was made under an Act of 1697, near the village of Ingatestone on the road from London to Harwich, and succeeded. After that, many more Acts were obtained. A number of Thames bridges were built to carry turnpike roads, including those at Shillingford and Lechlade (the 'Halfpenny' Bridge).

The administration of turnpike roads was originally entrusted to county magistrates, but from 1706 onwards Acts appointed trustees as administrators. The collection of tolls and work on the road were controlled by Surveyors and Commissioners of Turnpikes, whose powers and duties were listed in the Highway Act, 1773 (13 George 3, c. 78).

Turnpikes and the tolls levied at them were highly unpopular and sometimes even led to riots. Nevertheless, by the 1780s they had produced a road network on which stage-coaches could cover long distances more quickly than horse post. Eventually, more than 1,100 turnpike trusts operated some 23,000 miles of road.

The arrival of railways reduced the revenues of turnpike trusts. In 1841 Parliament authorised county magistrates to help trusts with money from highway rates, a provision that led, in South Wales, to bands destroying turnpike gates. The Government yielded and in 1844 abolished the trusts throughout the six counties of South Wales, transferring their work to County Roads Boards, which reduced the tolls payable. From then onwards turnpike trusts were wound up, the last in 1895.

Parish ratepayers, Highway Boards and Highway Districts (1835)

Earlier statute law on roads was replaced by the general Highway Act of 1835 (5 & 6 William 4, c. 50). This required a new bridge to be repaired by the authority responsible for repairing the highway in which it was built, and made a meeting of parish ratepayers the administrative body for highway management. A parish with more than 5,000 inhabitants could have a Highway Board. The Highway Acts, 1862 (25 & 26 Victoria, c. 61) organised parishes into highway districts formed by the justices and administered by Highway Boards.

The Metropolitan Board of Works (1855)

The Metropolis Management Act, 1855 (18 & 19 Victoria, c. 120), abolished numerous London bodies of trustees and commissioners and established the Metropolitan Board of Works, which received its powers on 1 January 1856. Members of the Board were elected by the City of London Corporation and certain vestries and district boards. The new board was responsible for highways and bridges.

The Metropolis Toll Bridges Act, 1877 (40 & 41 Victoria, xcix) enabled the Metropolitan Board of Works to purchase for £1,376,825 all the 11 bridges (except Westminster Bridge) from Waterloo to Hammersmith, and to free Lambeth, Vauxhall, Chelsea, Albert and Battersea Bridges from toll.

The Highways and Locomotives Amendment Act of 1878 (41 & 42 Victoria, c. 77) created the category of 'main roads', which included many of the turnpike roads described in the earlier section. Money for maintaining main roads was to be raised partly by the justices out of county rates and partly by the local highway authority. The County Surveyor became responsible for roads as well as bridges – his original responsibility.

County Councils, including the London County Council (LCC) (1888)

The Local Government Act, 1888 (51 & 52 Victoria, c. 41) introduced County Councils (including the London County Council) with democratically elected members. When it came into force on 1 April 1889 it made the Metropolis an administrative county and replaced the Metropolitan Board of Works with the London County Council. The Act also transferred the duties of repairing main roads and county bridges outside the Metropolis to the newly formed County Councils. These were given the powers of highway boards, powers soon extended by the Highways and Bridges Act, 1891 (54 & 55 Victoria, c. 63). They appointed County Surveyors who took over some duties from Justices in Quarter Sessions.

The Local Government Act 1972 (c. 70) made the local authority for highways outside Greater London the County Council. The Highways Act 1980 (c. 66) consolidated previous Acts and made County Councils the local highway authorities outside Greater London.

The Road Board (1909)

In the 1890s motor vehicles started to appear on Britain's roads, and by 1913 almost 125,000 cars, taxis and lorries, and more than 50,000 goods vehicles, were at work.

The first action of the Government to provide for the greatly increased road use was to constitute, by the Development and Road Improvement Funds Act, 1909 (9 Edward 7, c. 47), a body of Development Commissioners to advance money from Government funds for public purposes. A Road Board was established, which could make grants to local governing bodies, including councils, for improving existing roads and building new ones. The powers of the Road Board were transferred to the Ministry of Transport in 1919.

The Ministry of Transport (1919)

The Ministry of Transport was formed after the First World War by an Act of 1919 (9 & 10 George 5, c. 50) to regulate railways, tramways, waterways, roads, bridges, harbours and docks. It assumed the duties of the Road Board. The Ministry classified roads as 'first class' or 'second class' and bore a percentage, dependent on the class, of the cost of maintaining or improving them.

The Local Government Act, 1929 (19 & 20 George 5, c. 17) made the county responsible for all classified roads. However, those considered to form the most important traffic arteries were transferred back to the Ministry of Transport by the Trunk Roads Act, 1936 (1 Edward 8 & 1 George 6, c. 5). In most instances, execution of works on trunk roads was delegated to the county authorities. Work on the Chertsey Road between Chiswick and Shepperton, which required new Thames bridges at Chiswick and Twickenham, was delegated to Middlesex and Surrey County Councils in this way.

In 1949 the Special Roads Act (12, 13 & 14 George 6, c. 32) provided for the construction of roads (such as bypasses and ones leading to bridges) reserved for special classes of traffic. Before authorising a special road that crossed navigable water, the Minister had to consider the requirements of navigation.

The Greater London Council (GLC) (1965)

The London Government Act 1963 (c. 33) formed the Greater London Council, which replaced the LCC on 1 April 1965. The Act created 32 administrative areas, called 'London Boroughs', and authorities responsible for these, called 'London Borough Councils'.

The GLC was abolished in 1986 by the Local Government Act 1985 (c. 51), and most of its functions were transferred to the London Borough Councils and the Common Council of the City of London. Before abolition, the London Bridges Engineering Group (LOBEG) was formed with representatives from all the London boroughs, and currently advises Transport for London on the priorities for investment in London's borough-owned bridges.

Non-Metropolitan and Metropolitan County Councils (1974)

Under the Local Government Act 1972 (c. 70) Non-Metropolitan and Metropolitan County Councils replaced the old County Councils from 1 April 1974. The distinction between 'county' and other bridges maintained by a highway authority was abolished.

The Department of Transport (1976)

The functions of the Minister of Transport were transferred to the Secretary of State for Transport, head of a newly formed Department of Transport, by Statutory Instrument (S. I. 1976/1775).

The Ministry of Transport (1979)

A Ministry of Transport was formed from the Department of Transport by Statutory Instrument (S. I. 1979/571) and the new Minister took over some transport functions from the Secretary of State for Environment.

The Department for Transport (1981)

The Ministry of Transport was made into a Department again by Statutory Instrument (S. I. 1981/238).

The Local Government Commission for England and Unitary Authorities (1992-1998)

The Local Government Act 1992 (c. 19) created a new Local Government Commission for England, which recommended, among other changes, the formation of unitary authorities. Under powers given by this Act, numerous unitary authorities were formed, those bordering the Thames upstream of Greater London being Swindon (formed from April 1997) and Windsor & Maidenhead, Wokingham, Reading, and West Berkshire (formed from April 1998).

The Highways Agency (1994)

The Highways Agency was established on 1 April 1994 to manage, maintain and improve trunk roads and motorways. It was originally accountable to the Department for Transport, Local Government and the Regions, but became accountable to the Department for Transport in May 2002 upon the de-merger of the preceding Department.

The Department of Environment, Transport and the Regions (1997)

This Department was formed on 16 June 1997 by the merger of the Department of the Environment and the Department of Transport according to Statutory Instrument (S. I. 1997/1744).

The Greater London Authority (GLA) and 'Transport for London (2000)

London did not have an overall administrative body following the abolition of the GLC until a new one was formed by the Greater London Authority Act 1999 (c. 29). This Act provided for an elected Mayor of London and 25 separately elected London Assembly Members. The elections were held on 4 May 2000 and those elected took office on 3 July 2000. The 1999 Act created 'Transport for London' as the highway authority for all the GLA roads.

The Department for Transport, Local Government and the Regions (2001)

This Department was formed from the Department of Environment, Transport and the Regions by Statutory Instrument (S. I. 2001/2568).

The Department for Transport (2002)

This new separate Department was formed in May 2002 following de-merger of the Department for Transport, Local Government and the Regions. Some functions were transferred by Statutory Instrument (S. I. 2003/2626).

Listing of bridges as historic structures

In England (and Wales) many historic monuments, buildings and structures are 'listed' to protect them against alteration or destruction. Buildings are listed in three Grades:

Grade I: buildings of exceptional interest
Grade II*: particularly important buildings of more than special interest, and
Grade II: buildings of special interest warranting every effort to preserve them.

A number of Thames bridges are Listed Structures, but no list of these is readily available. The listings known to the author are included in the texts for the bridges concerned.

The listing of ancient structures dates back to the Ancient Monuments Protection Act, 1882 (45 & 46 Victoria, c. 73), which allowed owners of 50 particular ancient monuments, such as Stonehenge, to appoint the Commissioners of Her Majesty's Works and Public Buildings as guardians of them.

On 27 October 1908 the Royal Commission on the Historical Monuments of England was formed to identify sites and make recommendations about them.

Ancient Monuments Acts of 1913 (3 & 4 George 5, c. 32) and 1931 (21 & 22 George 5, c. 16) gave various powers to County Councils, enabling them to become guardians of monuments, to maintain, preserve and manage them, and also transfer them to or from the Ministry.

The Town and Country Planning Act, 1944 (7 & 8 George 6, c. 47) gave the Minister the right to compile lists of buildings of architectural or historic interest for guiding local authorities.

The Town and Country Planning Act, 1947 (10 & 11 George 6, c. 51) made it an offence punishable by fine to demolish, alter or extend a listed building without giving the County Council two months' written notice. The County Council could order the reinstatement of the building to the condition it was in before the unauthorised changes.

In 1953 the Historic Buildings and Ancient Monuments Act (1 & 2 Elizabeth 2, c. 49) formed the Historic Buildings Council for England to advise the Minister of Works.

In 1970 the Ministry of Housing and Local Government and the Ministry of Public Building and Works became parts of the Department of the Environment (S. I. 1970/1681).

The Ancient Monuments and Archaeological Areas Act of 1979 (c. 46) required the Secretary of State for the Environment to compile and maintain a schedule of monuments.

In 1983 the National Heritage Act (c. 47) dissolved the Ancient Monuments Board for England and the Historic Buildings Council for England, and formed the Historic Buildings and Monuments Commission for England (English Heritage).

A Royal Commission on the Historical Monuments of England was appointed by a Royal Warrant of 15 April 1992 to compile and maintain the National Monuments record (currently at Swindon) and identify and record all buildings of architectural and historic interest. On 3 July of the same year the Department of National Heritage was formed by the transfer of functions from the Department of the Environment by means of the Transfer of Functions (National Heritage) Order 1992 (S. I. 1992/1911).

In 1996 the Royal Commission merged with English Heritage, and on 14 July of the following year the Department of National Heritage was renamed the Department for Culture, Media and Sport. The Secretary of State was given a matching title just over a month later, on 22 August 1997.

4. THAMES NAVIGATION AND WATER AUTHORITIES

Since before the Norman Conquest of 1066, successive Thames authorities have had to balance conflicting interests of users of the river, especially mill-owners, navigators and fishermen.

The most serious conflicts were those between mill-owners and navigators. To provide a head of water for a water wheel, a miller had to have a weir across the river upstream of the mill. Small boats could be got past this weir by man-handling, but heavier craft could only continue their journey if a sizeable opening was made in the weir by removing a section of it. At some time in the Middle Ages, removable sections of Thames weirs came to be formed of a wall of wooden paddles in front of an array of squared timber shafts, called 'rymers'. The rymers were held in a line across the navigation opening by two beams, one vertically above the other. The lower beam was fixed to the river bed, and the upper beam was positioned above the high water level and pivoted at one end so that it could be swung out of the way of a passing ship. Both beams were notched at intervals on the upstream side, and the upper beam carried a walkway for the person handling the rymers and paddles. The navigation opening was closed by inserting the tips of the rymers into the notches of the lower beam, then moving the rymers to engage them with the notches in the upper beam. The paddles were then lowered into the water against the upstream faces of the rymers, where they were held in place by water pressure.

Because a downstream flash of water was produced when the paddles and rymers were removed, a weir of this kind came to be known as a 'flash weir' or 'flash lock'. Before a ship could pass the weir, the upstream and downstream water levels had to be allowed to equalise, more or less, so opening a flash weir usually slowed down, then stopped, milling over a period of hours. Millers therefore did not hesitate to delay opening, sometimes for days, to allow a good number of boats to assemble and pass through on a single occasion. Only when flash locks were replaced with pound locks (with adjacent weirs for passing the normal river flows) did conflicts between millers and navigators cease.

A 'pound lock' (nowadays called simply a 'lock') is a structure in which boats are raised or lowered in a chamber (the pound) that lies between upper and lower watertight lock gates. A boat is raised by sailing it into the chamber through the opened lower gates, closing those and sluices in or near them, then allowing water past sluices in or near the upper gates to fill the chamber. The upper gates are then opened to let the boat continue its journey. A boat going downstream is lowered analogously. The volume of water required to raise or lower a boat is vastly less than that which flowed when a flash lock was opened.

The first locks on the Thames were built in the stretch below Oxford in the 17th century primarily to provide deeper water, but the last of the numerous locks that now exist was not completed until the 19th century.

Some Thames authorities responsible for building locks also built bridges for the towpath and across the river for footpaths and, in a few instances, roads. These authorities sometimes specified widths and headways of bridges to be built by others to ensure that navigation was not unduly hindered.

Successive authorities

The Crown

The right of regulating the four Royal Rivers – the Thames, the Severn, the Trent and the Yorkshire Ouse – was assumed by the Crown before the Norman Conquest. Edward the Confessor decreed in 1065 that 'if mills, fisheries or other works were constructed which hindered navigation, they should be destroyed'.

Until 1350, when the first Act of Parliament regulating the Thames was passed (25 Edward 3, c. 4), jurisdiction over the River was a Crown prerogative, which came to be executed through temporary commissions mainly appointed by letters patent. The 1350 Act, like Edward the Confessor's decree of 1065, forbade the building of obstructions to navigation on the Thames. King Edward III might well have influenced the content of this Act because his Council, containing officers of the household, took a large part in formulating statutes. The Council could itself issue ordinances and proclamations, but these could not override common or statute law so had no more than a temporary legislative value.

The City of London (1197)

The City of London was, in effect, re-founded in 886 AD by King Alfred when he recaptured it from the Vikings and resettled the population inside the Roman walls.

To raise money for his second Crusade, Richard I sold his rights covering the whole River Thames in 1197 to the Mayor and Corporation of London, thus initiating the involvement of the City of London with the river that, for the tideway up to Teddington, continues today. Because the City wished to regulate only the tidal portion of the Thames, it erected in 1280 the London (or City) Stone just above Staines Bridge to mark the limit of its jurisdiction. This extent of control was confirmed in 1605 by the first charter of King James I.

In 1810 the City obtained its first Act (50 George 3, cciv)

authorising the construction of locks below Staines at (in upstream order) Teddington (1811), Sunbury (1812), Shepperton (1813) and Chertsey. Lord Lucan objected to the proposed siting of Chertsey Lock and a new Act was obtained in 1812 (52 George 3, xlvi) authorising its construction at its present site, where it was opened in 1813. The 1812 Act also authorised construction of a lock at Molesey, opened in 1815. A third Act was obtained in 1814 (54 George 3, ccxxiii) to allow the building of Penton Hook Lock (opened 1815). Much later, under an Act of 1890 (53 & 54 Victoria, ccxxiv), the City of London built Richmond Half-tide Lock (opened in 1894) to maintain a good level of water between Twickenham and Teddington.

The Burcot Commissioners (1605)

The water level in the 14½-mile stretch of the Thames from Burcot, just below Clifton Hampden, to Oxford, upstream, was not deep enough for the more sizeable barges coming into use by the 17th century. An Act was passed in 1605 (3 James I, c. 20) appointing Burcot Commissioners empowered to remove impediments to navigation but not to build locks. Clearly, they could never solve the problem. The 1605 Act was therefore replaced by an Act of 1623 (21 James 1, c. 32) by which the Lord Chancellor appointed eight Burcot Commissioners empowered to do anything necessary for improving navigation. By 1640 the new commissioners had raised the water level by opening pound locks at Iffley, Sandford, and in the channel that bypasses Abingdon known as the Swift Ditch. Surprisingly, no more pound locks were built in the Thames for 140 years.

Commissioners (1751)

An Act of 1751 (24 George 2, c. 8) established a commission of more than 600 members to watch the interests of those navigating the river above Staines. It thus established the first permanent general authority relating to the Thames.

The Thames Commissioners (1771)

The 1751 Act, like that of 1605, did not empower the commission to construct locks and was replaced by an Act of 1770 (11 George 3, c. 45) that did. The new Act additionally allowed the commission to build or acquire towpaths. Surprisingly, it also increased the already large number of commissioners and named them 'Thames Commissioners'.

The 1770 Act divided the river into six administrative districts and gave control of these to the Thames Commissioners. The first district covered the tidal stretch of the Thames from London Bridge to the London Stone, at Staines, and the second covered from there to Boulter's flash lock. Thus administration of the first district, recognised for centuries as belonging to the City of London, had apparently been transferred from the City Corporation to the new Commissioners. Yet elsewhere in the Act, the City's rights were expressly reserved. Clearly the Act was ambiguous.

In an attempt to resolve this problem, the Commissioners, who included officials of the City Corporation, passed a resolution in 1771 stating that they had no power to build any weir or pound lock below the London Stone. Now a clause in the 1770 Act prevented the Commissioners from building any lock below Boulter's Lock, so the Act and resolution together defined a stretch of river, from the London Stone to Boulter's Lock, in which neither the Commissioners nor the City of London could build a lock! Above Boulter's Lock there was no problem, and the Commissioners soon built a set of eight locks. The first, a substitute for Boulter's flash lock, was opened in 1772. The others, at Marlow, Temple, Hurley, Mill End (Hambledon Lock), Henley (Marsh Lock), Shiplake and Sonning, were all opened the following year.

The ambiguity of the 1770 Act was removed by an amending Act of 1774 (14 George 3, c. 91), which made clear that the tidal part of the river, from London Bridge to the London Stone, was controlled by the Navigation Committee of the City of London. Under the 1774 Act more locks were built between Sonning and Oxford, at Caversham (1778), Mapledurham (1777), Whitchurch, Goring and Cleeve (all 1787), Benson (1788), Day's (1789), and Abingdon (1790).

In 1783 the Commissioners recognised the need to improve navigation from Oxford to Lechlade in readiness for the traffic that would be generated upon the opening of the Thames & Severn Canal on 19 November 1789. The history of this canal was to be of decline and ultimate closure; towards the middle of the 19th century, traffic diminished because of railway competition, and the condition of the upper Thames worsened enough to impede navigation. Nevertheless, some traffic remained and the eastern section from Inglesham survived until 1933. Recently, a Cotswolds Canal Partnership obtained authority to restore 6 miles of the canal, from Stonehouse to Brimscombe Port, and to start doing this in 2005.

The main improvements for navigation recognised by the Commissioners in 1783 were at St John's (Lechlade), Radcot, Godstow and Folly (Oxford) Bridges. At St John's a lock approached by a new navigation channel, just south of the river, was decided upon in 1789 and opened in 1791; the new channel needed a new bridge. At Radcot a navigation cut crossed by a further bridge, with a single arch, was completed in 1787. At Godstow a cut and second bridge were made in 1780 and a lock was opened in 1790. At Folly Bridge the main arch was reconstructed in about 1790. This arch soon failed because the reconstruction did not remove a feature that made the bridge very difficult for boats to pass – the arch was not at right-angles to the road it carried – and this feature was only removed when a new bridge was built, opened in 1827.

An Act of 1795 (35 George 3, c. 106) gave the Thames Commissioners power to build further locks and also purchase land for a public horse towpath. However, land near a house or used as a garden or orchard could not be bought, and a continuous towpath was never achieved. Under the 1795 Act, locks were built at: Romney (1797), Boveney (1838), Bray (1845), Cookham (1830), Clifton (1832), and Culham (1809).

The Thames Conservancy (1857 and 1866)

In 1856 the City of London withdrew all claim to ownership of the bed and soil of the tidal portion of the Thames , and the Crown right was re-conveyed to a Board of Conservancy, having 12 members, constituted under an Act of 1857 (20 & 21 Victoria, c. 147). Five more Conservators were added by an Act of 1866 (29 & 30 Victoria, c. 89), and the Conservancy was given control of the whole tidal river from Yanlet Creek to Cricklade. Also, the weirs of the 28 mills then existing were transferred to the Conservancy so that private interests could have no further chance of hindering navigation.

The Thames Conservancy built more locks above Oxford, at King's (1927), Eynsham (1889), Northmoor (1896), Shifford and Rushey (both 1898), Radcot (1892), and Grafton (1896). Throughout its existence the Thames Conservancy continued to maintain locks, weirs and bridges, the latter including towpath bridges, footbridges across the river, and some bridges wide enough for vehicles, most of those being near locks.

After the Port of London Authority was formed in 1909 (see below), the Conservancy lost responsibility for the Thames below Teddington. The position where responsibility changes is marked by an obelisk 265 yards below the gates of Teddington New Lock.

In 1973 the Thames Conservancy moved from London to Nugent House in Reading, and the Conservators were disbanded on 1 April 1974 when the Thames Water Authority was formed.

The Port of London Authority (PLA) (1909)

By the end of the 19th century the increasing size of ships using the Port of London made extensive works in the river and docks essential. A Royal Commission was appointed in 1900, and in a report of 1902 recommended creation of a central authority. This was done by an Act of 1908 (8 Edward 7, c. 68), which transferred the powers of all the existing dock companies, the function and powers of the Thames Conservancy below Teddington, and certain duties of the Watermen's Company, to a new body called the 'Port of London Authority' (PLA). This started work on 31 March 1909.

In assuming control of Thames navigation below Teddington, the PLA became responsible for the operation and maintenance of Richmond Half-tide Lock with its twin footbridges.

The powers of the PLA are now contained in the Port of London Authority Act 1968 (xxxii).

The Thames Water Authority: Thames Conservancy Division (1973)

The Water Act 1973 (c. 37) established ten Water Authorities covering the whole of England and Wales. These became responsible for navigation of the rivers concerned, and the Thames Conservancy became the Thames Conservancy Division of Thames Water.

The National Rivers Authority (NRA): Thames Region (1989)

The Water Act 1989 (c. 15) established the National Rivers Authority (NRA), which took over the responsibilities of the ten Water Authorities. The work of the Thames Conservancy Division of Thames Water was taken over by the Thames Region of the new authority.

The Environment Agency (Thames Region) (1995)

The Environment Act 1995 (c. 25) abolished the National Rivers Authority on 1 April 1996. The Thames Region of that authority became the Thames Region of the Environment Agency, which embraces the Navigation and Recreation Service.

The Department for Environment, Food and Rural Affairs (2001)

The Environment Agency and the British Waterways Board, responsible for the canals, are now both parts of the Department for Environment, Food and Rural Affairs (DEFRA), formed by Statutory Instrument (S. I. 2001/2568).

The bridges, Dartford to the source

Hampton Bridge. *Murray*

QUEEN ELIZABETH II BRIDGE, DARTFORD

The Queen Elizabeth II Bridge crosses the Thames 20 miles below London Bridge from Dartford to Thurrock. It carries the A282(T), which links the eastern ends of the M25 London Orbital Motorway (Junctions 30, to the north, and 1b, to the south). The bridge carries only the southbound motorway traffic, the northbound passing through the two Dartford Tunnels; the first of those two-lane crossings had been opened in November 1963 and the second in May 1980.

The increase in traffic through the tunnels following partial opening of the M25 in 1984 made it clear that a further crossing would be needed not many years after the motorway had been completed. Therefore, in March 1986 the Department of Transport invited bids for the construction of a bridge. Out of eight bids submitted, that by Trafalgar House plc was accepted, and the company formed Dartford River Crossing Ltd (DRL) in April 1987 to carry out the project. The necessary Act of Parliament (1988, c. 20) was obtained in June and required DRL to lease the tunnels for the amount of the outstanding debt, build a four-lane, cable-stayed bridge, and operate the combined crossing for a maximum period of 20 years. In August 1988 DRL gave possession of the tunnels and site to two Trafalgar House subsidiary companies, Cementation Construction and Cleveland Bridge, and instructed them to start work.

At the site of the proposed bridge, just downstream of the tunnels, the Thames is 800m (2,625ft) wide and the main navigation channel is 305m (1,000ft) wide. A minimum headway of 54m (177ft) was stipulated and the foundations of the river piers had to be massive enough not to be shifted by the impact of a 65,000-tonne ship moving at 10 knots. The design adopted for the superstructure of a bridge that would satisfy these demands was largely due to the German engineer Dr Helmut Homberg. The main cable-stayed portion has two river piers, one at each side of the navigation channel, a central span over that channel, and two back spans between the river piers and transition piers where the main portion meets approach viaducts 1km (0.62 mile) long made necessary by the height of the central span.

Each river pier is built on a large cellular concrete caisson, which was floated into position above a flat surface, then sunk by filling the cells with water. The flat surface had been prepared by excavating the

18.10.93

river bed down to hard chalk, then depositing and levelling crushed limestone on the chalk surface. The interface between the caisson and crushed rock was grouted and the cells in the caisson were filled with concrete to bond the pier foundation to the river bed and give it the required mass. Each of the river piers has two hollow rectangular concrete columns up to road level and, on top of these, steel pylons to which the cable stays are attached.

Piers for the back spans (two for each between the river and transition piers) and approach viaducts (21 spans for the northern and 20 for the southern) are founded on reinforced concrete cast-in-situ piles with pile caps, except for the southern of the two transition piers where driven steel piles are used. The piers for the back spans have twin pillars, the transition piers are full-width slabs, and the piers for the viaducts are single pillars with cross heads.

The deck of each approach viaduct is formed of pier-to-pier spans of five longitudinal plate girders bearing transverse reinforced concrete planks on which a concrete deck slab was cast. The deck of the main span is formed of two outer and two intermediate, less deep, longitudinal plate girders connected by cross girders and carrying a stiffened steel deck having a concrete overlay on which the road surface is laid. The ends of the cross girders carry brackets to which are connected the lower ends of the 112 cable stays that fan out, 14 from each side, from the top of each of the four pylons.

The Queen Elizabeth II bridge was opened on 29 October 1991. A toll is collected for each vehicle using the Dartford crossing at booths about half a mile to the south.

Dimensions

Central span: 450m (1,476ft); each back span: 181m (594ft); cable-stayed length: 812m (8,664ft); lengths of approach viaducts: 1,052m (3,452ft) north, 1,008m (3,307ft) south; total length: 2,872m (9,423ft); height of each river pier: 137m (450ft), concrete columns: 53m (174ft), steel pylons: 84m (276ft); size of concrete caissons: 57m x 32m (187ft x 105ft) in plan, 22m (72ft) deep; width of carriageway: 14.6m (48ft) with two 1m (3.3ft) margins; minimum headway at centre of bridge: 54m (177ft).

TOWER BRIDGE
• Grade I listed •

Tower Bridge carries the A100 across the Thames between Tower Bridge Road, to the south, and Tower Bridge Approach, to the north. Since 17 February 2003 it has formed part of the Inner Ring Road that bounds the Central London Congestion Charge Zone. It spans the Upper Pool, the stretch of river extending from London Bridge to Wapping.

The need for a Thames road crossing below London Bridge was recognised in the early 19th century. In 1876 a Committee was set up by the Corporation of London to study the problem of the new crossing. This Committee considered a variety of schemes, including a rolling bridge, a swing bridge, a high-level bridge with hydraulic hoists at each end, and a steam-driven platform running on rails laid on the river bed, but did not adopt any one of them.

In October 1878 the City Surveyor and Architect, Horace Jones (1819-87), was asked to comment on a high-level bridge proposed by Sir Joseph Bazalgette (1819-91), Chief Engineer of the Metropolitan Board of Works. The authorities probably hoped that the two men would collaborate, but Sir Joseph did not wish to do this. On his part, Mr Jones considered that Sir Joseph's design ignored the views of wharfingers and ship-owners. He therefore suggested a low-level bridge with a pair of drawbridges that could be raised to provide a navigation opening. The drawbridges were to be hinged at central piers carrying towers that contained mechanisms for winding or unwinding chains for the drawbridges and were linked by a high lattice-steel arch.

In 1884, after further designs had been proposed and rejected, the Government assigned the task of bridging the river to the City Corporation. When the Tower Bridge Act (48 & 49 Victoria, cxcv) was passed in 1885, the design approved was a modification of the 1878 Jones design prepared jointly by him and John Wolfe Barry (1837-1918), a son of the designer of the Houses of Parliament. The most important modifications were (a) replacement of the drawbridges by twin bascules (sections of deck pivoted near one end and counterpoised about the pivot axis), which are more readily raised and lowered than drawbridges, and (b) replacement of twin lattice steel arches between the piers by a pair of straight lattice-steel spans between the tops of the towers. Jones was appointed as architect, and Barry and Henry Marc Brunel (1769-1849), son of the famous Isambard Kingdom Brunel (1806-59), were appointed as engineers.

Work on the bridge started on 22 April 1886 and the foundation stone was laid on 21 June that year by the Prince of Wales (who acted on behalf of Queen Victoria and was later to become King Edward VII), who then conferred a knighthood on the architect. Regrettably, Sir Horace did not live to see the bridge finished, dying the following year before even the foundations had been completed. The work was to take eight years and would cost, including the approaches, more than a million pounds. Tower Bridge was opened on 30 June 1894 by the Prince of Wales in the presence of the Princess of Wales (later Queen Alexandra) and the Duke of York. There were elaborate and spectacular celebrations.

For the foundations of each of the two piers that define the navigation opening, 12 caissons were sunk into the river bed. The clay was excavated from inside and between these, then replaced with concrete. The upper, visible, portions of the piers are of brickwork faced with stone. They support the bascules, contain the machinery for raising and lowering these, and carry the two main towers.

Foundations at each river-bank for abutments to carry smaller towers were built in cofferdams.

Each main tower comprises four octagonal steel columns braced together and encased in a Gothic structure of granite and Portland stone. Each of the two straight spans between the tops of the main towers has a pair of lattice girders supporting a footpath; these footpaths are reached by staircases and lifts in the towers. The smaller towers are also of steel encased in masonry, and all four towers are pierced by arches for the roadway. The latter is carried between the banks and adjacent piers by fixed spans suspended from cables which extend from shore anchorages, across the frames of the smaller towers to the tops of the main towers, where they are connected to the ends of straight links under the outer lattice girders of the footpaths. The cables are not like those normally used for suspension bridges but are curved structures of lattice-steel.

Each bascule has four longitudinal steel girders supporting a section of roadway and extending past the pivots where they are joined to a carrier for the counterpoise weighting inside a chamber within the adjacent pier. Toothed quadrants are fixed to the girders at each side of the counterpoise carrier so that the bascule can be rotated between its horizontal and upright positions by driving a shaft carrying pinions meshed with the quadrants. When the bascules are horizontal, locking bolts can be moved into position between the adjacent ends of the longitudinal girders. Until 1976 the pinion shafts were driven by hydraulic engines supplied with high-pressure water produced by a steam-driven pumping engine and stored in hydraulic reservoirs; the high-pressure water was also used for powering the lifts in the towers. Since 1976 the pinion shafts have been driven by electrically powered oil-hydraulic units and electric lifts have been installed in the towers.

To remove the possibility of mechanical failure preventing operation of the bridge, the essential components have always been in duplicate. Originally the bridge had in each duplicate set: (i) two boilers for raising steam; (ii) two steam pumping engines; (iii) three hydraulic accumulators; (iv) a smaller hydraulic engine in each pier; (v) a larger

Main contractors and costs

Mar 1886	Piers and abutments	Mr John Jackson	£131,344
Feb 1887	North approach and anchorage	Mr John Jackson	£52,882
Dec 1887	Cast iron parapet	Mr John Jackson	£5,596
Dec 1887	Hydraulic machinery	Sir W. G. Armstrong, Mitchell & Co Ltd	£85,232
July 1888	Southern approach	Mr William Webster	£33,383
May 1889	Iron and steel superstructure	Sir William Arrol & Co Ltd	£337,113
May 1889	Masonry superstructure	Messrs Perry & Co	£149,122
May 1889	Paving and lighting	W. Sugg & Co et al	£30.333
			£830,005
1972	Electro-hydraulic machinery	Cleveland Bridge & Eng Co Ltd	

Operating machinery

Power of steam pumping engines	360hp
Steam pressure	75lb/sq in
Water pressure	750lb/sq in

hydraulic engine in each pier for use when the wind pressure on the bascules was abnormally high; and (vi) pipework to convey high-pressure water from (ii) to (iii), (iv) and (v). All the boilers and steam pumping engines were in an engine house at the south end of the bridge. Two of the hydraulic accumulators were in an adjacent accumulator house and each pier contained two more. Since 1976 each pier has contained, in duplicate, an electric motor that drives an oil pump and a motor powered by high-pressure oil from the pump, which drives the original pinion shaft.

The opening and closing of the bridge and signals for river and road traffic were controlled from cabins on the eastern, downstream, ends of the piers. In the 1890s the staff, including the Bridge Master and the Resident Engineer, numbered 80. Until the Second World War there were ostlers to help, or provide replacements for, cart horses. After the installation of new machinery in 1976, one man could operate the bridge and the number of full-time staff was reduced to 12; north-east and south-west watchman's cabins were converted into new, more modern bridge-control cabins.

The idea of opening Tower Bridge as a tourist attraction was first considered in 1972. In 1976 the metal portions of the bridge were repainted and the cleaning and restoration of the stonework, windows and decorative features were started. The high-level walkways, which had been closed under an Act of 1906 (6 Edward 7, clxxx), were re-opened and glazed, and a museum was created in the engine house under the southern approach. This contains two boilers, two steam pumping engines, hydraulic accumulators and an hydraulic bascule-drive engine from the south pier. The bridge was opened to the public as the 'Tower Bridge Experience' on 30 June 1982 by the Rt Hon the Lord Mayor Sir Christopher Leaver in the presence of other officials. All the costs had been met by the Bridge House Estates Trust.

Dimensions

Distance between central piers: 230ft; navigation opening: 200ft; width of each central pier 70ft; span of each suspended section: 270ft; distance between abutments: 880ft; length including abutments: 940ft; length of northern approach: 1,260ft; length of southern approach: 780ft; headway at centre (bridge closed): 29ft 6in; headway at centre (bridge open): 135ft; height of main towers above river: 255ft; height of abutment towers: 44ft; width between parapets: opening span 49ft, suspended spans 59ft 6in; width of high-level footways: 12ft.

LONDON BRIDGE

1. The ancient bridges

It seems to be agreed that there was a bridge across the Thames at Londinium soon after AD50 when the Romans founded their settlement. Thousands of Roman coins were dredged from the river in 1832, following removal of the mediaeval bridge, and these were almost certainly offerings thrown from successive Roman timber bridges.

Much later, in the 10th century, several documents refer to a timber bridge. There is an account in the Olaf Sagas of how the bridge was destroyed in 1014 when King Aethelred the Unready, helped by King Olaf of the Norwegians, recaptured London from the Danes. The song of the Norse poet Ottar Svarte commemorating this event is the origin of the nursery rhyme 'London Bridge is broken down'. The timber bridge was rebuilt, and replaced at least twice, before being swept away in a flood in 1091. Its replacement was burned in 1135 and the last timber bridge, of elm, was built in about 1163 by Peter, Chaplain of St Mary's Colechurch, in the Poultry.

2. Old London Bridge *(above right)*

It was Peter of Colechurch who suggested that a stone bridge should be built. His suggestion was adopted and he worked on the new bridge, to the west of the timber bridge, until his death in 1205. The stone bridge was completed in 1209 under the direction of three city merchants, Serle, Almaine and Botewrite, and the timber bridge then removed. To help pay for the bridge, Henry II imposed a tax on wool, hence the legend that the foundations rested on woolpacks.

Old London bridge was 931 feet long between the river banks and had 19 arches and also a navigation opening spanned by a timber drawbridge. Each pier was founded on a boat-shaped island, called a 'starling', made by driving close-fitting elm sheet piles into the river bed and filling the enclosed space with stones. The masonry of the pier was built on a timber platform covered with pitch supported by an

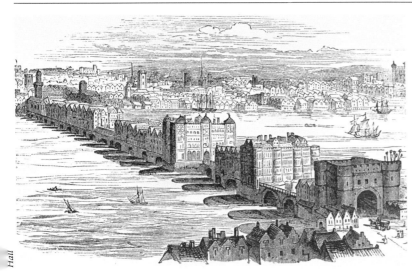

almost all the building and maintenance of the City bridges. Apart from dwellings, the main buildings of old London Bridge were shops, a chapel and two defensive gateways. The chapel was dedicated to St Thomas à Becket, who had been baptised in St Mary Colechurch, of which Peter of Colechurch was chaplain. It was built to the east of the roadway on the ninth pier from the north and had two storeys. Peter of Colechurch was buried in the lower one and his remains were found when the bridge was demolished in 1832. The upper part of the chapel was rebuilt at the end of the 14th century and, after becoming a grocer's shop in 1553, during the reign of Henry VIII, was always used as a secular building.

The Great Stone Gate stood on the second pier from the south. It collapsed in 1437 and its replacement was so damaged by fire in 1725 that it had to be rebuilt in 1727-28. The drawbridge gate was on the seventh pier from the south and was rebuilt between 1426 and 1428. It was pulled down in 1577 and replaced two years later by the ornate timber Nonesuch House, which had been prefabricated in Holland, and was so large that it needed support from the eighth, as well as the seventh, pier.

The many houses and shops on the bridge were frequently rebuilt. All the houses as far as the chapel were burned in 1633 and the gap produced had only been a quarter filled with a large new block by 1666, when the Great Fire of London raged. This consumed the new block but was prevented by the residual gap from spreading further. It was not until 1683 that all the houses had been rebuilt.

London Bridge was of great strategic importance being, until Putney was built in 1729, the only Thames bridge below Kingston. It resisted attack by Wat Tyler in 1381. In 1450 Jack Cade was allowed across with his Kentish rebels, but they murdered and plundered with such ferocity that the Londoners turned against, and defeated, them. Cade's head was displayed on the drawbridge gate. This gruesome custom of displaying severed heads probably started in 1305, with the head of William Wallace, and ended in 1678, with the head of William Stayley, who had been involved in the Popish Plot.

inner rectangle of larch piles. When it was necessary to repair a starling, another row of piles was driven around the outside, the gap being filled with more stones, so that over the centuries the openings were further reduced. When the bridge was measured in 1802, the aggregate waterway between the piers was 524 feet, but that between the starlings was only 231 feet. The obstruction to the flow of water caused by the starlings and piers was so great that there could be a difference of almost 6 feet between the water levels on either side of the bridge. The rush of water through the arches made it an adventure, not risked by some and not survived by others, to shoot the bridge by boat. Another result of the constricted flow was that in cold weather the Thames could freeze thickly right across. Frost fairs were held on the ice, the most famous in 1683-84 and the last in 1813-14.

Even before the bridge had been completed, King John had decreed that houses should be built upon it so that rents could supply money for bridge repair. This is the origin of the Bridge House Estates Trust, which, by careful investment of rents and tolls, has been able to finance

In 1581 Peter Morris, a Dutchman, obtained a 500-year lease, at 10 shillings per annum, of the first arch at the north end of the bridge for setting up a water-wheel and pump for supplying water to London. The system was a great success and further arches were subsequently leased in 1582, 1701 and 1761 and, at the south end, in 1767. Supply of water from the Thames continued into the 19th century, the wheels being removed following an Act of 1822 (3 George 4, cix). The flow of the river was also used to provide power for grinding corn, mills being set up in 1591 on starlings at the south end of the bridge.

Dimensions
Openings: 19 arches and a drawbridge; spans: 25-34ft; pier widths: 18-27ft; overall length: 931ft; total pier width: 407ft; total starling width: 700ft; width of roadway: 20ft.

Elmes (Shepherd)

3. The modified bridge of 1762 *(below left)*
Dissatisfaction with Old London Bridge grew when Westminster Bridge was opened in 1749, comparison being made between the dark, crowded and narrow old bridge and the airy and spacious new one. It was therefore decided to remodel the old bridge. Under an Act of 1756 (29 George 2, xl) the bridge was widened each side, the houses were cleared away, and the ninth pier from the south end was removed to make room for a great central arch. The rebuilt bridge had stone balustrades and alcoves, and the works took from 1758 until 1762. As soon as the great arch had been made, the flow of the river was much increased, to the detriment of the foundations not only of London Bridge but of bridges further upstream. It gradually became evident that an entirely new London Bridge was needed.

Dimensions
Width of roadway: 31ft; width of footways at each side: 7ft.

4. The bridge of 1831 *(right)*
On 15 June 1822 the City Corporation advertised prizes for designs for a new bridge. The first prize was awarded to a Mr William Fowler, but a House of Commons Committee overruled this decision and chose a design that had been submitted in 1821 (only two months before his death) by John Rennie senior (1761-1821), the designer of Waterloo and Southwark Bridges. The Act needed for building the bridge was passed in 1823 (4 George 4, l). Because of Rennie's death, the detailed work of designing and superintending the construction was carried out by his second son, also John (1794-1874). The contractors were Messrs Joliffe & Banks, and work was started in 1824.

The foundations were built within timber cofferdams and the foundation stone was laid inside the first of these on 15 June 1825, the tenth anniversary of the Battle of Waterloo, by John Garratt, Lord Mayor of London. The bridge had five arches of grey granite, the masonry below low water being of sandstone grit from Bramley Fall,

Elmes (Shepherd)

near Leeds. Another Act of Parliament was needed to authorise building the approaches. It was obtained, in the face of much opposition, in 1829 (10 George 4, cxxxvi) largely due to the efforts of the Duke of Wellington. Out of a total cost of £2,556,171, the bridge accounted for £680,232 and the approaches and street alterations £1,840,438, more than twice as much. The remaining £35,500 was for demolition of the old bridge, carried out between November 1831 and some time in 1834.

The bridge was opened on 1 August 1831 by King William IV and Queen Adelaide. When the old Pearl Assurance Co building was demolished in 1921, to make room for Adelaide House, an arch of the

old bridge was revealed, but the £7,000 needed to incorporate this relic could not be raised.

Between 1902 and 1904, under an Act of 1901 (1 Edward 7, xv), the roadway and pavements of Rennie's bridge were widened by corbelling out the pavements using granite brackets. The widening cost £100,000.

Dimensions

Spans and (pier) widths: 130ft (22ft) 140ft (24ft) 151ft 9in (24ft) 140ft 3 in (22ft) 130ft; length between abutments: 782ft; overall length: 1,006ft; length, including approaches: 2,350ft; width: 53ft (32ft 6in roadway and two 10ft 6in footways); width after widening: 65ft (35ft 0in roadway and two 15ft 0in footways).

5. The bridge of 1973 *(below)*

In 1965 the City council decided to rebuild the bridge, which, because of its enormous weight (some 130,000 tons) was gradually subsiding. The City Engineer, H. K. King, was put in charge of the project and the necessary Act of Parliament was obtained (1967, i). The consultants for design and construction were Mott, Hay & Anderson, and the Consultant Architects were William Holford & Partners. A tender of £4,066,573 for the construction, made by John Mowlem & Co Ltd, was accepted.

It was suggested at the meeting of the Bridge House Estates Committee during which the decision to rebuild was made that Rennie's bridge should be offered for sale. This suggestion was adopted and led to the purchase of 10,000 tons of elevational stonework by the McCulloch Oil Corporation of Los Angeles for $2,460,000 (£1,025,000). Twelve thousand pieces of granite were shipped to Lake Havasu City and fixed to each side of a double cantilever reinforced concrete bridge designed by Mott, Hay & Anderson to resist earth tremors; only the cut-off ends of large blocks were used.

The foundation stone of the reconstruction was laid by the Rt Hon

26.6.06

the Lord Mayor, Alderman Sir Gilbert Inglefield, on 23 September 1968, in the presence of the Governor of Arizona, the Hon Jack Williams. He was present also on 10 October 1971 when the bridge was opened by the Rt Hon the Lord Mayor, Alderman Sir Peter Studd. The celebration banquet was a faithful reproduction of the royal luncheon that had been held at the original opening in 1831.

Work on the new London Bridge was started in 1968 with the building of cofferdams and dismantling of the old bridge. The bridge has three spans and is supported by reinforced concrete columns (four for each pier, and two for the north, and three for the south, abutment) sunk deep into the clay of the river bed. The bridge deck comprises four parallel box beams, each made from pre-cast reinforced concrete segments stressed together with high-tensile wire strands. Gantries were erected to lift and position the segments, and throughout the building operation the bridge was kept open. The upstream beam was made first, then used for road traffic, pedestrians using the roadway of the old bridge. The downstream beam was made next, pedestrians being diverted to this so that the old bridge could be demolished and the two central beams built. The four quarters of the bridge thus constructed were then bonded together. The piers of the bridge were faced with axed Cornish granite and parapet walls were faced with polished granite and surmounted by a stainless steel handrail. The new bridge weighs 55,000 tons, less than half the weight of the old. The contract was extended by ten months because of problems in making the foundations, so that the final cost was almost £1 million more than the original tender.

New London Bridge was opened by HM Queen Elizabeth II on 16 March 1973 in the presence of the Rt Hon the Lord Mayor, the Lord Mais.

Dimensions
Spans: 260ft, 340ft (including suspended section of 107ft), 260ft; overall width: 107ft 0in; width between parapets: 104ft 0in (two 30ft 6in carriageways, central reserve 4ft, footways 23ft and 17ft).

CANNON STREET RAILWAY BRIDGE

Situated just above London Bridge, it carries trains from Kent and East Sussex across the Thames to Cannon Street terminus.

The South Eastern Railway Company (SER) opened its line from London Bridge to Dover in stages between 14 December 1836 and 7 February 1844. It originally intended to serve the City from London Bridge station and stations at the south end of Southwark Bridge and at Blackfriars Road, to be included in its extension to Charing Cross. That had been authorised by an Act of 1859 (22 & 23 Victoria, lxxxi) and eventually opened in 1864. However, when the rival London, Chatham & Dover Railway obtained an Act in 1860 (23 & 24 Victoria, clxxvii) for building a line across the river to Ludgate Hill and on to a junction with the Metropolitan Railway, the SER decided not to build the stations on the way to Charing Cross but to build instead a second extension across the Thames, to Cannon Street in the City, and obtained an Act of Parliament for doing this in 1861 (24 & 25 Victoria, xciii). The approach viaducts, Thames bridge and terminus were designed by Sir John Hawkshaw (1811-91), consulting engineer to the railway. Work began in July 1863 and the terminus opened on 1 September 1866. The bridge was originally called Alexandra Bridge, in honour of the future Queen of King Edward VII.

1. The bridge of 1866
The railway bridge was built by George Wythes, Cochrane Grove & Co and cost £193,000. It had five spans and carried five tracks. The deck was of wrought iron plates riveted to the flanges of deep wrought iron plate girders (continuous over the three middle piers), the outer ones with double web plates and resting on crossheads that transmitted the load to fluted cast iron columns. Each pier had four columns extending into the river bed, filled with concrete below low-

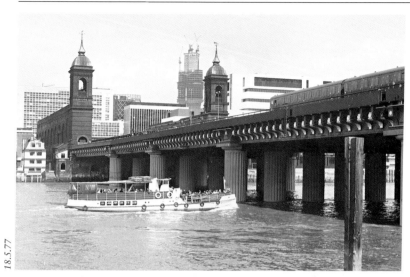

18.5.77

30.5.84

water level and brickwork above, and carrying granite bedstones. The bridge sported a considerable weight of cast iron decoration. At each side a footway was provided, the one upstream being open to the public from 1872 to 1877 on payment of a halfpenny toll, while the downstream footway was used by staff.

Dimensions
Clear spans: 125ft, 136ft, 136ft, 136ft, 125ft; width of piers: 12ft; width of deck: 80ft.

2. The widened bridge of 1892 *(above left)*
Between 1886 and 1892 the bridge was widened to 100 feet by F. Brady (?1829-1919), Engineer of the SER, so that it could accommodate ten tracks. Two cast iron columns were added to the upstream end of each pier and additional bearing girders were installed.

The bridge was strengthened between 1911 and 1914, six new main girders being inserted between the existing ones. Steam locomotives ceased to use the bridge regularly on 13 June 1959, when the last steam train left for Ramsgate.

3. The rebuilt bridge of 1983 *(below left)*
In 1977 it was found necessary to replace the rusted deck and crossheads of the bridge, and to do this without interrupting traffic. Because there was not room to insert prefabricated steelwork, in-situ cast concrete was chosen for the new crossheads, and also for collars (cast as quadrants) to be stressed to the tops of the cast iron cylinders, and jacking slabs to be supported by the collars. The slabs were to be used in raising the main girders to allow bearings to be inserted between them and the new crossheads. The concrete contained limestone aggregate and was cast in steel shuttering. The work was completed in 1983 and considerably changed the appearance of the bridge.

SOUTHWARK BRIDGE

Southwark Bridge carries the A300 northwards from Bridge Road to Queen Street.

1. The bridge of 1819 *(right)*

A company was formed in 1813 under an Act of 1811 (51 George 3, clxvi) to bridge the river at Southwark. The City Corporation and Thames Conservators insisted that the bridge should obstruct navigation as little as possible, so the engineer appointed, John Rennie (1761-1821), decided to build an iron bridge having only three arches. His first son, George (1791-1866), helped, working out jointly with Thomas Young (1773-1829) the profile and dimensions of the arches. An iron bridge was unusual at the time, the first one ever having been built in 1796, less than 20 years earlier, by Abraham Darby at Coalbrookdale.

The piers and abutments were of granite and were built on timber pile and raft foundations constructed inside timber cofferdams. Huge stone blocks for the abutments were obtained from Peterhead by Rennie's second son, John (1794-1874). Each of the three arches comprised eight solid ribs of 15 segments, and all the iron parts were kept in place by dovetailed sockets and cast iron wedges. The iron was cast by the Walker Foundry at Rotherham and the contractors were Joliffe & Banks.

The bridge took more than four years to build, and was opened at midnight on 24 March 1819 by Sir John Jackson, Chairman of the Southwark Bridge Company. There was no expensive ceremony for the good reason that the company had run out of money, the bridge having cost some £800,000.

Old Southwark Bridge was narrow and, together with the steepness of the approaches and the inconvenient road connections, never attracted much traffic. It was purchased by the City of London under an Act of 1867 (30 & 31 Victoria, iii) for £218,868 and freed from toll on 8 November 1864.

Elmes (Shepherd)

Dimensions
Clear spans: 210ft, 240ft, 210ft; overall length: 708ft; deck carried 29ft roadway and two 7ft footways.

2. The bridge of 1921 *(overleaf)*   • *Grade II listed* •

An Act for rebuilding Southwark Bridge was obtained in 1911 (1 & 2 George 5, cxx) and work started in 1913. However, the Great War delayed construction and a further Act had be obtained in 1921 (11 George 5, i) allowing further time for completion of the work. The bridge was opened later that year, on 6 June, at a ceremony performed by Their Majesties King George V and Queen Mary.

The new bridge was designed by Basil Mott CB (1859-1938), Alfred Bowman Yeates and the architect Sir Ernest George RA (1839-1922). The contractor was Sir William Arrol & Co of Glasgow. The bridge has five steel arches, each of seven ribs, between granite piers and abutments. Each pier was founded on a single steel

4.5.79

caisson sunk under compressed air. The cost of construction was £375,000.

London Transport ran electric trams across Southwark Bridge from its north end to destinations in south London from 14 July 1925 to 5 July 1952.

Dimensions

Clear spans: 123ft, 131ft 9in, 140ft 6in, 131ft 9in, 123ft; deck carried 35ft roadway and two 10ft footways.

MILLENNIUM BRIDGE

The Millennium Bridge was the first new bridge built across the Thames in London since the opening of Tower Bridge in 1894. It is a footbridge between the north bank, opposite St Paul's Cathedral, and the south bank, adjacent to Tate Modern (a gallery of modern British art housed in the shell of Sir Giles Gilbert Scott's building for Bankside power station).

It was the vision of David Bell, when Managing Director of the *Financial Times* (FT), which led to the bridge's construction. In 1996 he discussed the idea of a bridge with the Royal Institute of British Architects (RIBA,) which agreed to organise an international competition for a design funded by the newspaper. Instructions for entrants were prepared by the FT, RIBA and Southwark Council and distributed in July 1996, and 227 entries were received. Six were short-listed and the entrants were asked to develop their designs more fully. On 20 December 1996 it was announced that the winning design was that of Foster & Partners, Ove Arup & Partners, London, and Sir Anthony Caro.

In this design the deck was straight so that at night the bridge would appear as a 'blade of light'. The design was modified before construction started, the main changes being that the deck became a shallow arch, to allow improvements to the ramps and steps at the ends, and that aluminium was substituted for wood as the decking material.

To avoid the need for an Act of Parliament, the bridge was built under a licence from the Port of London Authority and planning permissions from the City of London and the London Borough of Southwark, the body organising the works.

The first steps in raising the money for the project were the application by Southwark Council for a Millennium Commission grant from National Lottery funds and the establishment of a Millennium Bridge Trust to raise money matching that of the grant. The Commission agreed to pay half the construction cost and granted £7.2 million. The Trust obtained contributions from the Corporation of London, through the Bridge House Estates Trust, and other sources.

1. The 'wobbly bridge' of 2000

Work at the site started in December 1998. Balfour Beatty carried out enabling works and Mowlem Marine Construction removed the Bankside jetty, which had been used for unloading coal. The main contractors for building the bridge were the British company Sir Robert McAlpine, for the reinforced concrete foundations, abutments and piers, and the Danish company Monberg & Thorsen of Odense, for the metal superstructure, including the cables, their supports and anchorages, and the deck and its suspension members.

The foundations were built in cofferdams and consist of bored piles of reinforced concrete. Those for the abutments – 12 for the north bank and 16 for the south – are just over 2 metres in diameter and are capped with a 3-metre thickness of reinforced concrete. Those for the piers – two for each – are 6 metres in diameter and extend to 25 metres below the river bed. They have reinforced concrete caps on which coned upper portions of elliptical cross-section were cast to carry vee-shaped hollow steel cable supports.

These supports were put in place in January 2000 and soon afterwards were fitted with temporary 'A'-frames for a pulley system to be used for transporting cables and deck parts.

There are four parallel suspension cables at each side of the bridge, held at their highest points at the tips of the vee-shaped supports and anchored at each end to the abutments. The cables form shallow catenary curves that, at the centre of the bridge, extend below deck level.

The deck consists of aluminium box sections fastened at their outer edges to brackets on top of steel tubes that span the river. It is suspended from the cables using transverse steel arms, fixed underneath, which are shaped to maintain the desired curvature of the cables both vertically and horizontally. The edges of the deck carry balustrades and concealed lighting units.

On 9 May 2000 Her Majesty Queen Elizabeth II, Prince Philip, the Lord Mayor of London and the Mayor of Southwark dedicated the bridge; on 8 June there was a firework display and the bridge was lit; and on 10 June the bridge was opened to the public. Under the influence of thousands of pedestrians it oscillated strongly and was immediately nicknamed the 'wobbly bridge'. At 10pm on 12 June it was closed.

2. The stable bridge of 2002 *(previous page)*

On the basis of practical experiments and calculations it was decided to install dampers to prevent oscillation. To suppress lateral vibration, 37 viscous dampers were added, mostly between the deck and the transverse arms, and four pairs of laterally tuned mass dampers were added to the central span. To suppress vertical oscillation, 26 pairs of vertically tuned mass dampers, supported by compression springs, were fitted between the deck and the transverse arms. Cleveland Bridge UK was in charge of the modifications.

The bridge was re-opened on 22 February 2002. It had cost about £23 million, £5 million of that being for the modifications.

Dimensions

Spans: 81m (north), 144m (between piers), 108m (south); width of deck: 4m; sag of cables, central span: 2.3m.

BLACKFRIARS RAILWAY BRIDGES

The present Blackfriars Railway Bridge carries trains from the South East of England across the Thames to Blackfriars station, on the north bank. This is predominantly a terminus, but has, at its western side, two platforms for First Capital Connect (before 1 April 2006, Thameslink) services serving stations further north.

Until 1984, when dismantling of the earlier bridge commenced, there were two Blackfriars Railway Bridges across the river just downstream of Blackfriars (road) Bridge, both built by the London, Chatham & Dover Railway (LCDR). The earlier bridge had been opened on 21 December 1864, as part of the LCDR's London extension to Ludgate Hill, built under an Act of 1860 (23 & 24 Victoria, clxxvii). On 1 January 1866 this extension was completed with a line running north from Ludgate Hill to a junction with the Metropolitan Widened Lines between Aldersgate Street (now Barbican) and Farringdon Street stations.

The later Blackfriars Railway Bridge, a little further downstream, was built under an Act of 1881 (44 & 45 Victoria, xciii) and had been opened on 10 May 1886 as St Paul's Bridge, using the name of the new terminus fronting Queen Victoria Street that it had been built to serve. Both terminus and bridge were renamed Blackfriars on 1 February 1937 to prevent confusion with St Paul's station on the Central Line, which London Transport had just created by renaming Post Office station.

On 16 May 1988 the tunnel between Blackfriars and Farringdon, which had not been used for some 20 years, was re-opened and a through station near the site of the old Holborn Viaduct terminus was brought into use. This allowed Thameslink services to be run between Bedford or Luton, on the St Pancras main line, and Sevenoaks or Brighton on Southern lines south of the Thames.

1. The bridge of 1864 *(right)*

Design of the first railway bridge was delayed because the design of the road bridge to be built as a replacement for the Blackfriars Bridge of 1769 had not been settled. The City Corporation had ruled that the piers of the two new bridges would have to be in line, but were slow in deciding how many spans there should be. Eventually five spans were specified and the railway bridge could be designed by Joseph Cubitt (1811-72) and F. T. Turner (1812-77). It was built by the Crumlin Iron Works with the Resident Engineer W. H. Thomas. Construction was allowed to start on 3 July 1862 and a test train ran across on 6 October 1864. The cost was £220,000.

23.10.69

The bridge was of lattice girder construction with three deep main girders that largely obscured the trains. The central girder was stronger than the outer ones and divided the deck into halves carrying two tracks each. The piers (which were left in place when the super-structure was removed in 1984-85) are in groups of three, one for each main girder, and each consists of a cylindrical stone pillar carrying a cluster of four iron columns with decorative capitals. The abutments were built using stone from the old Westminster Bridge and each of them carried a pair of large cast iron decorations embodying the arms of the LCDR.

The bridge was not used for trains from 3 May 1971, traffic being transferred to the bridge of 1886, and the superstructure was eventually removed. Demolition started on 18 June 1984. In January 1985 a Taklift floating crane from Rotterdam lifted the girder spans from the piers and lowered them on to barges for transit by water back to Rotterdam for scrapping. The two decorations on the south bank have been preserved and beautifully painted.

Dimensions

Spans: 160ft, 176ft, 185ft, 176ft, 160ft; depth of the main lattice girders: 15ft 6in; overall length: 1,014ft; distance between centres of piers in each group of three: 26ft 9in; diameter of stone pillars of each pier: 18ft.

2. The bridge of 1886 *(this page)*

This, the second Blackfriars Railway Bridge, was designed by W. Mills, Engineer of the LCDR, J. Wolfe Barry (1836-1918) and H. M. Brunel (1769-1849). It was built between 1884 and 1886 by the Thames Ironworks & Ship Co. It has five spans of wrought iron arched rib girders and is wide enough to carry seven tracks. The bridge fans out at its north end to accommodate the ends of the terminus platforms. The deck was replaced in 1976.

If proposed Thameslink 2000 works are carried out, the platforms of Blackfriars station will be extended across the railway bridge and a new entrance to the station will be built on the south bank.

Dimensions

Spans: 185ft, 175ft, 185ft, 175ft, 183ft; width between parapets: 81ft (123ft at station abutment).

BLACKFRIARS BRIDGE

Blackfriars Bridge carries the A201 across the Thames between Blackfriars Road, to the south, and New Bridge Street, to the north.

1. The bridge of 1769 *(below)*

The first Blackfriars Bridge was built for the Corporation of London under an Act of 1755 to a design by Robert Mylne (1734-1811). A foundation stone was laid on 31 October 1760 by the Lord Mayor, Sir Thomas Chitty, and the bridge was opened for foot passengers in 1766, as a bridleway in 1768, and completely on 19 November 1769.

When the works were started, it was intended to name the bridge after the Prime Minister, William Pitt the Elder, Lord Chatham (1708-78). However, by the time the bridge had been finished, Pitt was no longer in power and it was named 'Blackfriars Bridge' after the Dominican monastery (established in 1221) that used to stand nearby.

This elegant bridge was of Portland stone and had nine semi-elliptical arches built on timber pile foundations and provided with stone balustrades. The bridge was made wider above each pier to provide pedestrian refuges, and the additional paving and balustrading was supported by double Ionic columns. The bridge itself cost £152,840 and the total cost, including the approaches and £12,250 compensation to the Watermen's Company for loss of ferry revenue, was £230,000.

George Cooke 1827

The building of the bridge was accompanied by great improvements in the neighbourhood, the most noticeable being the covering in, at the northern river bank, of the Fleet Ditch. Until 1785 the bridge was a toll-bridge, but the tolls (for a pedestrian a halfpenny on weekdays and a penny on Sundays) were very unpopular, so much so that in 1780 the toll-house was burned by the Gordon Rioters.

The bridge was altered and repaired from 1833 to 1840 at a cost of £105,158. The crown was lowered and the approaches were raised to reduce the maximum gradient from 1 in 16 to 1 in 24, and the open balustrades were replaced with solid parapets. However, with the increased scour of the foundations caused by the removal of Old London Bridge, the bridge decayed, and was demolished in 1863 to make way for a replacement.

Dimensions

Clear span of three central arches: each 100ft; clear spans of outer groups of arches: 95ft, 85ft, 70ft; length between abutments: 935 ft; overall length: 995ft; width between parapets: 42ft.

2. The bridge of 1869

The rebuilding of the old Blackfriars Bridge was authorised by an Act of 1863 (26 & 27 Victoria, lxii). The foundation stone was laid by the Lord Mayor on 20 July 1865 and the bridge was opened on 6 November 1869 by Queen Victoria.

The new bridge was designed by Joseph Cubitt (1811-72). It has five iron arches between piers of granite-faced brick, which stand on metal caissons sunk into the river bed and filled with concrete and brickwork. Each pier end is decorated with an 11-foot-high, polished granite column weighing 30 tons and bearing a Portland stone capital ornamented with carved swans and herons. The bridge cost £401,131.

Dimensions

Clear spans: 155ft, 175ft, 186ft, 175ft, 155ft; width between parapets: 75ft (43ft carriageway and two 16ft footways); length between abutments: 923ft.

18.5.77

3. The widened bridge of 1909 *(above)*   • *Grade II listed* •

In July 1907, under an Act of 1906 (6 Edward 7, clxxx), work was started on widening the bridge to accommodate twin tramlines. The appointed engineer was Sir Benjamin Baker KCB (1840-1907), but he died shortly afterwards so Basil Mott (1859-1938) and E. M. Wood were engaged to take over the project. The contractors were Sir William Arrol & Co Ltd of Glasgow, and masonry work was carried out by Mitchell Brothers of the same city.

As built, each arch had nine wrought-iron ribs. During widening, this number was increased to 12 by the addition of steel ribs, but otherwise the appearance of the bridge was unchanged. The widened bridge was opened for traffic, including trams, on 14 September 1909 by the Lord Mayor of London, Sir George Wyatt Truscott, Baronet. The widening had cost £232,000. Tram services across the bridge ceased on 5 July 1952.

In connection with an improved road along the Embankment, authorised by an Act of 1960 (8 & 9 Elizabeth 2, xlviii), the northern bridgehead was altered. A plaque commemorating the start of this work bears the date 8 July 1963.

Dimensions

Width between parapets: 105ft (73ft carriageway and two 16ft footways).

WATERLOO BRIDGE

Waterloo Bridge carries Waterloo Road (A301) across the Thames to the Strand.

1. The bridge of 1817 *(below)*

Despite opposition from those who controlled London, Blackfriars and Westminster Bridges, a speculative company obtained an Act of Parliament in 1809 (49 George 3, cxci) enabling it to build a new Thames bridge from Lambeth to just by Somerset House. This Strand Bridge Company appointed George Dodd (c1783-1827) as engineer and he produced a design closely based on a famous bridge built across the Seine at Neuilly in 1774 by Jean Perronet (1708-94). The company was not satisfied with Dodd's design and consulted John Rennie (1761-1821) and William Jessop (1745-1814), who together severely criticised it. In 1810 the company appointed Rennie as engineer and Dodd as his assistant.

The foundation stone of the bridge was laid on 11 October 1811 by the Committee of Directors. The foundations were built inside timber cofferdams and comprised timber piles supporting rafts of timber, rubble and stone, which in turn supported timber platforms on which the stonework was built. The bridge had nine semi-elliptical arches and with its approaches had an overall length of almost half a mile. It was faced with Cornish granite and had Aberdeen granite balustrades. Each pier was ornamented with pairs of three-quarter Doric pilasters.

The bridge was built by Joliffe & Banks and cost £618,370 (including Parliamentary expenses); the cost including the approaches was £937,392. Before the works had been completed, further Acts of Parliament had to be obtained for raising more money, and the second

Elmes (Shepherd)

of these, passed in 1816 (56 George 3, lxiii), authorised changing the name of the bridge to Waterloo Bridge to commemorate the allied victory over Napoleon. The bridge was opened on the second anniversary of the battle, 18 June 1817, by the Prince Regent (later King George IV) in the presence of the Duke of Wellington (1769-1852). After the ceremony the Prince offered John Rennie a knighthood, an honour that he declined.

Waterloo Bridge was a toll bridge until 1878, when it was bought by the Metropolitan Board of Works under an Act of 1877 (40 & 41 Victoria, xcix) for £474,200. In 1880 it was found that the increased scour caused by the removal of Old London Bridge had uncovered the footings of the pier masonry, so between 1882 and 1884 timber sheet piling was driven around each pier and concrete spans were provided, this work costing £63,000. Between 1903 and 1908 a subway for single-deck trams was made between Theobald's Road and the Embankment; at the Embankment end it emerged from the abutment of the bridge, the north-west stair being removed to make way.

In 1923 the fifth pier, at the Lambeth side of the central arch, subsided, and on 11 May 1924 the bridge had to be closed. The structure was lightened by removing material from the roadway, and the failing fifth and sixth arches, at each side of the fifth pier, were propped up and the parapets above then taken away. A temporary bridge of timber and steel was built alongside, downstream, by Sir William Arrol & Co. This carried a 20-foot roadway and two footpaths and had a long navigation span adjacent to the old third and fourth arches. It cost £164,000 and was completed in August 1925.

For ten years Rennie's bridge was the subject of fierce aesthetic, technical and political controversy. It had always been considered his masterpiece: the Italian sculptor Canova (1757-1822) had described it as 'the noblest bridge in the world, worth a visit from the remotest corners of the earth'. A Royal Commission of 1925 recommended in its report of 30 November 1926 that the old bridge should be widened by corbelling, and supplemented by a new double-deck steel bridge at Charing Cross carrying six railway tracks on its lower deck and a

roadway on its upper deck. An alternative plan, which was worked out in 1929 by the LCC and agreed with the Southern Railway, involved the abolition of Charing Cross station and replacement of the railway bridge with a new road bridge. This was rejected twice by Parliament, in 1930 and 1931. In 1932 the Council tried to obtain leave to replace the Rennie bridge, but failed and reluctantly agreed to recondition and widen it. However, when Labour gained control of the LCC in 1934, this resolution was rescinded and the Council decided to build a new six-lane bridge without a Road Fund grant. On 21 June 1934 Herbert Morrison (1888-1965) ceremoniously wielded a sledge hammer to dislodge the first stone of the old bridge, and demolition was completed in 1936. The work cost £331,000. The following year the new bridge was started and Parliament finally agreed to a grant of 60% being made towards its cost.

Dimensions

Clear span of each of nine arches: 120ft; width of each of eight piers: 20ft; length of Middlesex approach: 370ft; length of Surrey approach: 1,380ft; deck carried 27ft 6in roadway and two 7ft 6in footways.

2. The bridge of 1944   • *Grade II* listed* •

The new Waterloo Bridge was designed by John Cuerel of Messrs Rendell, Palmer & Tritton in conjunction with the LCC Engineer, Sir Peirson Frank (1881-1951), and the consulting architect, Sir Giles Gilbert Scott (1880-1960). The contractors were Peter Lind & Co Ltd.

The bridge is of reinforced concrete faced with Portland stone and has five main spans and concealed shore spans. Although the bridge appears to have arches, it. is in fact a beam bridge. A pair of box beams extend from each end across three piers and overhang the central span. The overhanging portions act as cantilevers for supporting a central suspended span. The roadway is carried by a slab strengthened with secondary beams cast between the main beams. To obtain the desired headroom, it was necessary for these main box beams to be shallow, and they therefore had to be very heavily reinforced with steel bars welded together. The piers comprise concrete walls and jacks that allow any subsidence of the foundations to be counteracted. The piers are shrouded and protected by reinforced concrete shells. The lower parts of the sheet-steel cofferdams in which the foundations were made were left in the river bed. The new Waterloo Bridge cost about a million pounds, including £27,480 for the concrete in the superstructure, almost as much – £24,678 – for the facing stone, and £164,000 for the reinforcing steelwork.

20.9.79

Two lanes of the new Waterloo Bridge were opened on 11 August 1942, and on 21 December that year the footpaths were opened and the temporary bridge closed. The latter was dismantled in November 1943 and later used for repairing the Rhine bridge at Remegen during the Allied offensive against Germany. Waterloo Bridge was completed in December 1944, but not formally opened until 10 December 1945, the ceremony being performed, appropriately, by Herbert Morrison.

The tramway tunnel under the north approach had been deepened between 1929 and 1931 to take double-deck trams, but had been disused since trams had been abolished in 1952. It was decided to adapt the old tunnel as an underpass, light traffic from the bridge descending a ramp opposite Somerset House and emerging at the south end of Kingsway. This Strand Underpass was designed by Sir Frederick

Snow & Partners and built between 1962 and 1964 by John Mowlem. It was opened on 21 January 1964 by Herbert Morrison, then Lord Morrison of Lambeth.

In 1973 a memorial to John Rennie was set up on the remains of the first pier of the old bridge. It includes a replica of the foundation stone of his bridge and a fibreglass plaque showing the bridge in bas relief based on a watercolour by A. Yates. Between 1975 and 1976 the road was divided in two by a central island, which included new lamp standards.

Dimensions

Span of each of five arches: 252ft between centres; length of each of two concealed shore spans: 78ft; overall length: 1,236ft; before division in 1976, deck carried 58ft carriageway and two 11ft footways.

HUNGERFORD/GOLDEN JUBILEE FOOTBRIDGES AND CHARING CROSS RAILWAY BRIDGE

The present footbridges cross the Thames from near the Royal Festival Hall, on the South Bank, to the Victoria Embankment, on the North Bank, near its junction with Northumberland Avenue. The railway bridge stands between the footbridges and carries lines from London Bridge station, on the south bank, across the river to the terminus at Charing Cross.

The ten successive bridges at this crossing are described below in chronological order. For simplicity, the sections that contain footbridges beside the railway bridge are not split into downstream and upstream subsections.

Hall

1. The Hungerford Suspension Bridge of 1845 *(left and right)*

In 1669 the 16th-century house of the extravagant Sir Edward Hungerford (1632-1711) burned down and in 1682, to provide himself with additional income, he built Hungerford Market in its grounds. The original market building was replaced in 1833.

Between 1841 and 1845 a suspension footbridge – the first Hungerford Bridge – was built to attract custom to Hungerford Market from Lambeth, on the south bank. The land for the southern approach had been bought in 1840 from the Archbishop of Canterbury. The bridge was designed by Isambard Kingdom Brunel (1806-59) for the Hungerford & Lambeth Suspension Footbridge Company, with powers defined by Acts of 1836 (6 & 7 William 4, xxxiii) and 1843 (6 & 7 Victoria, xix). It cost £100,000 to build and was opened on 1 May 1845 as a toll-bridge.

The bridge pathway was suspended from eight chains, four each side, supported by brick towers built on large brick piers. These piers were used to provide access to river steamers and, with modification, still exist. A good photograph of the bridge when just built was taken by William Henry Fox-Talbot (1800-77), the inventor of negative-positive photography.

The bridge was largely demolished to make room for Charing Cross Railway Bridge and its suspension chains and ironwork were sold for £5,000 for use in completing the Clifton Bridge across the Avon Gorge near Bristol (opened in 1864).

Illustrated London News

Dimensions

Central span: 676ft; two shore spans each of 343ft; span between the centre lines of the piers: 702ft; span between abutments: 1,352ft; height above water of suspension towers: 80ft; height above water at piers: 28ft 6in; width of deck: 14ft.

2, 3 & 4. The Charing Cross Railway Bridge and the Hungerford Footbridges of 1863

The London Bridge & Charing Cross Railway was authorised by Parliament in 1859 (22 & 23 Victoria, lxxxi) and was built to provide direct rail communication between the West End and the South East of England, especially Dover, where boat trains were to be allowed to use the Admiralty Pier. An Act of 1860 (23 & 24 Victoria, cxlvii) dissolved the Hungerford Bridge Company and transferred its property to the railway company.

Acquiring the land for this short (1 mile 68 chain) railway was very expensive, partly because the Governors of St Thomas' Hospital (then near London Bridge) made the South Eastern Railway buy the whole hospital site for £296,000, even though only a sixth of an acre of that land was required. The new terminus, Charing Cross, was built on the site of Hungerford Market and the necessary railway bridge across the Thames was built on the site of the Hungerford Suspension Bridge.

The railway bridge was designed by Sir John Hawkshaw (1811-91) and built by Cochrane & Co of Dudley. It had six river spans and, at the terminus end, two land spans. The two brick piers from the suspension bridge were supplemented by six new piers, four in the river and two on the Embankment, of cast iron tubes. All the tubes were built up in sections and had wider lower portions, intermediate coned portions, and narrower upper portions visible above the river and adjacent land. Each river pier had two tubes and the land piers had seven and nine tubes to support a fan-shaped deck for the platform ends and trackwork of the terminus. The tubes for the river piers were sunk in open caissons into the river bed. All the piers were filled with concrete to low-water level and with brickwork above, and were capped with pad stones. The river and outer land pad stones carried lattice girders joined by lattice cross-girders that supported a deck wide enough to carry four railway tracks, and projected over the river to support upstream and downstream footpaths replacing the foot crossing that had been provided by the Brunel bridge.

The railway bridge was built between June 1860 and the middle of 1863 for £180,000, and the first trains, serving the Greenwich and mid-Kent lines, crossed it on 11 January 1864. Pedestrians paid a halfpenny toll until 1878, when the Metropolitan Board of Works paid the South Eastern Railway £98,000 to make the footbridges toll-free.

As described below, the bridge was supplemented between 1882 and 1887 with a new bridge upstream. In 1906, during repairs to the station roof, some new main girders were put into the 1863 bridge, and at the end of October 1916 minor strengthening work commenced. However, this part of the widened Charing Cross Bridge was still not as strong as the new. Therefore, when Southern Railway suburban services were electrified in 1926, it was arranged for the electric trains to use the older bridge and for the heavier main-line steam trains to use the newer. This arrangement continued until June 1961 when the Kent Coast lines were electrified so that steam locomotives no longer came to Charing Cross. Since 1926 only two lines on the old bridge have been used for traffic, a third line being used as a siding. The most extensive repair of the 1863 bridge was carried out in 1979 when the deck was replaced.

Dimensions

2 Railway Bridge: six clear spans from south bank of 154ft (river) and three of 100ft (land); river piers (counting from south bank): Nos 1, 3, 4 and 5 two cast iron tubes of lower diameter 14ft and upper diameter 10ft spaced 49ft 4in apart, Nos 2 and 6 brick piers from Brunel bridge of 1845, 30ft thick, land piers Nos 7, 8 and 9 cast iron tubes of lower diameter 10ft and upper diameter 8ft (end tubes) and 6ft (inner tubes); width: 61ft 3in over river, 49ft 4in to 168ft between main girders at fanned approach to station.

3 and 4 Footbridges: width 7ft 6in supported on 9ft 6in cross girder extensions.

5. The additional Charing Cross Railway Bridge of 1887

(opposite page)

Between 1882 and 1887 Charing Cross Railway Bridge was widened by building a new bridge of matching design on the upstream side of the old. It has two tubes per pier and carries two tracks. Also a third new track was accommodated by removing the attached upstream Hungerford Footbridge (4) and fitting a deck between the adjacent main girders of the new and old bridges. All the work was carried out under Mr F. Brady (?1829-1919), Engineer of the South Eastern Railway, by Messrs James Cochrane. The deck of the 1887 bridge was replaced in 1948.

Dimensions

River piers Nos 1, 3, 4 and 5 supplemented upstream with two cast iron tubes as for the original bridge, spaced 29ft apart, downstream tube being 19ft upstream of adjacent tube of original pier; third new track carried between girders 16ft 3in apart.

6. The Festival of Britain temporary footbridge of 1950

Bailey bridges were designed for military use and have pin-jointed standard parts, individually easy to handle. Large-scale production of the parts started in 1941 during the Second World War. In 1950 a Bailey bridge having its own timber-piled piers was built upstream of Charing Cross railway bridge to provide a wide footbridge across to the 1951 Festival of Britain exhibition. This bridge was removed after the exhibition.

The piers for the bridge, not in line with those of the railway bridge but irregularly spaced, were made by Richard Costain Ltd for the London County Council. The superstructure was constructed by Army engineers, using a 140-foot Bailey launching platform on the South Bank. This platform had rails along which a trolley could be winched towards or away from the river. The engineers lifted prefabricated 80-foot triple-single girders on to the trolley and joined these to form triple-triple bridge sections. Two of these sections were connected to form a first span of 156 feet, which was winched across the river until its outer end rested on rollers on the first pier. Another bridge section was then made, connected to the first, and the whole winched out. This process was repeated until all the bridge sections had been joined and the bridge extended across the rollers on all the piers. Finally, the upstream span was cut and slewed downstream.

Dimensions

Spans (from north bank): 170ft; 121ft; 170ft; 175ft; 85ft; 180ft; 152ft; width of deck: 14ft 3in; distance of centre line of bridge above railway bridge: 40ft.

7 & 8. The replacement downstream Hungerford Footbridge and temporary upstream Hungerford Footbridge of 1979 *(see page 18)*

In 1979 the wrought iron girders and timber flooring of the deck of the 1863 railway bridge were replaced. The attached downstream Hungerford Footbridge (3) was also replaced (7). To maintain a pedestrian crossing while this work was in progress, a temporary bridge (8) was attached to the upstream side of the 1887 bridge and consisted largely of tubular steel scaffolding.

The replacement downstream Hungerford Footbridge (7) was removed after the downstream Golden Jubilee cable-stayed bridge had been opened.

15.5.81

9 & 10. The Golden Jubilee (originally Hungerford) cable-stayed Footbridges of 2002 *(far right)*

In 1995 the Cross River Partnership was formed, comprising the Department of the Environment, Transport and the Regions, the London Borough of Lambeth, the Mayor of London, the Millennium Commission, Railtrack, the Railway Heritage Trust, Transport for London and Westminster City Council. The Partnership decided that an improved Hungerford pedestrian crossing was needed to stimulate regeneration of the South Bank, and it therefore held a design competition, which was won in 1996 by concept engineers WSP Group and concept architect Lifschutz Davidson. That year a Millennium Commission grant was obtained for the project. The winning design was for a pair of cable-stayed bridges, one upstream and one downstream of the Charing Cross Railway Bridge

In the winning design the decks were to be stayed from the tops of tapered steel pylons mounted on new concrete piers in line with the six piers of the railway bridge. The second and sixth of these, counting from the south bank, are the large brick Surrey and Middlesex piers retained from Brunel's suspension footbridge. The piers to be built upstream and downstream of the Surrey pier were each to carry two pylons inclined towards the railway bridge. The other ten piers, adjacent to the four rows of cast iron tubes and the brick Middlesex pier, were to be smaller and each was to carry a single pylon inclined away from the railway bridge. The pylons were inclined so as to bring their tops above the centre lines of the bridge decks and were held in place by backstays and backstay struts linked to the piers. Deck struts were also to be fitted between the decks and piers to prevent the bridges from swaying. For the pylons adjacent to cast iron tubes, the stays and struts were to be linked to steel collars surrounding, but spaced away from, the tubes and tied down to the piers. This arrangement was chosen to avoid direct contact between the rail and footbridges. Foundations for the new piers were to be of reinforced concrete and consist of clusters of four bored piles crowned with pile caps.

Detailed design by Gifford & Partners took three years and in July 1999 a construction tender of £21m made by Costain/Norwest Holst joint venture was accepted. In October work started on the bored pile foundations for the pylons. Fears that the boring might disturb unexploded bombs or breach Bakerloo and Northern Line tunnels under the Thames led London Underground to impose restrictions on the contractors' operations, which prevented the work being completed. After a long period of disagreement it was decided by November 2000 to redesign the bridges. This was done, the most northern river piers being moved to the Embankment, and the two pylons these were to have carried being replaced by 'A' frames. After additional funding had been agreed, a new contract for £39.5m was signed in January 2001.

As a result of the redesign, the clusters of piles for the two piers and abutment at the northern ends of the bridges were replaced with large single columns cast in hand-dug shafts. Once the foundations had been completed, new concrete piers were constructed on them. To protect the railway and new footbridges against a colliding ship, the pairs of new piers adjacent to the three tubular piers of the railway bridge in the navigation channel were connected at each side of the pier tubes by pre-cast concrete beams. Before these beams were sunk to the river bed, they were suspended beneath the railway bridge and shuttering was installed beneath them and around the tubular supports of that bridge to form a trough that was filled with concrete. The resulting massive structure was lowered to rest on the pile-caps beneath and connected to them with steel pins, then concrete.

The deck for each bridge was made of reinforced concrete by a technique known as 'incremental launching'. A first deck portion, approximately 50 metres long, was cast in a frame adjacent to the non-navigable span at the southern end of the railway bridge. Castings for connecting the stays were stressed on to the concrete and the portion was attached to a massive steel launch truss. This truss was moved northwards across the river and supported by a temporary pier of concrete blocks surmounted by a steel tower; such a pier was provided adjacent to each river pier of the railway bridge. A second deck portion was then cast at the tail of the first, attached to a further truss and, after the trusses had been bolted together, moved across the river. This process was repeated until the deck spanned the crossing.

The pylons, formed into frames with their stiffened backstays for easy handling, were lifted by a floating crane on to the piers for erection. The deck stays (28 per pylon), also stiffened for easy handling, were next lifted for attachment between 'angel wings' at the tops of the pylons and the castings stressed to the deck. Finally, the deck was lowered gradually until it was supported by the stays, allowing the stiffeners used during lifting and the launch trusses to be removed. Each bridge was completed by installing deck slabs, stainless steel handrails, lighting and, at each end, stairs and a lift.

The upstream footbridge was opened to the public on 13 May 2002 and the downstream in September that year. The deck of the upstream bridge contains the inscription 'Golden Jubilee Bridges opened by HRH Princess Alexandra on 2nd July 2003'. Each bridge carries a panel commemorating the Golden Jubilee of Her Majesty Queen Elizabeth II, gives details of successive bridges at the site, and identifies the features of the view from it.

Dimensions
River piers in line with those of railway bridge (see above); length of deck: 316m; width of deck: 4.7m. 'A' frame length: 35m; pylon length: 25m; pile diameter: 1.5m; diameters of foundation shafts near Bakerloo Line: 4m (land), 5m (river).

Upstream bridge, 12.11.03

WESTMINSTER BRIDGE

Westminster Bridge carries the A302 between Westminster Bridge Road, near Old County Hall, westwards across the Thames to Bridge Street, Parliament Square, and Victoria Street.

1. The bridge of 1750 *(below)*

The City of London long feared the possible consequences of a second bridge being built across the Thames to rival Old London Bridge. On 26 October 1664, when advancing a loan of £100,000 to King Charles II, the Common Council recorded the City's 'most humble thanks for the great instance of His Majesty's good and favour towards them expressed in preventing of the new bridge proposed to be built over the River of Thames betwixt Lambeth and Westminster which as is conceived would have been of dangerous consequence to the state of the City.'

It was not until 1736 that opposition to a new bridge was overcome and an Act of Parliament (9 George 2, c. 29) was obtained for building one. This and a succession of further Acts allowed money to be raised by lotteries. Compensation for loss of traffic was paid both to the Watermen's Company and to the Archbishop of Canterbury, as owner of a ferry at the site.

A prize for a design for the new bridge was won by James King

Elmes (Shepherd)

(d1744), whose bridge was to be of timber with stone piers. However, it was soon decided that the whole bridge should be of stone, and a new design was prepared by Charles Labelye (1705-81), a naturalised Swiss who had been commissioned to construct the piers of the first design. Work started in 1738 and the first stone was laid on 29 January 1739 by the Earl of Pembroke.

The piers, of which there were 14, were built in box-like caissons of heavy timber that were constructed on shore, floated into position, then sunk on an area of river bed that had been excavated down to a gravel bed. The masonry was built on the bottom of a caisson and its sides were then removed for re-use.

Old Westminster Bridge had 15 semi-circular arches, the central arch being the widest and the seven at each side narrowing towards the river banks. It was built largely of Portland stone, but Purbeck stone was used for the spandrels, causeways and paving. The piers had cutwaters at each end on which turrets of half-octagonal section were built. Twelve of these turrets, the four at each side of the central arch and the pairs carried by the first, second, 13th and 14th piers, were extended at the top and curved inwardly to form alcoves. The latter, because of their half-dome shape, focused sound so that a conversation held in one alcove could be clearly heard by a person in the alcove immediately opposite. Despite this snag, the alcoves were so favoured by sundry wrong-doers that the bridge commissioners had to appoint a dozen watchmen to keep order.

The bridge was completed on 25 October 1746. However, during the summer of 1747 the fifth pier, from the Westminster abutment, failed. Much work was needed to rebuild that pier on strengthened foundations and reconstruct the adjacent arches. The bridge was eventually opened (toll-free) on 18 November 1750, and had cost £380,500 to build.

The bridge proved very expensive to maintain: between 1810 and 1830 £83,000 was spent on repairs. Tolls were considered but not imposed. Also, in 1813, gas lighting was provided. During the year 1843, to lighten the load on the foundations, the roadway was lowered and some of the superstructure replaced with brick arches. Only three years later the roadway was lowered further, the stone balustrades and alcoves were replaced with timber palings, and three arches were propped up with timber centring. These measures were not enough to remedy the faults in the bridge, but it was not until 1852 that the Bridge Commissioners reported that a new bridge, of iron, should be built as a replacement.

Dimensions

Bridge was symmetrical about central arch and clear spans and (widths of abutments/piers) from either bank were: (76ft) 25ft (12ft) 52ft (12ft) 56ft (13ft) 60ft (14ft) 64ft (15ft) 68ft (16ft) 72ft (17ft) 76ft (central arch); overall length: 1,220ft; width of roadway: 30ft; width of footways: 6ft; width of parapets: 1ft.

2. The bridge of 1862 *(overleaf)* • *Grade II* listed* •

By an Act of 1853 (16 & 17 Victoria, c. 46), the Office of Works was empowered to replace Old Westminster Bridge and work was started in the following year. The first contractors failed after doing little, and it was not until 1856 that work was restarted. The new bridge was designed by Thomas Page (1803-77), who collaborated with Sir Charles Barry (1795-1860), architect of the Houses of Parliament. Construction was by Messrs Cochrane & Co.

The bridge has seven iron spans supported by granite-faced brick piers and abutments; granite from the old bridge was used in facing the abutments. The piers are supported on timber piles that were given protection by surrounding them with cast iron piles some distance apart, filling the gaps between them with ribbed cast iron plates, and replacing the clay in the resulting iron enclosure with concrete. Each span has 15 arch ribs that are of cast iron except in their central portions, where wrought iron was used. The deck was of Robert Mallet's buckled metal plates (patented in 1852) but is now of reinforced concrete. The parapets and spandrels are of cast iron and include the coats of arms of Queen Victoria, Albert the Prince Consort, the Prince of Wales, Sir William Molesworth (First Commissioner of

6.7.75

the Board of Works) and Lord Palmerston (1784-1865). The bridge was opened on 24 May 1862 (Queen Victoria's birthday in the 25th year of her reign). It had cost £393,190 and the approaches had cost an additional £109,054.

In 1906 lines for trams picking up current from a conduit were laid. Tram services ran over the bridge from 15 December 1906 until 5 July 1952.

Dimensions

Clear spans: 94ft 4in, 104ft 6in, 115ft, 120ft, 115ft, 104ft 6in, 94ft 4in; width of piers: 10ft; overall length: 811ft 6in; width of carriageway: 58ft 5in; widths of footways: 12ft 10in (east), 13ft (west).

LAMBETH BRIDGE

Lambeth Bridge links the triple junction, near Lambeth Palace, of Lambeth Palace Road, Albert Embankment (parts of the A3036) and Lambeth Road (A3203) with the junction of Millbank (A3212) and Horseferry Road (B323).

Lambeth Palace has been the residence of the Archbishops of Canterbury since the close of the 12th century. A ferry, commemorated in the name Horseferry Road, was licensed by the See of Canterbury to carry horses and coach traffic across the Thames between the Palace and Millbank, and when Westminster Bridge was built the Archbishop was compensated for loss of revenue from this ferry.

1. The bridge of 1862 *(above right)*

An Act of Parliament for building a bridge across the Thames at Lambeth was obtained in 1826 (7 George 4, lx) and two others were obtained, in 1836 and 1837, by the Metropolitan Suspension Bridge Co, but nothing came of these proposals. It was another private company that finally built a bridge under an Act of 1861 (24 & 25 Victoria, cxvii).

The bridge was designed by Peter William Barlow (1809-85) and was a suspension bridge having three equal spans. The deck was suspended from 28 wrought iron cables in four groups – two each side – which passed over iron towers on the piers and abutments to cast iron anchorage girders built in near the backs of the abutments. The deck comprised cross girders riveted to longitudinal box girders, which were connected to the cables by vertical and diagonal members. Each river pier consisted of two cast iron cylinders that were driven into the clay of the river bed then filled with concrete in the lower parts and with brickwork in the upper. It was the ease with which these cylinders were forced through the London clay that made Barlow realise that a tunnel could be made by forcing a cylinder through clay horizontally, a method that he was to use later when constructing the 'tube' railways.

Illustrated London News, 22.2.1862

Until 1879, when it was freed from toll under an Act of 1877 (40 & 41 Victoria, xcix), Lambeth Bridge was a toll-bridge. It began to fail after only 17 years. In 1887 Sir Benjamin Baker (1840-1907) was consulted about its stability because serious movement of the Westminster abutment had occurred. He thought that with reasonable care the bridge might last 30 years and suggested some remedial work, which was carried out, and a 3-ton weight limit was imposed. In 1905 vehicles were restricted to walking pace, and in 1910 the bridge was closed to vehicles altogether. Soon after this the LCC had so little confidence in the structure that it employed two men to watch the bridge and close gates at each end if it seemed likely that a crowd would collect!

Dimensions

Clear spans: three of 268ft; diameter of pier tubes: 12ft; spacing of pier tubes: 22ft; distance between abutments: 828ft; deck carried 20ft roadway and two 10ft footways.

2. The bridge of 1932 *(overleaf)*

An Act for building a new Lambeth Bridge was obtained in 1924 (14 & 15 George 5, lxvii). In 1929 the old bridge was demolished and a temporary bridge was built upstream of the site for the new bridge, which was to run from the old Westminster abutment to a point 81 feet upstream of the old Lambeth abutment; also, work on the new bridge was started. This was designed by Sir George Humphreys KBE, who until 1930 was Chief Engineer of the LCC, with Sir Reginald Blomfield RA (1846-1942) and A. Topham Forrest as architects. The contractors were Messrs Dorman Long & Co Ltd.

The new bridge has five spans. The four river piers are of mass concrete faced with Cornish granite founded on steel caissons that were sunk under compressed air 27 feet below the river bed. The abutments were excavated in open cofferdams. Each span comprises nine two-pinned steel arched ribs with segmental soffits.

Lambeth Bridge was opened on 19 July 1932 by HM King George V accompanied by Queen Mary. With approaches, it had cost £936,365.

Dimensions
Clear spans: 125ft 2in, 149ft, 165ft, 149ft, 125ft 2in; distance between abutments: 776ft 4in; deck carries 36ft roadway and two 12ft footways.

6.7.75

VAUXHALL BRIDGE

Vauxhall Bridge carries the A202 north-westwards across the Thames between Kennington Road and Vauxhall Bridge Road, and also links the Albert Embankment (along the south bank) with Millbank and Grosvenor Road (along the north).

In the early 19th century the north bank of the Thames at Pimlico was largely occupied with gardens and osier beds. On the opposite bank were the famous Vauxhall Gardens, which had been formed as a public resort in about 1661, during the reign of Charles II, and lasted until 1859. Anyone wishing to cross the river did so by ferry.

In 1809 a company obtained an Act (49 George 3, cxliii) authorising construction of a bridge at Vauxhall carrying a road (Vauxhall Bridge Road) that would link Belgravia with the south bank. The company originally appointed John Rennie (1761-1821) as engineer, and he designed a bridge to be built of blue sandstone from Dundee with seven segmental arches, the central one of 110-foot span. The estimated cost was £216,000. The first stone was laid on 9 May 1811 by Lord Dundas on behalf of the Regent, George, Prince of Wales.

After only a part of the Middlesex abutment had been built, the company decided that it could not afford to complete the work. Rennie therefore proposed a new design, estimated to cost only £100,000, for an iron bridge of 11 arches, the central one of 86-foot span and the others diminishing regularly on either side. However this design, also, was not adopted.

1. The bridge of 1816 *(right)*

The company obtained another Act in 1812 (53 George 3, cxlvii) and appointed a Mr J. Grellier to build a bridge to a design by Sir Samuel Bentham. Since the estimate for this later design was only £1,000 less than that for Rennie's stone bridge, it seems that the change of engineer was made for other than financial reasons.

In September 1813 the foundation stone for the Surrey abutment was laid by Prince Charles, eldest son of the Duke of Brunswick. As built, the bridge was largely to the design of the engineer in charge, James Walker (1781-1862). The piers were constructed in timber caissons and were of coursed masonry backed with rubble below the springing level and of brickwork faced with masonry above. The bridge had nine arched spans, each of which had ten cast iron ribs of 'I' section. It was made by William Jessop at the

Elmes (Shepherd)

Butterley Works and was the first cast iron bridge across the Thames. The bridge itself cost £175,000, but the total cost was about £300,000.

Regent Bridge, as it was known for a few years, was opened to the public as a toll-bridge (1d for foot passengers and up to 1s 6d for vehicles) on 25 July 1816. Under an Act of 1877 (40 & 41 Victoria, xcix) it was acquired by the Metropolitan Board of Works for £255,000 and freed from toll on 24 May 1879.

In the 1880s, under an Act of 1881 (44 & 45 Victoria, cxcii), two central piers were removed to provide a wide navigation opening. It was found that, as had occurred with other London bridges, the foundations had been exposed by the increased scour following the removal of Old London Bridge.

Dimensions

Clear spans: nine arches each of 78ft; width of piers: eight of 13ft; width between parapets: 39ft 3in; length between abutments: 809ft.

2. The bridge of 1906 *(below)*

In 1894 the LCC Bridges Committee decided to replace the failing bridge, and the necessary Act of Parliament (58 & 59 Victoria, cxxix) was obtained the following year. In 1897 a second Act was obtained authorising the building of a tramway across the bridge. Construction was started in 1898 under Sir Alexander Binnie (1839-1917), Chief Engineer to the LCC. He was succeeded, before the bridge was finished in 1902, by Mr (later Sir) Maurice Fitzmaurice (1861-1924). The Bridges Engineer was Mr E. Bazalgette until 1902, when he was succeeded by Mr W. C. Copperthwaite. The LCC architect, Mr W. E. Riley, also contributed to the design.

The bridge has a steel superstructure, built by the contractor Mr Charles Wall, and granite-faced concrete piers and abutments, built by Pethick Brothers. The superstructure has five spans each with 13 two-pinned plated arch ribs. The foundations for the piers and abutments are solid masses of concrete in sheet piling. The tramway was built by Mowlem & Co.

Because of trouble during construction of the fourth pier, the bridge was not completed within the time specified by the 1895 and 1897 Acts and an extension of time had to be obtained in an Act of 1902 (2 Edward 7, clxxii). The bridge was eventually opened in 1906. The bridge and approaches cost £340,917, and other expenses brought the total to £466,725.

Vauxhall Bridge had been authorised under the 1897 Act to carry trams, but not electric ones; the initial tram services, which started on 2 May 1906, were therefore horse-drawn. Authorisation of electric trams was hurriedly obtained so that electric services could be started on 6 August. They were the first to run across a bridge in central London and lasted until 6 January 1952, six months before the complete withdrawal of London trams.

Some years after the bridge had been completed, the piers were ornamented with large bronze statues symbolising various arts and sciences. These statues were designed by two Associates of the Royal Academy, Alfred Drury and F. I. Pomeroy, and represent, in order from the Pimlico to the Vauxhall shore, agriculture, engineering, architecture and pottery (upstream), and local government, education, fine arts and astronomy (downstream).

18.8.68

Dimensions

Clear spans: 130ft 6in, 144ft 5in, 149ft 7in, 144ft 5in, 130ft 6in; width of each pier: 14ft 8in; width between parapets: 80ft (50ft carriageway and two 15ft footways); length between abutments: 760ft.

VICTORIA (GROSVENOR) RAILWAY BRIDGE

This bridge carries trains from Surrey, Sussex and Kent across the Thames to the Victoria terminus. It was originally known as Victoria Bridge, but has subsequently often been referred to as Grosvenor Bridge.

In the early 1850s the only London termini available for the southern railway companies were London Bridge, Bricklayers Arms and Waterloo, and none of these was really convenient for the West End. The London, Brighton & South Coast Railway (LBSCR), which worked into London Bridge, therefore encouraged the West End of London & Crystal Palace Railway, promoted in 1853 (16 & 17 Victoria, clxxx), so that by 29 March 1857 LBSCR trains were serving Brighton and London Bridge from a riverside terminus at Pimlico. The Chelsea Suspension Bridge, which had been completed three days earlier, was close to this terminus and gave direct road access to the West End.

1. The bridge of 1860

In 1858 the Victoria Station & Pimlico Railway was authorised by Act of Parliament (21 & 22 Victoria, cxviii). This project was strongly backed by the LBSCR, which subscribed two-thirds of the capital. Construction started in 1859, work on the necessary Thames bridge commencing on 9 June. The first locomotive crossed exactly one year later.

The bridge was designed by John Fowler (1817-98) and had four segmental wrought iron arches over the river, and two land arches, one over Spicer's Wharf on the south bank, and the other over Grosvenor Road on the north. The foundations for the piers were concrete rafts and the piers were of brick, faced with limestone. The bridge was 30ft 9in wide between parapets and carried two mixed-gauge tracks to accommodate both standard gauge (4ft 8½in) and broad gauge (7ft 0¼in) GWR trains.

The new terminus was built in stages on the site of the basin of the Grosvenor Canal. The first part to open was the western side, which was leased to the LBSCR. That company started train services from there on 1 October 1860. London, Chatham & Dover Railway (LCDR) services followed on 3 December and continued to use the 'Brighton Station' until 25 August 1862, when the eastern side of the terminus was completed. GWR trains started using that side on 1 April 1863.

Dimensions

Spans: four (river) of 175ft (clear) and 187ft 4in (between pier centre lines), two (land) of 70ft (clear, Grosvenor Road) and 65ft (clear, Spicer's Wharf); overall length: 910ft; width between parapets: 30ft 9in.

2. The widened bridge of 1866

The approaches to the terminus soon became inadequate for the traffic, so widening plans prepared by Sir Charles Fox were adopted and authorised by an Act of 1863 (26 & 27 Victoria, ccxxvii). A second bridge, 98 feet wide, was built on the downstream side. Each pier extension was supported by four concrete-filled cast iron cylinders sunk into the river bed, and the wrought iron superstructure consisted of eight lines of arch ribs surmounted by continuous longitudinal girders. The ribs and girders were interconnected at the crowns and the two bridges were united by providing a continuous deck over the original and new arches.

The old part of the bridge was used for three LBSCR standard gauge tracks, while the new part carried two more standard gauge tracks for the LBSCR and two mixed gauge tracks to be shared by the LCDR and GWR. The bridge works were carried out between 22 February 1865 and 1 August 1866, and the new tracks were opened for public traffic on 20 December of that year. Being 132ft 3in wide between parapets, Grosvenor Bridge was then the widest railway bridge in the world.

3. The widened bridge of 1901

In 1898 the Brighton company obtained powers (61 & 62 Victoria, cxi) to add two further tracks to its Clapham Junction to Victoria line. A new bridge having mild steel arches was therefore built in 1901 on the upstream side of Grosvenor Bridge, the total width then becoming 178ft. All the widening works were completed in July 1907.

4. The reconstructed bridge of 1967 (below)

Although the bridge had been strengthened in 1920, it was in poor condition by the 1950s. Therefore, in 1959 Freeman Fox & Partners were asked to prepare a design for a new bridge twice as strong as the old. The company's design was accepted, and between the middle of 1963 and the end of 1967 the bridge was rebuilt, section by section and without significantly interrupting traffic, to consist of ten new separate steel bridge spans, each carrying a single track and supported by reconstructed piers. The latter involved stripping the masonry from the

pier shaft and enveloping the shaft and its foundation with reinforced concrete. The embedded portion of the cofferdam required for this work was left to form part of the new foundation. Each new bridge river span has, at its sides, support arches of welded steel box-section ribs. The new land spans are of shallow battledeck construction. All the spans were made and erected by Dorman Long (Bridge & Engineering) Ltd, being assembled in halves at Nine Elms and floated to the site on pontoons. After removal, the old spans were also transported by river. The main contractors for the rebuilding were Messrs Marples Ridgway & Partners, and the work was supervised by A. H. Cantrell, Chief Civil Engineer of British Railways, Southern Region.

Dimensions

Four river spans reduced to: 164ft; width across ten new spans: 162ft; length of piers at top of foundation: 214ft 9in.

19.5.77

CHELSEA BRIDGE

Chelsea Bridge carries the A3216 northwards across the Thames from Queenstown Road to Chelsea Bridge Road. At the north bank the A3216 crosses the road alongside the river at the point where it changes its name from Grosvenor Road to Albert Embankment.

1. The bridge of 1856 *(below)*

The construction of a new bridge across the Thames near the Chelsea Hospital was recommended by a Government Commission in 1842. An Act of 1846 (9 & 10 Victoria, xxxix) authorised the Commissioners of Her Majesty's Woods and Works to arrange this, and work was started in September 1851. The bridge, designed by Thomas Page (1803-77), was a suspension bridge. It had two piers built on timber piles encased in cast iron, which carried portal-braced cast iron suspension towers; in the archways of these towers the road was 7 feet narrower than for the remainder. The deck was of wrought iron and suspended at each side from two chains, also of wrought iron, which were fixed at each end of the bridge to massive anchorages. The ironwork was made in Edinburgh.

Chelsea Bridge was opened as a toll-bridge on 30 March 1856, having cost £85,319. The original intention was to free it from tolls as soon as £80,000 had been recouped; however, the bridge was not profitable enough for this to be possible. After only five years, on the advice of John Hawkshaw (1811-91) and Edwin Clark, the bridge was strengthened by stiffening the longitudinal girders and providing a third suspension chain at each side. Despite this work (which cost £11,000), a vehicle weight limit of 5 tons was imposed. Under an Act of 1875 (38 & 39 Victoria, clxvii) the bridge was freed from tolls for pedestrians on Sundays and public holidays, but all tolls were not abolished until 1879, two years after acquisition by the Metropolitan Board of Works for the sum of £75,000 under an Act of 1877 (40 & 41 Victoria, xcix). Between 1921 and 1922 the ornamental cast iron pinnacles were removed from the towers, but the picturesque stone toll-houses survived for the life of the bridge.

Dimensions

Clear spans: 165ft, 333ft, 165ft; width between parapets: 47ft 3in; width of roadway: 29ft 4in (22ft 5in at towers); width of piers: 15ft; length between abutments: 703ft.

Hall

2. The bridge of 1937 *(below)*

The 1926 report of a Royal Commission on cross-river traffic recommended rebuilding Chelsea Bridge, and in 1933 it was decided to do this. The Ministry of Transport agreed to pay 60% of the cost from the Road Fund. Work started in 1934 with the erection of a temporary footbridge, which had been used when Lambeth Bridge was rebuilt. The old Chelsea Bridge was demolished the following year.

The new bridge was designed by the engineers Rendel, Palmer & Tritton in conjunction with the architects G. Topham Forrest and E. P. Wheeler, and the contractors were Holloway Brothers Ltd. It is a self-anchoring suspension bridge, a type of bridge in which the suspension cables are not anchored at each shore but are attached to the ends of stiffening girders that carry the deck. The piers of the new bridge were built where the old piers had been; they and the new abutments were constructed inside open sheet-steel cofferdams and are of concrete, faced with granite above low-water level. Each pier carries a pair of steel suspension towers, hinged to allow longitudinal movement. There is one suspension cable at each side of the bridge, made up of 37 locked-coil wire ropes of 1⅞in diameter bundled to form a hexagon. The stiffening girders on each side of a four-lane carriageway each comprise a pair of vertical plate girders, and two pavements are cantilevered out from the outer ones.

The bridge was ready for opening five months before the completion date and had cost about £300,000. It was opened on 6 May 1937 by the Rt Hon L. Mackenzie King CMG, Prime Minister of the Dominion of Canada, just before the Coronation of King George VI.

Dimensions

Clear spans: 163ft, 332ft, 163ft; width between parapets: 82ft; width of roadway: 40ft; width of footways: 14ft (12ft at towers); width of piers: 20ft; height of towers above bearings: 69ft 2in; length between abutments: 698ft.

19.5.77

ALBERT BRIDGE

Albert Bridge links Albert Bridge Road (A3031) with Oakley Street (B304) at a crossroads with the A3212 (which runs along the north bank), at the point where it changes name from Chelsea Embankment (downstream) to Cheyne Walk (upstream).

1. The bridge of 1873 *(below)*

It seems that the idea of building a bridge across the Thames from Cadogan Pier, Chelsea, to Albert Road, Battersea, was put forward by the Prince Consort, and a company was formed for the purpose under an Act of 1864 (27 & 28 Victoria, ccxxxv). The project had been strongly opposed by the owners of the next bridge upstream, Battersea Bridge, who had succeeded in having included in the 1864 Act the conditions that the Albert Bridge Company should (a) pay them £7,000 for repairing their decrepit wooden bridge, (b) agree to maintain that bridge, (c) pay them £3,000 per annum until Albert Bridge had been completed, then (d) purchase their bridge. Preliminary work on the new bridge was carried out in 1864, but construction had to be delayed until the Metropolitan Board of Works had settled its plans for rebuilding the Chelsea embankment. Work was not resumed until 1870, following an Act of 1869 (32 & 33 Victoria, xliv), which extended the time for completion.

Albert Bridge was designed by R. M. Ordish (1824-66) according to a principle (the Ordish-Lefeuvre principle) that he had patented in 1858 and used successfully in bridging the River Moldau in Prague. It is a stayed suspension bridge with two pairs of cast iron suspension towers, each tower consisting of a central column surrounded by eight octagonal cylinders and standing on a cast iron tube having an upper portion of lesser diameter joined by a coned section to a lower portion of greater diameter sunk into the river bed and filled with concrete. Pairs of wrought iron ties extend from near the top of each tower to wrought iron stiffening girders at the sides of the deck. These girders are also supported by vertical suspenders, which hang from suspension chains passing over the tops of the towers. Some further support for the girders is derived from their being anchored in cast iron pits at each bank. The bridge was built at a cost of some £200,000 and opened on 23 August 1873 as a toll-bridge; however, tolls were levied for less than six years because the Metropolitan Board of Works bought it and Battersea Bridge together under an Act of 1877 (40 & 41 Victoria, xcix) for £170,000, and freed it from toll on 24 May 1879.

Albert Bridge has never been very strong, and in 1884 it was overhauled at a cost of some £25,000 under the direction of Sir Joseph

18.8.68

Bazalgette (1819-91). The suspension chains, which were initially wire ropes, were replaced with steel eye-bar chains and other strengthening work was carried out. A 5-ton weight limit was nevertheless imposed.

2. The strengthened bridge of 1973 *(below)* • *Grade II listed* •

In 1959 the London County Council proposed to pull the bridge down, but was dissuaded by Chelsea conservationists under Sir John Betjeman (1906-84). Instead, between 1972 and 1973 some £250,000 was spent on repairs. Two cylindrical concrete piers were provided in the middle of the river to give the deck more support so that the bridge became a curious hybrid of the beam, suspension and stayed types. Despite this improvement, the bridge was again threatened with closure and was saved this time by a campaign organised in 1973 by the Royal Automobile Club.

Dimensions

Clear spans: 147ft 2in, 384ft 9in, 147ft 2in; diameters of pier tubes: 15ft above coned section and 21ft below, in river bed; height of towers: 66ft; diameters of tubes of towers: 4ft (central column), 1ft (octagonal cylinders); width of carriageway: 27ft; width of each footway: 7ft.

6.7.75

BATTERSEA BRIDGE

Battersea Bridge carries Battersea Bridge Road (A3220) across the Thames to a junction with Cheyne Walk (A3212), which runs along the left bank, and Oakley Street.

1. The bridge of 1772

There had been a horse ferry at Battersea at least since the reign of Queen Elizabeth I. After changing hands a number of times it finally passed with the Bolingbroke estate to John, Earl Spencer, and in 1766 he obtained an Act (6 George 3, c. 66) to build a bridge. Eventually he raised enough money, by selling £1,000 shares to 14 partners and contributing himself, to build a bridge of timber (the final cost was £17,662).

Old Battersea Bridge was designed by Henry Holland (?1746-1806), who had designed Claremont and the Brighton Pavilion, and was built by John Phillips (c1709-75), nephew of Thomas Phillips (c1689-1736), the builder of Putney Bridge. It had 19 openings of differing spans. Construction started in 1771 and enough work on the bridge was done that year to allow it to be opened for foot passengers at a halfpenny toll. It was opened for carriage traffic in 1772, with a toll for a horse and cart of fourpence. The bridge proved expensive to keep in repair and the shareholders did not do well.

In 1799 the bridge was lit with oil lamps, and these were replaced by gas lamps in 1824, when iron railings were also fitted.

In 1873 the bridge was bought by the Albert Bridge Company, which strengthened it with girders and additional piles and replaced four of the old spans with two girder spans to ease navigation. The bridge was loved by artists, including Walter Greaves (1846-1930) and Whistler (1834-1903), but by few users. It was acquired (together with Albert Bridge) by the Metropolitan Board of Works under an Act of 1877 (40 & 41 Victoria, cxii), and freed from toll on 24 May 1879.

Dimensions

Openings: 19 from 15ft 6in to 32ft, fourth pier removed to give span of 71ft and ninth pier removed to give span of 77ft in 1873; length between abutments: 734ft; width: 24ft.

2. The bridge of 1890 *(below)*   • *Grade II listed* •

In 1881 the Board obtained an Act (44 & 45 Victoria, cxcii) to authorise rebuilding, but in 1883, before any work was done, it was found necessary to close the bridge to vehicles. The following year the Board obtained another Act (47 & 48 Victoria, ccxxviii) allowing the new bridge to be built on a different alignment.

It was not until 1886, when yet another Act (49 & 50 Victoria, cxii) was obtained giving more time for compulsory purchase of property, that work on the new bridge started. A temporary footbridge was first erected and the old bridge then taken down. The following year the Duke of Clarence and Avondale laid a memorial stone.

The bridge was designed by Sir Joseph Bazalgette (1819-91) and built, under the direction of his son Edward, by Messrs Williams, Son, & Wallington. The contract price was £143,000 and the bridge was opened on Monday 21 July 1890 by Lord Rosebery.

The bridge has five cast iron arches, each arch having seven segmental ribs each formed of five segments. The spandrel framing, bracings and deck plates are of wrought iron. The greater part of the width of each pavement is carried by cantilevers, which project beyond the adjacent outer rib and are hidden by ornamental iron castings. The piers and abutments are of granite and were built in timber cofferdams.

Originally the bridge carried a line for horse trams adjacent to each footway, then electric tramcar services (to King's Road, Chelsea) were introduced on 22 June 1911. After 23 March 1950, when a ship collided with the bridge, trams terminated at a crossover on the south side until services were withdrawn on 30 September 1950.

There have been other occasions when ships have collided with the bridge. On 21 September 2005 a dredger cracked the main girders and these had to be repaired, by 'stitching' with stainless steel links, before normal road traffic could be resumed.

Dimensions

Spans: 113ft 6in, 140ft, 163ft, 140ft, 113ft 6in; length between abutments: 725ft 6in; width: 40ft (24ft roadway and two 8ft footways).

BATTERSEA RAILWAY BRIDGE

Battersea Railway Bridge carries the West London Line across the Thames between Kensington and Clapham Junction. The bridge has sometimes been referred to as Cremorne Bridge, the name being that of gardens that existed until 1877 on the north bank.

In 1836 an Act (6 & 7 William 4, lxxix) was obtained to build a Bristol, Birmingham & Thames Junction Railway to link those cities with a rail terminus near the basin of the Kensington Canal, which opened in 1828 and ran from the Thames near Battersea Bridge to Hammersmith Road. The railway company changed its name, in 1840, to the West London Railway (WLR) and, after buying the decaying canal, opened its railway in 1844. The WLR did not prosper and was taken over by the Great Western Railway (GWR) and the London & North Western Railway (LNWR) under an Act of 1854. In 1859 the companies obtained, jointly with the London, Brighton & South Coast Railway (LBSCR) and London & South Western Railway (LSWR), an Act (22 & 23 Victoria, cxxxiv) to build the West London Extension Railway (WLER), extending the WLR southwards from its Kensington terminus and across the Thames to junctions with the LBSCR and LSWR near Clapham Junction.

The railway was opened on 2 March 1863 and provided an important north-south route, now called the West London Line, with numerous useful connections. Since nationalisation it has belonged successively to British Railways Western Region, London Midland Region and Southern Region, then Railtrack and Network Rail.

The bridge of 1863

The new Thames bridge was designed by Benjamin Baker (1840-1907) and T. H. Bertram of the GWR and LNWR respectively, and the contractor was Brassey & Ogilvie. The bridge has five iron segmental arch river spans (made by Calvert & Co of York) and brick approach viaducts having six arches on the Middlesex bank and four on the Surrey. Each river span consists of three pairs of wrought iron girders connected to each other and to segmental arch ribs by latticework. The original deck was of timber and carried two mixed gauge tracks to accommodate both GWR broad gauge and standard gauge traffic; however, the broad gauge rails were soon removed, in November 1866. The timber deck was replaced by one of steel in 1969 and the bridge was further strengthened in 1991 with lightweight foamed concrete before the onset of international traffic (including Eurostar trains).

The lines from Clapham Junction to Kensington Olympia were electrified with the third rail system in July 1993 and passenger journeys continuing from there to Willesden Junction were made in diesel multiple units. In 1994 conductor rails were laid to allow Eurostar trains to reach the North Pole depot, alongside the Paddington main line. Overhead electrification of the northern mile and a half of the railway in 1996 enabled Silver Link dual-voltage trains to work a Clapham-Willesden service and Eurostar services to run from the Continent to main lines north of London.

Dimensions

Clear spans: five of 144ft each; width of arches in approach viaducts: 40ft each; length between abutments: 775ft; length including approach viaducts: 1,270ft; width of piers: four of 14ft; width of platform: 30ft.

18.8.78

WANDSWORTH BRIDGE

Wandsworth Bridge carries Wandsworth Road (A217) south-eastwards across the river to a roundabout also joined by York Road (A3205), Trinity Road (A214) and Swandon Way (A217).

1. The bridge of 1873 *(right)*

An Act incorporating the Wandsworth Bridge Company was obtained in 1864 (27 & 28 Victoria, ccxxxviii), the company being authorised to raise £80,000 and build a suspension bridge to the design of R. M. Ordish (1824-86), designer of the Albert suspension bridge downstream. A second Act was obtained in 1867 (30 & 31 Victoria, cci) to authorise raising an additional £50,000 capital. However, the company then decided to build a lattice girder, instead of a suspension, bridge and obtained a third Act in 1870 (33 & 34 Victoria, cxxv) authorising this change of plan.

The new bridge was designed by J. H. Tolmé (1836-78) and had five wrought iron lattice girder spans supported by brick abutments and piers that consisted of twin wrought iron cylinders filled with concrete. It was opened as a toll-bridge on 27 September 1873. Construction had cost £150,000, but litigation with local authorities about the northern approaches incurred further expense. Under an Act of 1877 (40 & 41 Victoria, xcix) the Metropolitan Board of Works bought the bridge for £53,000 in 1878 and it was declared toll-free in June of the following year by the Prince of Wales.

Dimensions

Clear spans: 106ft (Nos 1 and 5), 138ft 4in (Nos 2, 3 and 4); diameter of each pier cylinder: 7ft 6in; spacing of pier cylinders: 30ft; length between abutments: 620ft; width between parapets: 29ft 9in.

2. The bridge of 1940 *(overleaf)*

In 1935 the London County Council decided to replace the old Wandsworth Bridge. The LCC's chief engineer, Sir Pierson Frank

Dredge

(1881-1951) and architects E. P. Wheeler and F. R. Hiorns together designed a steel three-span cantilever bridge. It has concrete abutments and piers built in open cofferdams on hard London clay and faced above low-water level with granite. The central span includes a section suspended between the outer ends of the cantilevers, the other ends of these being anchored at the abutments. Each span comprises seven longitudinal girders. In the cantilevers there are five lattice girders under the roadway and two plate girders under the parapets; in the suspended span, there are seven plate girders. The bridge carries a roadway for four lanes of traffic and two footways.

Work was started by Holloway Brothers (London) Ltd in 1938 with erection of a temporary bridge and demolition of the old structure. The abutments and piers were completed in good time, but the Munich Crisis and the outbreak of the Second World War delayed manufacture

11.8.06

of the steel superstructure so that the bridge could not be opened until September 1940. The total cost was £262,000.

Dimensions

Clear spans: 165ft (Nos 1 and 3), 284ft (including 120ft suspended span) (No 2); width of each pier: 16ft; length between abutments: 646ft; width between parapets: 60ft 6in; width of roadway: 40ft.

PUTNEY RAILWAY BRIDGE

This bridge carries London Underground (District Line) trains to Wimbledon across the Thames between Putney Bridge and East Putney stations.

1.6.71

The railway bridge and attached footbridge of 1889 *(below left)*

Under an Act of 1878 (41 & 42 Victoria, cliv), the Metropolitan District Railway extended its line from West Brompton to a terminus called Putney Bridge & Fulham on the north bank of the Thames. Services commenced on 1 March 1880.

The following year, a Kingston & London Company obtained an Act for building a railway from Surbiton across Wimbledon Common and the river to join the 'District' at that terminus. There was strong opposition to building a line across Wimbledon Common and this led the London & South Western and District Railways to form, by an Act of 1882 (45 & 46 Victoria, ccxlviii), a joint company to construct a line from Wimbledon, instead of Surbiton, which kept to the east of the Common. Before this line had been built, however, there was a further change of plan calculated to minimise incursion of the District Railway south of the Thames. An Act of 1886 (49 & 50 Victoria, cx) vested the undertaking wholly in the London and South Western Railway (LSWR) and allowed that company to abandon the original Surbiton to Putney project. The LSWR had to work the Wimbledon line either alone or jointly with the District Railway.

The contract to build the line and its Thames bridge was let to Lucas & Aird on 31 March 1887. The bridge was designed by William Jacomb (d1887) and W. H. Thomas, and built between April 1887 and April 1889 by Head Wrightson & Co of Stockton-on-Tees. It has eight wrought iron lattice truss spans (five over the river, one on the Middlesex shore and two on the Surrey shore) supported by pairs of cast iron cylinders. A footbridge is attached to the downstream side.

District services to Wimbledon started on 3 June 1889 and have always been worked by District Line trains; successive owners of the bridge have therefore never run their own trains across it. Electric trains were authorised by an Act of 1902 (2 Edward 7, ccxx) and introduced on 27 August 1905.

Dimensions

Five river spans of 153ft, three land spans of 100ft, one on Middlesex shore, two on Surrey shore; each pier of two cast iron cylinders 30ft apart and 10ft in diameter above river bed; in river bed tubes are of 14ft diameter and filled with concrete.

PUTNEY (FULHAM) BRIDGE

Putney Bridge links Putney Bridge Approach and Fulham High Street (A304), on the north bank of the Thames, with the junction of Putney High Street (A219) and Richmond Road (B306) on the south.

For many centuries, the City of London successfully prevented the building of any new bridge between Old London Bridge and Kingston Bridge. It was not until the 18th century, that such a bridge was authorised by Parliament and built. The bridge crossed the Thames at a site, just over 7 miles above London Bridge, where there had been a ferry since at least the date of the Domesday Book. It linked the then villages of Fulham, on the north bank, with Putney on the south; of these villages, Fulham was the better known because the parish contained Fulham Palace, the summer residence of the Bishops of London, and also contained market gardens that, with those in adjoining parishes, grew at least half the fruit and vegetables sold in Covent Garden Market. It was therefore Fulham that gave its name to the bridge. The ends of the bridge were near the respective parish churches, and the embattled tower of All Saints, Fulham, and the 14th-century tower of St Mary's, Putney, have enhanced many pictures of the crossing.

1. Fulham Bridge of 1729 *(overleaf)*

Fulham Bridge was built for a syndicate of 30 and was authorised by Acts of 1725 (12 George 1, c. 36) and 1727 (1 George 2, c.18). The design initially chosen was by Sir Jacob Ackworth, but a St Thomas's Hospital surgeon, William Cheselden (1688-1752), seems to have been in charge when the bridge was built in 1729 by the King's Carpenter, John Phillips (c1709-75), at a cost of £23,975. The bridge was built on piles and had 26 openings, termed 'locks', of different spans. The largest of these was named Walpole's Lock in honour of Sir Robert Walpole (1676-1745), the first ever Prime Minister.

The bridge was a toll-bridge – a foot passenger paid a halfpenny on weekdays and a penny on Sundays. There was a small red-brick toll-house at the Putney end and a double toll-house at the Fulham end, which had a roof spanning the roadway. At first the bridge was lit by oil lamps, but in 1845 these were replaced with gas lighting.

In 1855 the Chelsea Waterworks Co obtained an Act (18 & 19 Victoria) for building an aqueduct of nine spans a little upstream of Fulham Bridge, which further impeded navigation.

An Act of 1863 (26 & 27 Victoria, ccxii) formed a company for rebuilding the bridge. Despite obtaining a further Act (29 & 30 Victoria, cccxxxii) in 1866 for raising more capital, the company managed to do nothing. Desperate to improve navigation past the bridge, the Thames Conservancy obtained an Act in 1870 (33 & 34 Victoria, cxlix) that compelled the company to create two wider spans, which it did in 1870 and 1870 by removing two piers and bridging the gaps so produced with girder spans.

Under the Metropolis Toll Bridges Act of 1877 (40 & 41 Victoria, xcix) the Metropolitan Board of Works bought out the shareholders of the bridge company for £58,000, and in 1880 freed the bridge from toll. However, the bridge was too decrepit to cope with the resulting threefold increase in traffic; also, despite the widening of the two spans, it and the nearby aqueduct still hindered navigation. Fulham therefore became the first Thames bridge to be replaced by the Metropolitan Board of Works.

Dalton

Dimensions

Spans: 26 of 14-32ft; length between abutments: 764ft; width between parapets: 22ft 6in; width of two navigation spans: 72ft each.

2. Putney Bridge of 1886

(right)   • *Grade II listed* •

The Board obtained the necessary Act of Parliament in 1881 (44 & 45 Victoria, cxcii). The new bridge was designed by Sir Joseph Bazalgette (1819-91) and built by John Waddell & Sons on the site of the aqueduct. A foundation stone was laid in July 1884 by the Prince of Wales and the bridge was opened by the Prince and Princess of Wales in 29 May 1886. It had cost £244,000.

Putney Bridge is of white Cornish granite and has five segmental arches. The foundations for the piers were constructed by driving tongued and grooved timber piles into the clay river bed around the site of each pier to form a cofferdam. The water was pumped out of the cofferdam and three wrought iron caissons were built up in it and sunk in free air to a depth of about 24 feet below the river bed. Each caisson had a double skin, with a 3ft 6in space between, which was filled with concrete before sinking. To minimise obstruction to navigation, wrought iron centres were used to support the arch stones during construction.

Electric trams ran over the bridge from 23 January 1909 until they were replaced by trolleybuses on 12 September 1937; the latter were withdrawn on 9 November 1960. Between 1931 and 1933 the bridge was widened on the downstream side, the original granite facing being used. The extension to each pier was made in a steel caisson sunk under compressed air. It was found possible in the new work to reduce the arch thickness by 6 inches and thereby save the use of some 12,000 cubic feet of granite.

Putney Bridge has been associated with all but the first of the Oxford and Cambridge University boat races. The first race was rowed at Henley in 1829, and the next five, in 1836 and 1839 to 1842, were rowed from Westminster to Putney Bridge. All subsequent races, from 1845 onwards, have been rowed between Putney Bridge and Mortlake, Putney being the normal starting point.

The widened 1937 bridge, 1.6.71

Dimensions

Clear spans: 112ft, 129ft, 144ft, 129ft, 112ft; width of piers: 19ft (two outer), 18ft (two inner); width between parapets: initially 44ft, after widening 74ft; length between abutments: 700ft.

HAMMERSMITH BRIDGE

Hammersmith Bridge links Castlenau (A306), at the south end, with Hammersmith Bridge Road, at the north.

1. The bridge of 1827 *(below)*

The building of a bridge at Hammersmith was authorised by an Act of 1824 (5 George 4, cxii). The bridge built was a suspension bridge designed by William Tierney Clark (1783-1852) who had been engineer to the West Middlesex Water Works at Hammersmith. A foundation stone for the new bridge was laid by HRH the Duke of Sussex on 7 May 1825.

The piers and abutments were made of brickwork faced with Portland stone. Portland stone suspension towers with central arches for the roadway were then built on the piers. Inconveniently, these arches were narrower than the roadway elsewhere on the bridge. The deck was of timber, supported by transverse cast iron beams, and included a pair of footways in addition to the roadway. It was suspended with wrought iron links attached at the bottom to the ends of the cast iron beams and at the top to wrought iron suspension chains, of which there were four at each side of the roadway, disposed in pairs one above the other. They were supported at the tops of the towers by cast iron saddles resting on rollers, and their ends were anchored at the abutments. All the ironwork used was supplied by Brown, Lenox & Co of Newbridge, near Cardiff.

The bridge cost £80,000, of which £45,000 was for its construction and the remainder for the purchase of land. At the opening, on 6 October 1827, there was a firework display to make up for the absence from the ceremony of the Dukes of Clarence and Sussex.

When the Oxford and Cambridge Boat Race came to be rowed between Putney Bridge and Mortlake in 1845, Hammersmith became a favourite grandstand. It was estimated that 11,000-12,000 people would go on to the bridge to watch, giving the owners both profit from the tolls and anxiety for the structure. During the last few years of its life, the bridge was closed at Boat Race time. Under an Act of 1877 (40 & 41 Victoria, xcix), the bridge was bought by the Metropolitan Board of Works and freed from toll on 26 June 1880 at a ceremony attended by the Prince and Princess of Wales.

Murray

Dimensions

Clear spans: 142ft 6in, 400ft, 145ft 6in; width of piers: 23ft; length between abutments: 734ft; overall length: 822ft; width of roadway: 20ft; height of suspension towers: 64ft; width of tower archways: 14ft.

2. The bridge of 1887 *(right)*
• *Grade II listed* •

In 1883 the Board obtained an Act (46 & 47 Victoria, clxxvii) authorising replacement of the old Hammersmith Bridge. Work started in November the following year to a design by the Board's Chief Engineer, Sir Joseph Bazalgette (1819-91). The contractors were Dixon, Appleby & Thorne. The abutments and piers of the old bridge were strengthened and enlarged, and wrought iron suspension towers, to be encased in ornamental cast iron, were then constructed on the piers. Two sets of mild steel suspension chains were put at each side of the bridge across the tower frames and their ends were anchored at each bank deep below ground. At the ends of the bridge further ornamental castings decorated with coats of

1.6.71

arms, including those of the Metropolitan Board of Works, Middlesex, Kent and Guildford, were installed to conceal the upper portions of the chain anchorages. A timber deck was laid on longitudinal main girders carrying cross girders extending beyond the suspension chains to support footways As with the previous bridge, the width of the archways through the towers was made markedly less than the width of the roadway. The works cost £82,177 and the bridge was opened on 18 June 1887 by Prince Albert Victor, Duke of Clarence.

In its more recent history, Hammersmith Bridge has been threatened with replacement more than once but has managed to survive. Extensive repairs were carried out in 1973-76, which allowed the upper weight limit to be increased to 12 tons, and in 1997-98 work was done to free the chain bearings.

Dimensions
Clear spans: 143ft 6in, 400ft 6in, 146ft; width of piers: 22ft; length between abutments: 734ft.

BARNES RAILWAY BRIDGE

This bridge carries a loop line to the north of the main line from Clapham Junction to Windsor, and crosses the Thames between Barnes Bridge and Chiswick stations.

The Richmond Railway Co was formed under an Act of 1845 (8 & 9 Victoria, cxxi) and built a line from Battersea (now Clapham Junction) to Richmond, which was opened for traffic on 27 July 1846. In that year an Act was obtained (9 & 10 Victoria, cxxxi) under which the Richmond Company was sold to the London & South Western Railway (LSWR). In 1847 the LSWR was authorised by a further Act (10 & 11 Victoria, lviii) to extend its Richmond line to Datchet (near Windsor) and also to build a loop to the north of the Datchet line from just beyond Barnes station, east of Richmond, across the Thames, then through Brentford and Hounslow to a junction west of Richmond at Feltham. The engineer for the Datchet and loop lines was Joseph Locke (1805-60) and the contractor was Thomas Brassey (1805-70). The Richmond to Datchet line was opened on 22 August 1848 and the loop was opened from Barnes to a temporary station just east of the present Isleworth station on 22 August 1849 and on to Feltham junction on 1 February 1850.

1. The bridge of 1849

The Thames bridge designed by Joseph Locke (1805-60) for Barnes was very similar in appearance to the railway bridges at Richmond and Kingston and had three spans of arched rib girders supported by brick piers and abutments. It carried two railway tracks and, on the downstream side, a footbridge, much used as a grandstand for the Oxford and Cambridge University Boat Race – in 1879 the LSWR sold 1,050 tickets at 15 shillings (75p) each, as well as issuing 180 free tickets.

Dimensions
Three clear spans: 120ft; width of piers: 10ft.

2. The reconstructed bridge of 1895   • *Grade II listed* •

On 21 July 1891 an Act was obtained for renewing and widening the first bridge. Design was by E. Andrews (1833-1912) and the work was supervised by A. W. Szlumper (1858-1934), who later became Chief Engineer of the Southern Railway. Building work was carried out by Perry & Co of Bow East, with ironwork by Head Wrightson & Co.

In the reconstructed bridge, the lines are carried by three wrought

24.5.69

iron bowstring girder spans supported by extensions to the piers and abutments. The southern, upstream, portion of the old structure was retained, hence the present hybrid appearance of the bridge. Downstream, a new footbridge was built to replace the original one. In January 1895 up trains were diverted to the new part of the bridge and the rebuilding was completed on 9 June of that year. In 1975-76 the decking of the bridge was renewed.

Dimensions
Spans as for 1849 bridge; width of new footbridge: 8ft.

CHISWICK BRIDGE

Chiswick Bridge carries the A316 south-west across the Thames between Great Chertsey Road and Clifford Avenue. The A316 is an arterial road built in the years between the First and Second World Wars to relieve Hammersmith and Richmond Bridges of heavy traffic; this needed two new Thames bridges, at Chiswick and Twickenham, and made it necessary to rebuild Hampton Court Bridge. All this work was authorised by an Act of 1928 (18 & 19 George 5, lxxii).

The bridge of 1933
Chiswick Bridge was designed by the architect Sir Herbert Baker (1862-1946) and the County Engineer of Middlesex, Alfred Dryland (1865-1946), in association with Considère Constructions Ltd of Darlington, specialists in reinforced concrete design. The bridge was built by the Cleveland Bridge & Engineering Co at a cost of £175,700, while purchase of land, work on the approaches, and sundry fees brought the total cost to £227,600.

The bridge has mass concrete foundations constructed in open sheet-steel cofferdams and a cellular superstructure of reinforced concrete having three river and two land arches. The roadway, with a footway at each side, is carried by a platform supported from the arches by columns and beams. Except for under the arches, the concrete surfaces are faced with Portland stone, which is also used for the balustrades.

Chiswick Bridge, Twickenham Bridge and the rebuilt Hampton Court Bridge were all opened by the Prince of Wales (later King Edward VIII) on 3 July 1933.

Dimensions
Clear spans: 61ft 4in, 125ft, 150ft, 125ft, 61ft 4in; length between abutments: 436ft; overall length: 606ft; width: 70ft (40ft roadway and two 15ft footways).

24.5.69

KEW RAILWAY BRIDGE

Kew Railway Bridge carries London Underground (District Line) and Silverlink Metro (North London Line) trains across the Thames from North London to Kew Gardens and Richmond. The bridge crosses the north bank of the river near Strand-on-the-Green, and the south bank near the National Archive (the former Public Record Office).

To provide more convenient routes from north of the Thames to Richmond, the London & South Western Railway (LSWR) obtained, in July 1864, an Act (27 & 28 Victoria, clxvi) for building (i) a line from Kensington (Addison Road), through Hammersmith, Brentford Road (now Gunnersbury) and southwards, across a new Thames bridge at Kew, to Richmond, and (ii) a junction at Acton between the new line and the North & South West Junction Railway (opened in 1853), which ran from Willesden Junction to a junction at Kew with the LSWR Barnes and Hounslow loop (see the entry for Barnes Railway Bridge).

The bridge of 1869

Construction of the Kensington to Richmond line, including the Thames bridge and Acton Junction, was started by Brassey & Ogilvie in 1865. Owing to delay caused by changes of plan, train services were not able to start until 1 January 1869.

Kew Railway Bridge was designed by W. R. Galbraith (1829-1914) and carries two tracks by means of five wrought iron lattice girder spans supported by brick abutments and pairs of cast iron cylinders sunk into the bed of the Thames. In 1922 the bridge was strengthened on account of the weight of North London Railway (NLR) electric trains.

The first passenger services across the bridge were run by the

19.8.76

LSWR and the NLR. The LSWR service was from Richmond to Kensington (Addison Road), then south, over Battersea Railway Bridge, to Latchmere Junction (near Clapham Junction), and finally either to Waterloo or to Ludgate Hill, via Brixton. The NLR service was from Richmond to Broad Street, using the new Acton Junction.

Previously the NLR had provided a Richmond service with trains that called on their way to Kingston and followed a zigzag route through Kew and Barnes (on the Hounslow loop), Mortlake and Twickenham (on the Datchet line), and Strawberry Hill (on the line from Twickenham to Kingston). That line had been opened in 1863 as a branch and extended six years later through Norbiton to join the Waterloo main line just beyond New Malden, thus forming what became known as the Kingston Loop.

Passenger services, some short-lived, were also run across Kew Bridge by other pre-Grouping companies, including the Great Western Railway (from 1870) and the Midland Railway (from 1875). In 1877 the LSWR gave running powers over the Hammersmith to Richmond line to the Metropolitan District Railway and that company started a service between Mansion House and Richmond on 1 June of that year. Electric trains were introduced between Whitechapel and Richmond on 1 August 1905, which were forerunners of the present-day services.

The NLR service from Broad Street to Richmond was electrified on 1 October 1916 and passed successively to the London & North Western Railway (1922), the London, Midland & Scottish Railway (1923), and British Railways (London Midland Region) (1948). After privatisation, train services were provided by Network SouthEast, North London Railways, and, from 1997, by Silverlink Metro, North London Line.

Dimensions
Five lattice girder spans: 9ft deep, 115ft long, 106ft clear spans; piers of two cast iron cylinders 28ft apart, 9ft diameter in river bed and 6ft 9in diameter for upper 14ft 6in.

KEW BRIDGE

Kew Bridge carries the A205 Mortlake Road northwards across the Thames to merge with the A315 at the point, near Strand-on-the-Green, where its name changes from Chiswick High Road to Kew Bridge Road.

1. The bridge of 1759 *(see page 8)*
There had been a ferry at Kew at least since 1605, in the reign of King James I. In 1730 Frederick, Prince of Wales (1707-51) took a lease of a mansion at Kew belonging to the Capel family and lived there with his own family for 20 years. His presence increased use of the ferry so much that the proprietor, Robert Tunstall, decided to build a bridge. He therefore obtained an Act of Parliament in June 1757 (30 George 2, c. 63) to build a toll-bridge from Smith's Hill, at Brentford in Middlesex, to the Surrey shore. Barge owners petitioned against this scheme, so Tunstall obtained an amending Act in March 1758 (31 George 2, c. 46) authorising construction of the bridge in a more acceptable position.

The new bridge was designed and built by John Barnard and had 11 arches, the seven central ones being of timber founded on oak piles, with the others (two at each end) and abutments being of brick and stone. The foundation stone was laid on the Surrey side on 29 July 1758 and the bridge was opened, less than a year later, on 4 June 1759. The date was appropriate, being the birthday of Prince Frederick's son George (1738-1820), who was to become King George III in 1760. He, his mother Augusta, the Dowager Princess of Wales, and the Royal Family had already passed over the bridge on 1 June and had given £200 to the proprietor and 40 guineas to the workmen.

Dimensions
Clear spans of timber arches: 32ft, 40ft, 43ft, 50ft, 43ft, 40ft, 32ft; width of roadway: 30ft.

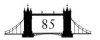

85

2. The bridge of 1789 *(below)*

The first Kew Bridge proved costly to maintain and needed extensive repair in 1774, so Tunstall's son, also named Robert, obtained an Act in 1782 (22 George 3, c. 42) to build a bridge of stone just to the east (downstream) of the old one. It was designed by James Paine (1725-89) and had five main arches and two small land arches. Work started on 4 June 1783 and the bridge was opened on 22 September 1789. The cost of £16,000 had been raised by tontine insurance: according to this system, annuities were shared by subscribers to a loan with the benefit of survivorship, so that as subscribers died, the annuities were divided between fewer people. Ultimately, all the annuities went to the last, or last few, subscribers, according to the terms of the agreement.

In 1819 the bridge was sold to Thomas Robinson for £22,000. It was sold again under Acts of 1868 (31 & 32 Victoria, c. 17) and 1869 (32 & 33 Victoria, xix) to the Metropolitan Board of Works in 1873 for £57,300, and freed from toll on 4 May of that year.

Dimensions

Clear main spans: 38ft 4in, 45ft 10in, 55ft 0in, 45ft 10in, 38ft 4in with two small shore spans; width between parapets: 24ft.

3. The bridge of 1903

(above right)   • *Grade II listed* •
The Surrey and Middlesex County Councils obtained an Act for rebuilding Kew Bridge in 1898 (61 & 62 Victoria, clv). A temporary bridge was first erected and the old bridge was demolished in 1900.

The new, and present, bridge was designed by Sir John Wolfe Barry (1836-1918) and Cuthbert Brereton, and built by Easton

Tombleson

Gibb & Son of Aberdeen. It is of granite and has three semi-elliptical arches with piers founded on mass concrete. There are also two narrow shore spans and small arches in the approaches (six on the Middlesex shore and nine on the Surrey shore). The bridge was opened on 20 May 1903 by King Edward VII and named after him.

Dimensions
Clear spans: 116ft 6in, 136ft, 11ft 6in with two shore spans of 18ft, width between parapets: 57ft; overall length: 1,500ft.

RICHMOND LOCK AND FOOTWAYS

Richmond Half-tide Lock and Weir spans the Thames just downstream of Twickenham Bridge. It includes twin footways providing pedestrian access between Ranelagh Drive, on the left bank, and Old Deer Park Recreation Ground on the right.

As early as 1770, the canal engineer James Brindley (1726-72) suggested the building of a dam across the Thames between Mortlake and Kew Bridge with a lock at each bank. In the 19th century, from 1859 onwards and especially in the 1880s, the Richmond Vestry and the Twickenham Local Board campaigned for a lock because the removal of Old London Bridge, the rebuilding of other bridges in

London, the building of the Embankments and dredging had all enabled tidal water to flow downstream more quickly and reveal great areas of mud.

In 1889 a resident of Richmond, J. B. Hilditch, learned of sluices patented by F. G. M. Stoney (1837-97) that, with a pound lock and boat rollers, could provide a barrier for maintaining a depth of water upstream of at least the half-tide level without unduly hindering navigation. The Joint Committee of the Richmond and Twickenham Vestries soon campaigned for such a barrier, but were opposed by various interests including barge-owners, land-owners, ratepayers, Isleworth traders and the Thames Conservancy. Fortunately, the opposition was overcome and in 1890 the Richmond Footbridge, Sluice, Lock and Slipway Act (53 & 54 Victoria, ccxxiv) was obtained. The Conservancy contributed to the cost of the works and agreed to run them when complete.

24.5.69

The lock and footbridges of 1894   • *Grade II* listed* •

Richmond Half-tide Lock was designed by James More, engineer of the Thames Conservancy. In 1887 Stoney had become Manager of Ransomes & Rapier, of Ipswich, and this firm built the sluices, which floated to adjust the opening through which water could pass beneath. Work on the structure started in 1891 and on 17 May 1894 the sluices were let down for the first time. Two days later the lock was formally opened by the Duke of York, who later became King George V. The works had cost £61,000.

Richmond Lock and Footbridge has five openings: three at the centre for counterbalanced wrought iron sluices of the Stoney design, one at the Surrey bank for the pound lock, and one at the Middlesex bank for the boat rollers. The openings, between stone-faced concrete abutments and piers, are spanned by pairs of steel arches, with cast iron spandrels, which support downstream and upstream footbridges. Steel supports for the sluices and the mechanisms for moving them

between their lowered (vertical) and raised (horizontal) positions are between the footbridges. Originally the sluice mechanisms were operated manually, but they are now electrically powered. Usually, the sluices are lowered for two-thirds of the time, when the downstream water-level is below that for half-tide.

Ownership of Richmond Lock passed to the Port of London Authority when that body came into being on 1 April 1909. Since then the structure has been repaired, in 1944-45 following Second World War bomb damage, and renovated in 1990-94. Until some time during the war a penny toll was levied from a person crossing the bridge, whereas a sightseer who went on to and left the bridge at the same side had to pay twopence.

Dimensions

Clear spans: 50ft, 66ft, 66ft, 66ft, 50ft; lock: 250ft x 37ft; width of footways: 6ft; footway separation: 17ft; sluice height: 12ft.

TWICKENHAM BRIDGE

Twickenham Bridge is the second of the two new crossings of the Thames – the other being Chiswick Bridge – needed when the A316 arterial road (now a feeder for the M3 motorway) was built in the years between the two World Wars under an Act of 1928 (18 & 19 George 5, lxxii). It links Twickenham Road, Richmond, with The Avenue, Twickenham. The new road had also required replacement of the old Hampton Court Bridge with a new one built just downstream of the old. All three new bridges were opened on 3 July 1933 by the Prince of Wales.

The bridge of 1933 • *Grade II listed* •

Twickenham Bridge was designed by Alfred Dryland (1865-1946), County Engineer of Middlesex, in association with reinforced concrete specialists Considère Constructions Ltd and the architect Maxwell Ayrton. Originally, Ayrton had included in his design monumental towers at the Surrey end of the bridge, but the Fine Arts Commission considered that these made the structure look heavy, so he lightened the appearance of both ends of the bridge to produce the design that was accepted and built. The contractors were Aubrey Watson Ltd and the costs were £124,000 for the bridge and road works, £60,500 for the approaches, and £32,800 for land, fees and supervision, making a total of £217,300.

The foundations are of mass concrete and were built in sheet-steel cofferdams, the lower portions of which were retained. The bridge

has three river spans and two smaller spans on land, all constructed of reinforced concrete bush-hammered to give a rough finish. The deck is supported directly by ribs on the hidden outer surfaces of the arches. Hinges are provided for the three river arches to allow them to adjust to changes of temperature, and expansion joints are fitted in the deck and elsewhere in the structure. At each side of the bridge there are bronze openwork balustrades and lamp standards.

Dimensions

Spans: 56ft 0in, 98ft 4in, 103ft 4in, 98ft 4in, 56ft 0in; width between parapets: 70ft (40ft roadway and two 15ft footways); length above arches: 477ft 6in; length including abutments: 1,235ft.

24.5.69

RICHMOND RAILWAY BRIDGE

Richmond Railway Bridge carries the South West Trains services from Waterloo to Staines and Windsor across the Thames between Richmond and St Margaret's stations.

A line was built by the Richmond Railway Company from the London & South Western Railway (LSWR) line at Battersea to Richmond under an Act of 1845 (8 & 9 Victoria, cxxi) and opened on 22 July 1846. In 1847 a further Act (10 & 11 Victoria, lviii) formed a Windsor, Staines & South Western Railway Company to extend the line from Richmond across the Thames to Twickenham, Staines and Datchet. That extension was opened on 22 August 1848 and further extended, under an Act of 1849 (12 & 13 Victoria, xxxiv) to reach Windsor on 1 December of that year.

1. The bridge of 1848

The bridge was designed by Joseph Locke (1805-60), Engineer of the LSWR, and built by Thomas Brassey (1805-70). It had three cast iron ribbed arches, there being six ribs in each arch – two for each railway track and one for each parapet. At the eastern end an ornamental brick approach viaduct of seven arches was built and is still in use.

2. The rebuilt bridge of 1908 *(left)*

Between 1906 and 1908 the 1848 bridge was replaced with one of very similar appearance constructed of mild steel. The new bridge was designed by J. W. Jacomb Hood (d1914), Locke's successor, and built by the Horsley Bridge Company of London and Tipton.

Between November 1983 and May 1984 the main girders of the bridge were repaired and the deck replaced.

Dimensions

Three clear river spans: 100ft; two land spans: 20ft; width of each pier: 9ft.

5.9.76

RICHMOND BRIDGE

Richmond Bridge carries the A305 between Richmond and Twickenham south-westward across the Thames from Bridge Street, in the town, to the Richmond Road.

There had been a ferry across the Thames from Richmond to the Twickenham Meadows since at least 1442. Towards the end of the 18th century the local inhabitants became discontented with the ferry, which, because of the steep approach on the Richmond side, was unsuitable for laden vehicles and which in times of flood or frost did not operate at all. They accordingly campaigned for a bridge.

The lessee of the ferry, a Mr William Windham, realised that he might profit from this demand by selling the remaining term of his lease, using the proceeds to build a timber bridge at the site of the ferry, then enjoying an income from tolls. He therefore petitioned the House of Commons to bring in the necessary Bill, offering the remainder of his lease to the Crown Commissioners for £6,000. To his surprise there was strong local opposition to his plan, claiming that a timber bridge was inappropriate and that the site was unsuitable. In the end he withdrew his bill.

1. The bridge of 1777

In 1773 an Act for building a bridge at Richmond was at last obtained (13 George 3, p. 83).

The bridge was to be of stone, and the Crown Commissioners insisted that it should be built at the ferry site.

The 1773 Act provided for the payment of £6,000 to Mr Windham as compensation for the loss of the ferry and authorised the raising of £25,000 by the issue of tontine shares of £100 each, which would yield 4% per annum. As mentioned in the Kew Bridge entry, in the tontine system the shares of shareholders who died were divided among the shareholders who survived. There were two tontines for Richmond Bridge: the first, of 200 shares, had given a lady who died in 1859 at the age of 86 £800 a year for more than five years, and the second, of 50 shares, had given a lady who died in 1865 aged 91 years £200 a year for nine years.

Richmond Bridge was designed by the architect James Paine (1725-89) in collaboration with Kenton Couse (1721-90), and was built by

26.12.64

Thomas Kerr. The foundation stone was laid by the Hon Henry Hobart on 23 August 1774 and the bridge was opened on 12 January 1777.

The bridge has five main arches, of masonry faced with Portland stone, and the approaches are carried by brick arches, three on the Surrey shore and five on the Middlesex. The interiors of the Surrey arches were converted for private use. Tolls were removed in 1859, following the death of the lady who had come to own all the shares of the first tontine.

In 1927 the County Surveyors of Middlesex and Surrey recommended that a new bridge should be built downstream, just north of Richmond Railway Bridge, to relieve Richmond Bridge of heavy traffic. An Act of 1928 (18 & 19 George 5, lxxii) authorised construction of a bridge there as part of a new arterial road (the A316), and the new bridge – Twickenham Bridge – was opened in 1933. The 1928 Act also vested the bridge in the Middlesex and Surrey County Councils and the assets were transferred from the Richmond Bridge Commissioners to the County Councils on 31 March 1931. The bridge is now in the Greater London Borough of Richmond upon Thames.

Dimensions
Clear spans: 10ft, 45ft, 50ft, 60ft, 50ft, 45ft, 10ft; width between parapets: 24ft 9in (16ft 9in roadway and two 4ft footways); length between approaches: 330ft

2. The widened bridge of 1938 (previous page) • *Grade I listed* •
As early as 1925 it had been proposed to widen Richmond Bridge and this was eventually done between the spring of 1937 and the summer of 1939. The bridge was widened on the upstream side, using the original facing stones. The Cleveland Bridge & Engineering Co carried out the work at a cost of £73,000.

Dimensions
Width between parapets increased by 12ft to provide 21ft roadway and two 7ft 6in footways.

TEDDINGTON FOOTBRIDGE

The two footbridges that provide a Thames crossing above Teddington Lock link Ferry Road, which provides the upstream end of the Thames Path along the north bank, with the Thames Path along the south bank. Because the Thames flows north-westwards here, the 'north' (left) bank is, confusingly, south of the 'south' (right) bank.

The first lock at Teddington was built by the City of London under an Act of 1810 (50 George 3, cciv), which also authorised construction of three further pound locks at Sunbury, Shepperton and Chertsey. Teddington Lock was opened on 20 June 1811 and was near the site of the present footbridge. Because of lower water levels resulting from the removal of Old London Bridge, boats were grounding in the lock, so it was rebuilt, further downstream, in the years 1857-58. Early in the next century, the rebuilt lock was augmented with a fine double lock opened on 11 June 1904.

The Teddington Lock footbridges
In 1882 the Teddington Local Board sought permission to build a footway across the Thames at the site of the 1811 lock. Permission was obtained, and north and south footbridges, designed by George Pooley and built by Goddard & Massey of Nottingham, were constructed and opened in the years 1885-89. The total cost, shared by the authorities of Ham, Petersham and Teddington, was £2,684.

The north footbridge (*opposite left*) crosses the navigation channel leading to the locks. Its superstructure is a steel truss, made using material from a temporary bridge at Hammersmith, which is supported by concrete abutments that include flights of steps. The south abutment, on the island, is pierced by an arch for a footpath.

The south footbridge (*far right*) crosses from the left bank to an island between the navigation channel and the backwater below Teddington weir and sluices. It is a suspension bridge, and each side of the deck is attached to hangers from two steel wire cables. The four cables are carried by twin iron pillars that lean slightly towards each other and are braced together. Steps up to the deck are provided at each end.

Dimensions

North footbridge: clear span: 99ft; width of footway: 6ft.
South footbridge: main span: 160ft; north span: 80ft; width of footway: 6ft; headway: 18ft.

Both 28.3.76

KINGSTON RAILWAY BRIDGE

This bridge carries South West Trains services between Kingston station, near the east bank, and Hampton Wick station, near the west.

In 1859 the London & South Western Railway (LSWR) obtained an Act (22 & 23 Victoria, xliv) for building a line from Twickenham (on the railway from Richmond to Windsor) to Kingston. Kingston station was to have been built in Middlesex, near the left bank of the river, but in 1860 the company obtained a further Act (23 & 24 Victoria, clxxxv) for extending the line eastwards across the Thames to a station near the centre of the town The line was opened on 1 July 1863. The final railway development was under an Act of 1865 (28 & 29 Victoria, cii), which authorised the LSWR to extend the Kingston line

further east to join the main line from Waterloo at a junction just beyond New Malden station, thus forming what became known as the Kingston Loop, opened on 1 January 1869.

1. The bridge of 1863

The bridge was designed by J. E. Errington (1802-62), Locke's successor, and built by Thomas Brassey (1805-70) under the supervision of W. R. Galbraith (1829-1914). The design was very similar to that for Richmond Railway Bridge, but there were five (instead of three) cast iron arches, each of six ribs, with the three central arches above the river.

2. The rebuilt bridge of 1907 *(overleaf)*

The 1863 bridge was replaced in 1907 by a bridge of closely similar appearance and dimensions having mild steel arches. It was designed by J. W. Jacomb Hood (d1914), Engineer of the railway company, and built by the Horsley Bridge Co.

Dimensions
Five clear spans: 74ft 6in; width between parapets: 25ft.

25.5.81

KINGSTON BRIDGE

Kingston Bridge carries the A308 westward across the Thames from Horse Fair, Kingston, to its junction with the A310 at Hampton Wick. The A308 continues, via Hampton Court, on its way to Windsor and Maidenhead, and the A310 starts northwards to Twickenham and the A4.

1. The mediaeval (probably 13th-century) bridge
The earliest documentary reference to a bridge at Kingston dates from 1219 when the bridge had fallen into decay and was transferred with the estate, first to the keeping of two wardens appointed by King

Henry III, and afterwards to the bailiffs of Kingston. Leland (?1506-52), writing in 1539, alludes to the existence of a Saxon bridge downstream of the mediaeval bridge, itself downstream of the present bridge.

The mediaeval bridge was of timber, and was repaired and altered throughout its life. In 1710 it had 20 openings, two in the middle being big enough for barges. The income from the estates with which the bridge was endowed was never enough for its maintenance, so the wardens had to rely on tolls and benefactions. A gift of land valued at £40 a year was made in 1565 by Robert Hamond to make the bridge toll free for ever more. However, by 1720 tolls – for river traffic at least – had been re-imposed.

Old Kingston Bridge was strategically important throughout most

of its life because, until the opening of Putney Bridge in 1729, it was the first Thames bridge above London Bridge.

For centuries a ducking stool was used from Kingston Bridge, and the ducking of the hostess of the King's Head alehouse before a large crowd on 17 April 1745 was one of the last recorded cases of this punishment.

Dimensions
Length between abutments: 378ft; lengths of abutments: 90ft (east), 36ft (west).

2. The bridge of 1828
The first stone bridge at Kingston was built for Kingston Corporation under an Act of 1825 (6 George 4, cxxv) and designed by Edward Lapidge (d1860). The first stone was laid on 7 November 1825 by the Earl of Liverpool (1770-1828), who was both Prime Minister and Steward of the Borough; the bridge was opened on 12 July 1828 by the

Duchess of Clarence (1792-1849), who became Queen Adelaide in 1830. Following Acts of 1868 (31 & 32 Victoria, c. 17) and 1869 (32 & 33 Victoria, xix) tolls were abolished in 1870 at a cost of £15,600. At a freeing ceremony on 12 March, the toll-gate was drawn across the bridge on a trolley and publicly burned at Hampton Wick.

Kingston Bridge was built with five main and two flood arches and had a stone toll-house with gates at each end. The bridge and approaches cost £40,000.

Dimensions
Spans and (width of piers): 50ft 10in (10ft 6in) 54ft 10in (11ft) 58ft 11in (11ft) 54ft 10in (10ft 6in) 50ft 11in; length between abutments: 313ft 4in; width between parapets: 25ft 1in.

3. The widened bridge of 1914 *(overleaf)*
Between 1912 and 1914 the bridge was widened on the upstream side by the Middlesex and Surrey County Councils, the engineers being Basil Mott and David Hay and the contractors Walter Scott & Middleton Ltd. The toll-houses were removed.

Electric tram services were run across the bridge from 1 March 1906 until 14 June 1931; on 15 June they were replaced by trolleybus services, which were continued until 8 May 1962.

Dimension
New width between parapets: 55ft 1in.

4. The widened bridge of 2001   • *Grade II* listed* •
Since 1986 Kingston Bridge has been the responsibility of the Royal Borough of Kingston upon Thames. In 1993 the Borough commissioned Travers Morgan, consulting engineers, to inspect the bridge and assess its strength. The inspection showed that strengthening was needed, and vehicles above 38 tonnes in weight were prohibited from crossing. However the strengthening was done, it was deemed essential to maintain four lanes for traffic across the

bridge throughout the work. This could be achieved either by providing a temporary bridge during the work, or by widening the bridge, then using the new portion while the remainder was strengthened. The second option cost little more than the first and gave a better result, and was therefore chosen.

Various schemes for widening and strengthening were considered in consultation with English Heritage, but in the event the widening was done upstream on new pier foundations made in sheet pile cofferdams. A base for the cofferdam was made underwater by excavation and the placing of concrete 2 metres thick, then cast-in-situ bored concrete piles were sleeved through the base. Before this could be done, bores had to be made through old foundations not shown on the drawings. The new piers were made of reinforced concrete clad in Portland stone. The extensions for each arch were made from 12 individually shaped pre-cast half arch units incorporating brickwork facing. When these

had been installed, reinforced concrete spandrel walls were cast in situ and the space between these and the outer surface of the arch extension was filled with reinforced lightweight concrete to form a saddle.

The original part of the bridge was strengthened by casting a lightweight concrete saddle slab, similar to that of the extension, following excavation above the brick arches and the epoxy grouting of 6,500 stainless steel hoops into holes drilled in the brickwork.

The work was planned by Symonds Group and carried out by M. J. Gleeson between the autumn of 1997 and the summer of 2001. The bridge now carries a cycle track on each side and a central bus lane as well as the original twin traffic lanes in each direction and footways next to the parapets.

Dimension
New width between parapets: 76ft 1in.

24.5.69

HAMPTON COURT BRIDGE

Hampton Court Bridge carries Hampton Court Way (A309) between East Molesey, on the south bank, across the river to a roundabout on Hampton Court Road (A308) near Hampton Court Palace.

The present bridge was built as a replacement for, and just downstream of, the previous bridge to cater for the increased traffic expected when the Chiswick to Chertsey Arterial Road (A316) was opened. That road, the new Thames bridges at Chiswick and Twickenham that it necessitated, and the new Hampton Court Bridge, were all constructed under an Act of 1928 (18 & 19 George 5, lxxii) by the Middlesex and Surrey County Councils, and all three bridges were opened by the Prince of Wales (later the uncrowned King Edward VIII) on 3 July 1933.

1. The bridge of 1753

James Clarke, owner of the ferry at Hampton Court and lessee of the Manor of East Molesey, petitioned Parliament on 12 January 1750 for permission to build a bridge at the site of the ferry. He obtained the necessary Act (23 George 2, c. 37) on 15 April 1750.

The bridge was built by the designers Samuel Stevens and Benjamin Ludgator. Work started in 1752 and the bridge was opened on 13 December 1753. It was a timber bridge of Chinese appearance, having seven steeply humped arches between brick abutments and a pair of turrets at each end of the central arch.

Dimension
Length between abutments: 260ft.

2. The bridge of 1778

The next Hampton Court Bridge was also of timber and had 11 openings constructed between the brick piers of the previous bridge. It was designed and built by a Mr White of Weybridge, who had commissioned the building of the first bridge at Walton-on-Thames.

Dimension
Length between abutments: 260ft.

3. The bridge of 1865 *(below)*

The third Hampton Court Bridge was built under an Act of 1863

Illustrated London News

(26 & 27 Victoria, cxcvii), obtained by T. N. Allen, proprietor of the 1778 bridge, which formed the Thames Bridges Co '…for making and maintaining Bridges over the River Thames at Hampton and Shepperton…'. The name 'Shepperton bridge' was used here to refer to the bridge at Walton-on-Thames.

The new Hampton Court Bridge was designed by E. T. Murray and built by T. N. Allen between 1864 and 1865 for £11,176. It had five spans between brick abutments with pairs of cast iron octagonal columns for the piers, wrought iron girders for supporting a timber deck, and wrought iron latticework for the balustrades. The abutments, with battlemented brick walls added to stop people falling into the river, were preserved when the next bridge was built a few yards downstream.

The bridge was bought from Mr Allen by the Metropolitan Board of Works for £50,000 following an Act of 1869 (32 & 33 Victoria, xxi).

Dimensions
Spans: 66ft, 71ft, 76ft 3in, 71ft, 65ft 9in; width of piers: 5ft.

4. The bridge of 1933 *(below)* • *Grade II listed* •

The present bridge was designed by the County Engineer of Surrey, W. P. Robinson, and the architect Sir Edwin Lutyens (1869-1944). It was built by Holloway Brothers (London) Ltd with L. G. Mouchel & Partners Ltd acting as consulting engineers for the ferro-concrete work. Work on the bridge was started in 1930 and completed three years later at a cost of £200,000.

Hampton Court Bridge has three main spans across the river, with two small arches at the south bank and one at the north. It is of reinforced concrete with seven ribs for each arch concealed between the soffits and the deck slab. To be in keeping with the Palace, the bridge is faced with brickwork and Portland stone, more of this stone being used for the carved balustrades.

In 1991 or 1992 the bridge was strengthened by introducing more columns between the soffits and deck slab, and also waterproofed.

Dimensions
Spans: 90ft, 105ft, 90ft; width of piers: 14ft; distance between abutments: 313ft; overall length: 410ft; width between parapets: 70ft (40ft roadway and two 15ft footways).

22.6.69

SUNBURY LOCK CUT FOOTBRIDGE

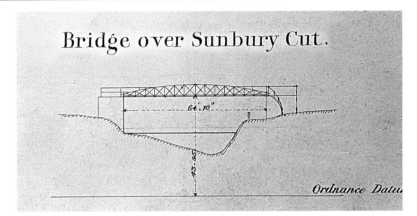

This footbridge crosses from the towpath (now the Thames Path) along the south bank of Sunbury Lock Cut to Sunbury Lock Island (or Ait) from which it is possible to cross first a weir footbridge to Wheatley's Ait, then a footbridge to Sunbury.

Sunbury Lock was built according to a proposal of 1809 by John Rennie (1761-1821) and opened in 1812. By 1852 it had become dilapidated and was therefore rebuilt, and a bridge was constructed across the lock cut by June 1856. The lock was rebuilt again in 1886.

1. The bridge of 1856 *(above right)*
The bridge preceding the 1957 reconstruction had a bow-string truss supported and approached by brick abutments having cobbled ramps, instead of steps, for the benefit of towing horses.

2. The bridge of 1957 *(right)*
The present Sunbury Cut Footbridge has a reinforced concrete span supported by the abutments of the previous bridge. The ramps and deck are provided with tubular steel handrails.

Dimensions
Distance between abutments: 64ft 9in; width of deck (1957): 4ft 3in.

28.3.76

WALTON BRIDGE

The bridge at Walton-on-Thames carries the A244 Esher to Hounslow road. There have been five bridges at the site and a sixth is to be built to replace temporary bridges of 1954 and 2000.

1. The bridge of 1750 *(below)*

The first Walton Bridge was built for Samuel Dicker, Member of Parliament for Plymouth, under an Act of 1747 (20 George 2, c. 22). It is shown in the famous 1754 picture painted for Thomas Hollis by Canaletto (1697-1768), now in the Dulwich College picture gallery. Published information about the designer and builder is not consistent. According to Thacker, the bridge was designed by White of Weybridge, but later authors attribute the design to William Etheridge and suggest that Etheridge had modelled his design on one by Palladio (1508-80). Mr White was probably the builder. There is no doubt about the structure of the bridge: it was a 'mathematical bridge', which allowed any timber to be replaced without disturbing any contiguous timber. At each side of it, straight timbers were arranged as tangents to the curves of the three arches. These timbers were fixed to each other, to supports for the deck, and to a handrail and its supports. The structure was carried by stone piers and abutments. There is a small 'mathematical bridge' at Iffley Lock, and a somewhat larger one provides an entrance to Queen's College, Cambridge.

A few years after the first Walton Bridge had been completed, the earthen ramps at each end were replaced with five-arch stone approaches.

Dimensions
Spans of arches: 44ft, 132ft, 44ft.

2. The bridge of 1787

Etheridge's timber structure was replaced by a bridge of four brick and stone arches in the years 1783 to 1787, the stone approaches of the earlier bridge being retained. The new bridge was built for Michael Dicker Sanders (William's nephew) under an Act of 1780 (20 George 3, c. 32). It was designed by James Paine (1725-89) and cost £2,000.

In 1859 a storm caused part of the bridge to collapse and repairs costing £500 had to be carried out.

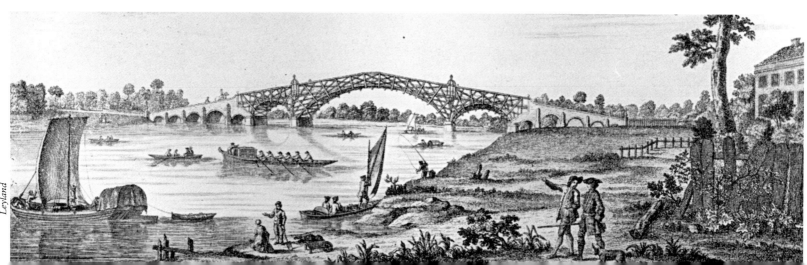

Leyland

3. The bridge of 1864 *(below)*

The repaired bridge of 1787 was replaced with an iron bridge designed by E. T. Murray during the years 1863 and 1864. The abutments and three piers were of brick and stone and supported continuous girders. Transverse girders supported longitudinal troughing filled with concrete on which the road surfacing was laid. Lattice iron balustrades completed the structure.

In 1870 the bridge was freed from toll at a cost of £7,000 following Acts of 1868 (31 & 32 Victoria, c. 17) and 1869 (32 & 33 Victoria, xix). Eight years later a brick approach viaduct of 13 arches was built at the Surrey (eastern) end.

The bridge was unsettled by a bomb during the Second World War, and after 1954 was no longer used for road traffic. Although a listed structure, it was demolished in 1985 at an approximate cost of £240,000.

Dimensions
Spans: 43ft 6in, 61ft 6in, 61ft 6in, 43ft 9in; thickness of piers and abutments: 7ft; width between parapets: 21ft.

4. The bridge of 1954 *(below)*

The bridge of 1864 was relieved of traffic by a Callender-Hamilton bridge built alongside, downstream, between September 1952 and the opening date of the fourth bridge, 5 June 1954. The bridge was supplied by the Callender Cable & Construction Co and erected by Dorman Long Ltd for a cost of £53,736. Following construction of a new temporary bridge on the site of the bridge of 1864, the Callender-Hamilton bridge has been used for pedestrians.

Dimensions
Spans between pier centres: 53ft 2in, 68ft 10in, 68ft 10in, 53ft 2in; overall width: 35ft 5in; width of roadway: 20ft; width of downstream footway: 6ft 6in.

28.8.95

5. The bridge of 2000 *(overleaf)*

A new temporary bridge was built on the site of the 1864 bridge for Surrey County Council and was opened in January 2000. Planning permission for the bridge lasts until March 2009, by which time a

28.8.02

permanent bridge is due to have been completed. The bridge was designed by Fairfield Mabey and built by Mabey Construction Ltd, a Gleesons company. Including work on the road and approaches, it cost £1.7 million.

The new bridge has foundations of circular driven steel piles supporting three piers of steel tubes in the river and three piers of steel girders on land, providing seven spans. The superstructure has two 'H' girders connected by cross-girders that support galvanised steel panels on which the road surface is laid.

Dimensions

Spans between pier centres: 58ft 10in, 75ft 10in, 68ft 6in, 68ft 6in, 50ft 6in, 59ft 0in, 42ft 8in; overall width: 25ft 11in; width of road surface: 20ft 0in.

THE EAST AND WEST DESBOROUGH CHANNEL BRIDGES

Between Shepperton Lock and Walton Bridge, the Thames flows round a pair of loops, the first near Shepperton and the second near Lower Halliford. The Desborough Channel (or cut), three-quarters of a mile long and 100 feet wide, was excavated for the Thames Conservancy to the south of these loops, between March 1930 and June 1934, to bypass them and so shorten the navigation route by about three-quarters of a mile. It was opened in 1935 and is named after Lord Desborough (Sir Wilfrid Grenfell, 1856-1945), who became a Conservator in 1896 and was Chairman of the Thames Conservancy from 1905 to 1937.

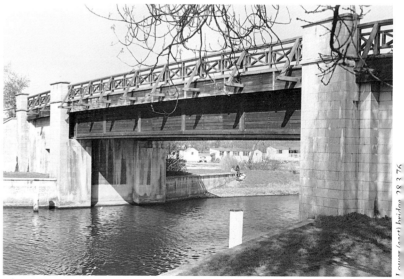

Lower (east) bridge 28.3.76

Cutting the channel produced an island and a road was built across the south of this, close to the north bank of the channel, linked at each end by a bridge to an existing road along the south bank from Walton Bridge to Weybridge. The eastern bridge provides convenient access to a water works on the island.

The two bridges were completed in 1933 and are virtually identical. Each has stone block abutments supporting a pair of massive steel beams encased in timber-clad concrete and carrying a concrete deck surfaced with tarmac. The abutments and deck have timber balustrades.

Dimensions (each bridge)
Span: 80ft; deck width: 19ft 8in.

Upper (west) bridge, 28.8.95

CHERTSEY BRIDGE

Chertsey Bridge carries the B375 from Walton-on-Thames to Chertsey.

1. The bridge of c1410
The first bridge at Chertsey was built, under a licence granted by Henry IV in 1410, to replace a ferry, and was probably constructed by the Benedictines of Chertsey Abbey. Writing in about 1530, Leland described the bridge as a 'goodly bridge of timber newly repaired'. Some 50 years later a certificate relating to an inquiry as to who should be responsible for its repair gave details, including some dimensions, of the bridge, and stated that it was divided into 23 bays.

For 200 years large sums of money were spent on periodic repairs. Then, in 1779, a Commission of the Middlesex and Surrey justices,

including the architect James Paine (1717-89), was set up to decide what type of bridge should be built as a replacement for the old one. Their decision was to invite Paine to design a stone bridge.

Dimensions
Length over water: 210ft; width between parapet rails: 15ft; width at each side beyond rails: 7ft.

2. The bridge of 1785
Money for building a bridge of James Paine's design was obtained under an Act of 1739 (13 George 2, c. 29) concerning the levying of the County Rate. The bridge was built at a site above that of the old bridge by Charles Brown of Richmond between 1780 and 1785 at a cost of £7,325. As initially built, the bridge had inconvenient approaches, and these had to be improved, the necessary purchase of land and further

work costing £2,786. A relatively small sum of £120 was raised in 1784 by auctioning the materials of the old bridge.

Chertsey Bridge is of Purbeck stone and has seven arches, five spanning the river and one on each bank. Its stone balustrades have openings filled with metal grilles.

To commemorate the 200th Anniversary of the bridge, the Worshipful the Mayor of Runnymede, Councillor A. W. Read, unveiled a plaque at a ceremony on 9 June 1985.

Dimensions

Spans and (widths of pier): 20ft (6ft 9in) 29ft 6in (6ft 7in) 36ft 3in (7ft) 41ft 10in (7ft 2in) 36ft 3in (6ft 8in) 29ft 9in (6ft 9in) 20ft; width: 17ft 6in carriageway and two 3ft 3in footways.

3. The refurbished bridge of 1991 *(below left)* • *Grade II listed* •

The bridge was partly rebuilt in 1894, and further repairs were carried out thereafter. However, a thorough investigation of 1986 showed that the steadily increasing weight and amount of traffic had caused many defects. Surrey County Council therefore strengthened and refurbished the bridge in 1991. To prevent serious disruption of traffic in the area, a two-way temporary bridge of five spans was provided while the works were in progress.

The bridge was strengthened by removing the existing fill and replacing it with mesh-reinforced concrete to 'saddle' the arches and provide a surface for a waterproofing membrane. Ducts for services were cast into the saddle. Stonework was repaired and the parapets were taken down and re-erected. During the latter work, the metal grilles were moved from above the centres of the piers to above the centres of the arches, arguably making the bridge less beautiful.

24.9.04

CHERTSEY MOTORWAY BRIDGE (M3)

Chertsey Motorway Bridge carries the M3 motorway across the Thames a little upstream of the 1785 road bridge. It crosses from east to west at an angle of 14 degrees to the river.

The bridge of 1974

This bridge was built for the Department for the Environment and designed by Courtney Theobald in collaboration with Posford, Pavry & Partners. Steelwork was by Sir William Arrol & Co Ltd, who subcontracted concrete and road-making work to Caffin & Co. The bridge was opened on 11 July 1974 but had been used by the contractors for some months before then. The bridge has three spans with separate decks for eastbound and westbound three-lane carriageways and their associated hard shoulders. The east pier (at the left bank) is founded on piles, whereas the west pier is founded on gravel. The piers and abutments are of concrete and support longitudinal steel girders, nine for each deck, connected by cross-members and having lower edges of parabolic profile. These girders were built up by welding manufactured sections together. A reinforced concrete deck was then made section by section on the completed steelwork. Aluminium post and rail parapets are fitted.

Dimensions

Spans between pier centres: 95ft, 210ft, 95ft; distance between parapets: 118ft; width: two carriageways of 36ft 8in and two hard shoulders of 9ft 10in.

24.9.04

STAINES RAILWAY BRIDGE

Staines Railway Bridge crosses the Thames between Staines and Egham stations and carries South West Trains services from Waterloo through Staines to Windsor & Eton, Reading or Weybridge (on the main line from Waterloo to Portsmouth or the West of England).

An independent company, the Staines, Wokingham & Woking Junction Railway, was authorised by an Act of 1853 (16 & 17 Victoria, clxxxv) to build a railway from Staines, on the London &

South Western Railway (LSWR) line to Windsor, to Wokingham, on the South Eastern Railway line from Reigate to Reading. The new railway was opened to Ascot on 4 June 1856 and Wokingham on 9 July 1856. From 25 March 1858 it was worked by the LSWR.

A second new route from Staines, to Weybridge, was completed ten years later. This started as a branch from Weybridge to Chertsey, authorised by an Act of 1846 (9 & 10 Victoria, clxxiv) and opened on 14 February 1848. It was completed by extending that branch to the north-west from Chertsey to Virginia Water, on the Staines to Wokingham line, under an Act of 1864 (27 & 28 Victoria, lxxxvii), and opened on 1 October 1866.

The bridge of 1856

This bridge, for two railway tracks, was designed by John Gardner (?1851-1915) and built by Cochrane & Co. It has three wrought iron plate girder spans between brick abutments. Each of the two piers is a group of three cast iron cylinders, concrete-filled and braced together. There are four flood arches on the Surrey bank.

The main girders were strengthened in 1915 and the deck was repaired in 1952.

Dimensions

Spans: 85ft 3in, 88ft 6in, 85ft 3in, each flood arch 25ft; depth of main girders: 8ft; pier cylinder diameter: 6ft (upper 15ft 4in section), 7ft 4in (lower section).

20.1.69

STAINES BRIDGE

Staines Bridge carries the A308, which starts at Wandsworth, London, and ends at Bisham, on the Thames just south of Marlow.

Just upstream of Staines Bridge on the north bank, in Ashby Recreation Ground, stands the London Stone. This is generally considered to be a 17th-century monument and once bore the inscription 'God preserve the City of London, AD 1280'. Standing at the former boundary of Middlesex and Buckinghamshire, it used to mark the limit of jurisdiction up the Thames of the Corporation of London and later (from 1857 to 1866) of the Thames Conservancy. It still marks the upper limit of public fishing rights.

1. The Roman bridge

In Roman times Staines was called Pontes after bridges there across the Thames and its tributary, the Colne. These carried the Via Trinobantica, which ran from Staines to Bath, and were probably timber structures.

2. The 13th-century bridge *(below left, in distance)*

There was a timber bridge across the Thames from before 1223, when the first of numerous grants of timber was made by the Crown for its repair. An Act of 1509 (1 Henry 8, c. 9) appointed fresh trustees because the tolls for the repair of the bridge were being improperly applied. There was a further Act of 1739 (13 George 2, c. 25) concerning maintenance. The bridge was not taken down until 1807, because successive bridges intended to replace it, completed in 1796 and 1803, had very short lives.

3. The bridge of 1796 *(below left, foreground)*

In 1791 an Act of Parliament (31 George 3, c. 84) was obtained for building a stone bridge. A design for it was prepared by Thomas Sandby (1721-98), who had been the first Professor of Architecture at the Royal Academy and had succeeded Sir Robert Taylor (1714-88) as Architect of the King's Works.

The bridge was built, just downstream of the timber bridge, between 1792 and 1796 by Townsend & Watson of Oxford and cost £9,000. It had three arches and its very short life was due to the pier foundations being shallow – one pier started to settle within a year.

Dimensions
Spans: 52ft, 60ft, 52ft;
width of piers: 8ft.

4. The bridge of 1803

In 1801 the engineer James Wilson was called in, and he designed a new bridge having a single, and therefore wide, iron arch supported between stone abutments. This was completed in 1803 and its almost immediate failure was due to spreading of the abutments caused by the considerable lateral thrust of the arch.

Dimensions

Span of single arch: 181ft; rise of arch: 16ft 6in.

5. The bridge of 1807 *(below)*

The next bridge was authorised by an Act of 1804 (44 George 3, lxxviii) and designed and built by two carpenters, Joseph Kimber and Lewis Wynes. It had an arched timber deck carried by eight rows of wooden piles irregularly spaced across the river to give alternate narrower and wider openings. The deck was reinforced with iron and fitted with iron railings as balustrades. When this bridge was completed in 1807 (at a cost of £4,526), the ancient timber bridge was at last taken down.

This third hoped-for 'permanent' bridge was sounder than its two predecessors, but nevertheless had to be replaced after only 21 years.

Dimension

Distance between abutments: 180ft.

6. The bridge of 1832

The new bridge was authorised by Acts of 1828 and 1829 and designed by George Rennie (1791-1866), eldest son of the John Rennie (1761-1821) who had made the design ultimately chosen for the London Bridge of 1831. It was built by Joliffe & Banks between 1829 and 1832 for £44,000. An opening ceremony was performed on 23 April 1832 by King William IV and Queen Adelaide.

Staines bridge was made of white Aberdeen granite, with three segmental arches across the river and a smaller arch on each bank. The approach viaducts were of brick and contained six flood arches, two on the Surrey bank and four on the Middlesex.

Tolls for crossing Staines Bridge were levied until 25 February 1871, when they were abolished under Acts of 1868 (31 & 32 Victoria, c. 17) and 1869 (32 & 33 Victoria, xix) at a cost of just over £20,000.

Dimensions

Spans: 10ft, 66ft, 74ft, 66ft, 10ft, with flood arches of 20ft; width between parapets: 33ft (24ft roadway and two 4ft 6in footways).

W. Cooke

7. The widened bridge of 1958 *(right)*
• *Grade II listed* •

In 1958 Rennie's bridge was widened by cantilevering out the footpaths to project a little way over the river. The stone balustrades across the main spans were also replaced with steel railings.

28.3.76

RUNNYMEDE M25 BRIDGES

Two bridges carry the A30 Staines bypass and the M25 London Orbital Motorway across the Thames near Bell Weir Lock. The older, upstream, bridge to the west carries the northbound (clockwise for the M25) traffic and the newer, east, bridge the southbound.

Runnymede (east) bridge of 1986 *(overleaf above)*

When it had been decided that the M25 and A30 would cross the Thames together, the design and siting of the necessary new bridge posed problems. Widening the bypass bridge would have produced a long tunnel, while the foundations of that bridge also precluded construction of an adjacent arch. These problems were solved by building a bridge of open structure, founded on piles, 10 feet downstream. The new bridge was designed by Ove Arup & Partners, and Arup Associates were the consulting architects. The contract price was £1,704,000. The foundations are bored piles resting on London clay. The superstructure has four pre-stressed white concrete frames linked by a reinforced concrete deck. Each of the frames is formed of two half-frames joined by a beam above the middle of the river. The parapets are pre-cast units of white concrete having a single aluminium rail.

The bridge was constructed by Fairclough Civil Engineering Ltd. The half-frames were made on land, and slid and jacked into position on their bearings. The remaining stages of construction, including filling the gaps between the half-frames, casting the deck and pre-stressing the reinforced concrete, were carried out conventionally.

The bridge came into use with the opening of the M25 by Margaret Thatcher on 29 October 1986.

Dimensions

Length between expansion joints: 137.6m; overall width: 34m; width of main span: 54.66m.

17.5.71

Runnymede (west) bridge of 1961 *(below)*

The first bridge at Runnymede was built to carry the A30 Staines bypass. The architectural design was completed before the Second World War by Sir Edwin Lutyens (1869-1944) and was used after the war when the bridge could at last be built. However, the pre-war structural design by the consulting engineer Mr H. Fitzsimons was replaced by a more modern design prepared by C. W. Glover & Partners; the contractors were W. & C. French Ltd.

Although it looks like a straightforward arch structure of brick and stone, it is more complex, being a two-pinned spandrel-braced arch. The abutments are cellular concrete structures that bear on London clay 24 feet below ground level. Eighteen welded steel ribs were built by constructing a spandrel-braced springing section from each abutment and fitting a plate girder section into the remaining gap. The upper and lower portions of the ribs were then encased in concrete to form deck and soffit slabs respectively. The elevations of the bridge were finished with red brick, Portland stone and white concrete.

The cost of the bridge was £476,180 and it was opened in November 1961.

Dimensions
Length: 415ft; width: 100ft; span of main arch: 173ft 6in; spans of side arches: 31ft.

28.3.76

HAM (OLD WINDSOR LOCK CUT) BRIDGE

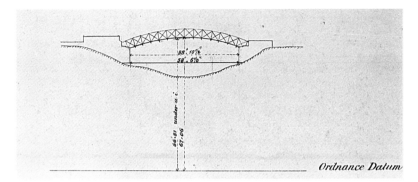

Ordnance Datum

Ham Bridge crosses the New Cut made for Old Windsor Lock in 1822, and now provides access to a sewage works on Ham Island.

It seems that there were two early bridges across the lock cut. The first, opened with the lock on 27 September 1822, collapsed only four months later, on 17 January 1823. This bridge will have been replaced fairly soon afterwards.

1. The bridge of 1871 *(above right)*
The early lock cut bridge was replaced jointly by the Thames Conservancy and the Crown in 1871, the Crown reserving the right to lay sewage pipes across it. The new bridge had a single arched lattice steel span supported by brickwork abutments.

Dimension
Span: 58ft 10½in.

2. The bridge of 1934 *(right)*
The 1871 bridge was replaced in 1934 by a steel girder bridge having a flatter and wider span suitable for vehicles. The brick abutments of the previous bridge were modified to carry the new span.

Dimensions
Span: 70ft 6in; width of deck: 12ft 2in.

3.9.70

ALBERT BRIDGE (DATCHET)

Albert Bridge carries the B3021 across the Thames from Old Windsor to a junction at Datchet with the B470 road to Windsor.

In 1845 it was suggested to Her Majesty's Commissioners of Woods and Works that the Home Park, between the town and castle of Windsor and the River Thames, could be made more private if the old bridge from Datchet to the middle of the Park was removed and replaced with new bridges adjacent to the downstream and upstream limits of the Park. Doing this would have the advantage of providing a better route from Old Windsor through Datchet to Windsor Town.

It so happened, as described in the account of Richmond Railway Bridge, that the London & South Western Railway (LSWR) opened a terminus at Datchet on 22 August 1848 and was eager to extend its line to the town of Windsor. Also, the Great Western Railway (GWR) wanted to build a branch line from Slough southwards to Windsor. The Commissioners and Windsor Corporation were therefore in a strong position when negotiating with the two railway companies, and obtained an Act of 1848 (11 & 12 Victoria, liii) obliging the LSWR to pay £60,000 and the GWR £25,000 for the new road bridges and the removal of Datchet Bridge. As a result the GWR and LSWR railway companies were authorised to build their lines to Windsor by Acts of 1848 (11 & 12 Victoria, cxxxv) and 1849 (12 & 13 Victoria, xxxiv) respectively.

1. The bridge of 1851

The bridge was designed by Thomas Page (1803-77), designer of Westminster Bridge, and opened on 2 June 1851. Henry Taunt (1842-1922), and later Fred S. Thacker, both wrote that Prince Albert (1819-61) had contributed to the design.

The bridge had a single span with five cast iron ribs supported by masonry abutments. In 1914 it was found that all the ribs had cracked, but it was not until after the First World War had ended that a replacement bridge could be built.

Dimensions
Main span: 119ft 6in; overall length: 228ft.

2. The bridge of 1928 *(below left)*

The new bridge was designed by Lt-Col J. F. Hawkins and E. Winfield, County Surveyors of Berkshire and Buckinghamshire respectively, and was built between 1927 and 1928 by A. Jackaman & Son Ltd of Slough. The Trussed Concrete Steel Co Ltd was responsible for reinforced concrete work.

Albert Bridge has two reinforced concrete river arches and retains on the Berkshire bank three flood arches from the previous bridge. Three half-turrets were built adjacent to the main arches, using stone from the earlier bridge, to provide pedestrian refuges. Between June 2003 and January 2004 the bridge was refurbished. The main work carried out by the contractors, Yoldings Ltd, was replacing the parapets, fitting high kerbs to prevent vehicles mounting the pavement and damaging the new parapets, treating metal against corrosion, and redecorating.

Dimensions
Clear spans: 75ft 6in (Berks), 110ft 9in, and three flood arches of 21ft (Bucks); width between parapets: 30ft 9in (22ft 8in roadway and two 4ft footways).

20.1.79

DATCHET BRIDGE

There is no longer a bridge across the Thames from Datchet village to the Home Park adjoining Windsor Castle, as it was removed in 1851 after the Albert and Victoria Bridges were built at the downstream and upstream boundaries of the Park following its enclosure.

1. The bridge of 1706
The first Datchet Bridge was built in 1706 in the reign of Queen Anne (1702-14) to replace a ferry. It was built of timber from Windsor Forest and had to be extensively repaired in 1734 at a cost of £800.

2. The bridge of 1770 *(below)*
The 1706 bridge was replaced in 1770 with a timber bridge of nine openings carried by stone piers. The piers failed, due to scour of the foundations, so that in 1794 the bridge was closed and a ferry re-introduced.

3. The bridge of 1812 *(below)*
The residents of Datchet campaigned for the building of a new bridge and, following legal proceedings, Berkshire and Buckinghamshire were each directed to pay half the cost. The bridge was built by Robert Tebbott of Windsor and had a timber superstructure supported by the surviving, and presumably repaired, stone piers.

4. The bridge of c1836
The final Datchet Bridge resulted from an unwilling co-operation of the Berkshire and Buckinghamshire authorities in repairing the 1812 bridge. The Datchet end needed extensive repair by 1834 and the Berkshire end collapsed in 1836. Buckinghamshire repaired the Datchet end with timber while Berkshire repaired the Home Park end with iron. The curious resultant structure was demolished under the Act of 1848 (11 & 12 Victoria, liii) that authorised the construction of the Victoria and Albert Bridges.

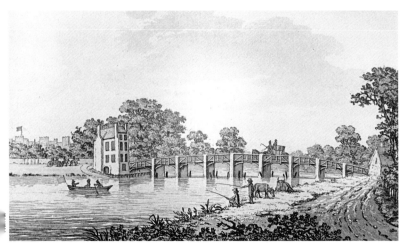

Tombleson

VICTORIA BRIDGE (DATCHET)

Victoria Bridge carries the B470 across the Thames between Datchet and Windsor. It and the Albert Bridge were built under an Act of 1848 (11 & 12 Victoria, liii) to replace Datchet Bridge, which was removed when the Home Park at Windsor was enclosed.

1. The bridge of 1851 *(below)*

The design of the Victoria Bridge was produced by Thomas Page (1803-77), probably in collaboration with Prince Albert (1819-61), and was closely similar to that of Albert Bridge. It had a single main arch, now replaced, of five decorative cast iron ribs, between stone abutments, which have been retained. Each abutment has, near the river, an arch flanked by half-turrets providing alcoves for pedestrians and, further from the river, two flood arches. All the original arches were of the slightly pointed Tudor form.

Dimensions

Main span: 117ft 9in; shore spans: 23ft 6in; width between kerbs: 22ft; width of footways: 4ft; overall length: 228ft.

2. The bridge of 1967 *(below)*

The 1851 bridge was declared unsafe in 1963 and a temporary Bailey bridge was erected to maintain the crossing.

The main arch of the old bridge was replaced between April 1966 and April 1967 by two high-tensile steel ribs of box-section carrying vertical mild steel tubular pillars that support a reinforced concrete deck. The consulting engineers were Mott, Hay & Anderson and the contractor was the Cementation Construction Co; the steelwork was made by Joseph Westwood & Co Ltd. The cost of the work was about £77,000, and the major part of this was borne by British Rail and Berkshire, while Buckinghamshire contributed to the remainder. Since the rebuilding, responsibility for maintaining the bridge passed first to Berkshire, then to the Unitary Authority of Windsor & Maidenhead.

The abutments of the 1851 bridge were little changed in appearance by the reconstruction. The alcoves now carry an original plate with the wording 'Constructed for the Commissioners of Her Majesty's Woods and Works, 1851 Thos Page Engineer J. A. Rigby Contractors', and a new plate reading 'The VICTORIA BRIDGE – CENTRAL ARCH RECONSTRUCTED 1966'.

Dimensions

Main span: 126ft; width between parapets: 30ft.

BLACK POTTS RAILWAY BRIDGE

Dredge

This bridge carries the line from Waterloo to Windsor across the Thames between Datchet and Windsor & Eton (Riverside) stations.

As described in connection with Richmond Railway Bridge and Albert Bridge (Datchet), the London & South Western Railway (LSWR) was authorised by an Act of 1849 (12 & 13 Victoria, xxxiv) to extend its line beyond the terminus opened at Datchet on 22 August 1848 to a new terminus in Windsor. This required the building of a further bridge across the river, which was given the name Black Potts, from a little fishing house used by Sir Isaac Walton (1593-1683) and his friend Sir Henry Wootten, then Provost of Eton.

1. The bridge of 1849

The first railway bridge was designed by Joseph Locke (1805-60) and built by Thomas Brassey (1805-70). It had four spans, each having six ribbed arches and vertically ribbed spandrels of cast iron, carried by brick piers and abutments. The bridge was rather similar in appearance to the present Richmond Railway Bridge. Because it was in sight of the castle, it was given decorative cast iron parapets. The piers were built on iron platforms supported by six cast iron cylinders sunk into the river bed. When the track was laid, two of the piers subsided, so that instead of reaching Windsor on the expected date of 9 August

1849 (before the arrival of the Great Western Railway on 8 October), the LSWR did not reach the town, at a temporary terminus, until 1 December.

2. The bridge of 1893 *(above)*

The deck of the 1849 bridge was replaced by Perry & Co using straight wrought iron girders and corrugated floor plates supplied by the Horsley Company. The ornamental external ribs and parapets were retained. In addition, flood arches were replaced with an embankment. All these works were completed in November 1893.

3. The bridge of 1954 *(below)*

In 1954 the ornamental cast iron external ribs and parapets were removed, greatly altering the appearance of the bridge.

Dimensions (all bridges)
Four spans, each of 51ft 9in (75ft on the skew); width of each brick pier: 10ft 9in.

WINDSOR (TOWN) BRIDGE

Windsor Bridge is now a pedestrian crossing from Thames Street, near the castle on the south bank of the Thames, to Eton High Street, leading to Eton College, on the north bank. Before the opening of the Windsor & Eton bypass in 1966, it used to carry the main road from Bagshot to Gerrards Cross.

1. The ancient bridge

A timber bridge existed at Windsor before 1172, a record of that year stating that Osbert de Bray derived £4 6s 6d from tolls levied on vessels passing under it. As for all timber bridges, Windsor Bridge needed periodically to be repaired or rebuilt, and during that work the crossing was maintained by ferry. An Act of 1736 (9 George 2, c. 15) enabled 'the mayor, bailiffs and burgesses of the borough of New Windsor to repair and maintain their great bridge over the river of Thames' and charge 'tolls for pontage and passage over and under the said bridge'.

The bridge was inconvenient for navigation and in 1793 was described by Robert Mylne (1734-1811) as having only one opening, out of 12 or so, fit for a barge. Barges passing upstream had to be hauled by a winch. By 1811 the bridge had decayed so much that it was referred to by Cooke as 'a tottering ruinous, rotten old fabric'.

Dimension
Length: 165ft.

2. The bridge of 1824 *(above right)* • *Grade II listed* •

An Act of Parliament for building a new bridge was obtained in 1819 (59 George 3, cxxvi). To design the bridge, Windsor Corporation engaged Charles Hollis, engineer to the architect Jeffry Wyatt, then restoring the Castle. Construction started in 1820 but, because of unforeseen delays, the cornerstone could not be laid until 10 July 1822

when a ceremony was performed by Frederick, Duke of York (1763-1827). The bridge was eventually opened on 1 June 1824 by the Mayor, local dignitaries and others (including the architect) concerned with the works.

The levying of tolls for crossing the bridge was maintained; however, a resident of Eton, Mr Joseph Taylor, considered that the powers for doing this had lapsed, and in 1895 started a campaign that, after proceedings in the Court of Queen's Bench, the Court of Appeal and the House of Lords, resulted in the removal of the toll-gates on 1 December 1898.

Windsor Bridge has three cast iron arches, each of seven ribs, supported by granite piers and abutments. The road surface was originally laid on cast iron plates but these were later replaced by plates of steel.

Following the opening of the Windsor & Eton bypass in 1966, vehicular traffic across the Town Bridge declined and the bridge was restricted to pedestrian use in April 1970. It is a Grade II listed structure.

Dimensions
Spans: 43ft 4in, 55ft 6in, 43ft 4in; width between parapets: 25ft 6in; width of each pier: 8ft 1in.

WINDSOR RAILWAY BRIDGE

Windsor Railway Bridge carries the branch line that runs south from Slough to Windsor Royal station.

The Great Western Railway (GWR) opened its main line west from Paddington as far as Maidenhead in June 1838, but, largely due to the antagonism of the Eton College authorities, was unable to obtain an Act for building the Windsor branch until 1848 (11 & 12 Victoria, cxxxv). Because of the eagerness of the GWR and the London & South Western Railway (LSWR) companies to gain access to Windsor, they had agreed – as a condition for obtaining the Acts they needed – to pay Her Majesty's Commissioners of Woods and Works and Windsor Corporation substantial sums to fund improvements in and around Windsor. These included replacement of Datchet Bridge with the Victoria and Albert Bridges, respectively upstream and downstream of the village. The GWR line to Windsor was opened on 8 October 1849.

1. The bridge of 1849

The bridge carrying the Windsor branch across the Thames was designed by the famous Isambard Kingdom Brunel (1806-59), Engineer of the GWR, in a typically original manner. It has three 'bow and string' (or 'bowstring') girders, each consisting of a wrought iron arch (the bow) of inverted triangular section from which is suspended by braced hangers a wrought iron flanged plate girder (the string), which ties the ends of the arch together. The central bowstring girder, between the two railway tracks, is twice as strong as those at the edges. The bows are cross-braced at the top, and the lower flanges of the strings are connected by cross-members, which, together with those flanges, support a timber deck. In the bridge as built, each bowstring girder was supported at each end by two cast iron cylinders filled with concrete.

The bridge is approached from the north by a viaduct more than half

7.6.06

a mile (about 1km) long and crosses the Thames at an angle of 60 degrees. The viaduct was originally of timber, but was replaced by one of brick, having 300 arches, between 1861 and 1865.

The tracks on Windsor Bridge were originally of the GWR broad gauge (7ft 0¼in), but in the spring of 1862 were converted to mixed gauge, by adding intermediate rails for the standard (4ft 8½in) gauge, so that Queen Victoria could use the line on her way to Scotland. The broad gauge was removed on 30 June 1883. More recently, one track has been removed.

Dimensions
Length of bowstring girders: 202ft; clear span: 187ft (skew); diameter of cast iron cylinders: 6ft; overall width: 37ft 6in; spacing of cylinders: 9ft in direction of bridge, 17ft 6in transversely.

2. The modified bridge of 1908 *(above)* • *Grade II listed* •

The cast iron cylinders supporting the bowstring girders were replaced by brick abutments in 1908. At the same time, the cross-girders and rail bearers were renewed in steel.

Dimensions
Clear span: 163ft 6in (square), 184ft 6in (skew).

WINDSOR & ETON BYPASS (QUEEN ELIZABETH II) BRIDGE

The Queen Elizabeth II Bridge carries the Windsor & Eton Bypass across the Thames upstream of Windsor Railway Bridge. The bypass forms the southern end of the A355 route south from Amersham, which becomes the A332 for its continuation to Bagshot.

The bridge of 1966

The building of the bridge and bypass was authorised by an Act of 1961 (9 & 10 Elizabeth II, xv). The bridge was built between 1964 and 1966 to designs prepared by K. P. Brow, County Surveyor of Berkshire, and E. H. Frankland, County Surveyor of Buckinghamshire, in association with the architect Courtney Theobald.

The structure of the bridge is similar to that used for the 1972 Marlow Bypass Bridge (on the A404 further upstream) for which Courtney Theobald was once more engaged as consulting architect. It is a three-span structure of reinforced concrete with outer box sections resting at intermediate points on the two piers and anchored at the abutments to form cantilevers that extend towards each other across the river to provide about two-thirds of the main span. The remaining third is provided by a central section suspended between the free ends of the cantilevers.

The works on the road and bridge were carried out by Richard Costain (Civil Engineering) Ltd and Higgs & Hill Ltd at a cost of £4½ million, of which almost £300,000 was spent on the bridge. The bypass was opened on 11 July 1966.

Dimensions

Spans: 63ft, 175ft 2in, 63 ft (main span has suspended central section of 68ft 6in); length of each cantilever: 120ft; distance between abutments: 301ft; overall length: 461ft; overall width: 84ft (two 24ft carriageways, two 13ft side reservations and 10ft central reservation).

SUMMERLEAZE BRIDGE

Summerleaze Bridge, named after the company for which it was built, carries a path for pedestrians and cyclists across the Thames half a mile downstream of the Maidenhead M4 motorway bridge. It connects the towpath on the east (left) bank at Dorney with a road on the west bank at Bray. It is unique among Thames footbridges in having a gravel conveyor under its deck.

Robin Prior (1893-1978), an engineer brought up in Oxford, spent some years extracting gravel from sites owned by various land-owners, then decided to form a company so that he could obtain and work sites for himself. Summerleaze Ltd was incorporated in 1946, then in the 1960s the company diversified into landfill, to allow restoration of former gravel workings, and power generation using the gas produced by decaying landfill waste.

After agreeing to make an international-standard rowing lake for Eton College, Summerleaze Ltd decided to build a combined gravel conveyor and footbridge. The conveyor could carry the 4.5 million tonnes or so of gravel that would have to be excavated towards a processing plant at Bray on the opposite side of the Thames. Richard Irons Associates, consulting engineers from Northampton, produced a design, and planning permission was obtained late in 1995. Construction started in August 1996 and the bridge was opened on 29 October that year by Richard Simmonds CBE, Chairman of the Countryside Commission.

Summerleaze Bridge has a suspended span between spans cantilevered out from the river banks. Each of these spans consists of a pair of plate girders rigidly connected at intervals by cross-girders arranged vertically in groups of three. The plate girders are deep enough to hide the conveyor belt and are profiled to make the bridge appear to have a wide central arch and part-arches on either side. The upper reach of the conveyor belt is supported as a trough by horizontal and inclined rollers mounted on the middle cross-girders. The return

18.11.02

reach of the belt is supported by single rollers mounted on the lower cross-girders. The deck is carried by the upper cross-girders, so as to hide the conveyor belt, and is provided with handrails fixed to the plate girders.

The cantilever spans are anchored to reinforced concrete abutments at their shore ends and are supported part-way along their lengths by pairs of inclined steel piers bearing on reinforced concrete foundations at the river edges. Access to the ends of the deck is provided by ramps of 1 in 12 gradient.

The main structure was built by John Martin Construction Ltd of Thetford, Norfolk, and. the hardwood decking and handrails were supplied by H. Somerscales Ltd. The total cost of building the bridge was about £400,000.

Dimensions

Spans (between centrelines): 9.893m (32½ft), 52.445m (172ft), 9.893m; distance between river abutments: 53.0m; width between handrails: 3.0m (10ft); headway at centre: 7.478m.

NEW THAMES BRIDGE, MAIDENHEAD (M4)

The New Thames Bridge, Maidenhead, carries the M4 motorway across the river near Bray, between Junctions 7 and 8, about 1½ miles downstream of Maidenhead Railway Bridge.

The bridge, from the parish of Bray to the parish of Taplow, was authorised by an Act of 1937 (1 Edward 8 & 1 George 6, xlii). Construction started in 1939 and the foundations and abutments had been largely completed when work was stopped in 1940 because of a steel shortage resulting from the Second World War.

The bridge of 1961

After the war it was decided to include the bridge in the London to South Wales Motorway (M4) and the superstructure was redesigned for the Ministry of Transport by the Buckinghamshire Bridge Section staff and, as consulting engineers, Freeman, Fox & Partners. It was built for £184,000 between 1959 and 1960 by Horseley Bridge and Thomas Piggott Ltd, and opened for traffic in March 1961.

The superstructure has eight welded high tensile steel girders connected by welded steel cross-frames grip bolted in position. The girders were simultaneously built out from each side of the river by cranes moving over the steelwork, and were completed by dropping closing sections into position and welding them in. A reinforced concrete deck slab was then cast to act compositely with the steelwork. Originally the deck carried two dual carriageways, two cycle tracks and two footways, but between 1969 and 1971 these were replaced by two three-lane carriageways and two footways.

10.8.68

Dimensions

Main span: 270ft; two anchor spans: 38ft 9in; width: 100ft; spacing of main girders: 12ft 6in; deck thickness: 8½in.

MAIDENHEAD RAILWAY BRIDGE

Maidenhead Railway Bridge takes the main line from Paddington to the West of England across the Thames between Taplow and Maidenhead stations.

The Great Western Railway (GWR) main line from London to Bristol was built under an Act of 1835 (5 & 6 William 4, cvii), and opened on 4 June 1838 from a temporary terminus at Paddington to a station at Taplow, on the east bank of the Thames. This station was also made to serve Maidenhead, well over a mile away, on the west bank. The line was extended 9 miles west to Twyford on 1 July 1839, crossing the river at Maidenhead by the most famous of the four Thames railway bridges designed by Isambard Kingdom Brunel (1806-59). Surprisingly, it was not until November 1871 that Maidenhead was given a convenient station in the centre of the town.

The bridge of 1838

To meet the demands of the Thames Commissioners for an unobstructed navigation channel and towpath, Brunel designed a brick bridge having two main semi-elliptical arches, each of 128-foot span and only 24-foot rise. The pier between them was to be built on a conveniently situated island, and the bridge was to have four semi-circular land arches on each bank of the river. Brunel was helped in producing this astonishing design by experiments and sketches made by his father, Marc Isambard Brunel (1769-1849) (see the biography of Marc by Harold Bagust). The main arches were to be the widest and flattest brick arches anywhere in the world, and Brunel's critics predicted (and probably hoped!) that they would fall down as soon as the centring on which they were to be built was taken down.

The contractor Chadwick began to build the bridge early in 1837. During the spring of 1838 the centring was eased and, to the delight of the critics, a separation of about half an inch occurred between the three lowest courses of bricks for about 12 feet on each side of the crown of the eastern arch. The

separation had occurred because the centring had been eased before the cement had hardened completely. In July the faulty work was replaced and, on 8 October, the centring was eased once more but left in place. When, in the autumn of 1839, the centring blew down in a storm and the arches stayed up, the critics were finally silenced. The bridge had cost £37,000.

The widened bridge of 1893 (*previous page*) • *Grade II* listed* •
Maidenhead Bridge originally carried two broad gauge (7ft 0¼in) tracks, but these were converted to mixed gauge (with an additional rail at the standard gauge of 4ft 8½in) on 1 October 1861. When it was decided to abolish the broad gauge it was also decided to quadruple the main line between Taplow and Didcot. Sir John Fowler (1817-98) was appointed consulting engineer for the widening, and the bridge

was made able to carry four tracks by widening on each side. The two additional tracks reached the eastern end of the bridge on 8 September 1884 and came into use as far as Reading on 4 June 1893, just over a year after the abolition of the broad gauge on 20 May 1892.

In 1975, European Heritage Year, an elliptical stone plaque was fixed to the south side of the bridge between the towpath (now the Thames Path) and the river. The inscription on the plaque refers to 'The Sounding Arch', a name given to the eastern arch because of the echoes it provides.

Dimensions
Span of two semi-elliptical main arches: 128ft; rise: 24ft 6in; spans of semi-circular arches at each end: 21ft, 28ft, 28ft, 28ft; width as built: 30ft; width after widening: 60ft; overall length: 778ft.

MAIDENHEAD BRIDGE

Maidenhead Bridge carries the main road west from London to Bath (A4) across the Thames between Taplow to the east (on the left bank) and Maidenhead. The present bridge was built in the 18th century to replace a mediaeval bridge upstream.

1. The mediaeval bridge
The first Maidenhead Bridge was built of timber in about 1280, and had a bridge chapel dedicated to St Andrew. The bridge needed frequent repairs and money for these was obtained (i) from Royal grants of pontage over the years 1297 (in the reign of Edward I) to 1433 (in the reign of Henry VI); (ii) from tolls and alms collected by the Guild of St Andrew & St Mary Magdalene, which existed from 1451 to 1547 (in the respective reigns of Henry VI and Edward VI); and (iii) from tolls levied by a body incorporated by a charter of Queen

Elizabeth I. When this charter was confirmed by James I, he allowed the Corporation to take three oaks each year from the Royal Forest of Bray. Later, oaks were obtained under the Commonwealth and, after the Restoration, the Crown.

In January 1400 the bridge was the scene of military action when the brother of Richard II, the Duke of Surrey, defended it against the men of King Henry IV. In 1688 it was fortified to impede the approach of the Prince of Orange to London.

2. The bridge of 1777 (*above right*)   • *Grade I listed* •
When the cost of repairing the mediaeval bridge became high in the mid-18th century, the Corporation considered building a timber replacement but wisely decided to build a bridge of stone. An Act of Parliament was obtained in 1772 (12 George 3, c. 41) and the foundation stone was laid on 19 October of that year.

Maidenhead Bridge was designed by Mr Robert Taylor (1714-88), who was subsequently knighted when he was Sheriff of London for the

period 1782-83. It was built by John Townesend, of Oxford, between 1772 and 1777, and has seven stone arches across the river and three arches with brick vaults on each bank; it cost £19,000.

Tolls were levied from road-users until 30 October 1903. The freeing from toll resulted from legal proceedings based on evidence of mismanagement by the Corporation of the money collected. The event was promptly celebrated by members of the public throwing the toll-gates into the river.

Maidenhead Bridge is a Grade I listed structure.

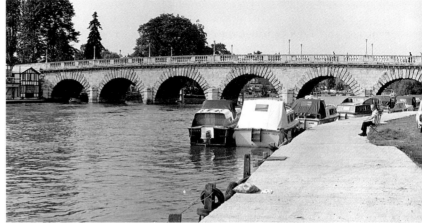

10.8.68

Dimensions

Spans of river arches: Nos 1 and 7 28ft, Nos 2 and 6 30ft, No 3 32ft 3in, No 4 (central) 34ft 6in, No 5 32ft 6in; total length: 474ft 4in; thickness of piers: from 8ft 3in, on either side of central arch, to 7ft 3in between pairs of river arches at each end; width between parapets: 30ft (20ft roadway and two footways of 4ft 10in).

BOULTER'S LOCK BRIDGE

Flowing south from Cookham, the Thames divides into four channels just north of Boulter's Island, about a mile upstream of Maidenhead Bridge. The east channel is the mill-stream for Taplow Mill and was made the upper end of the Jubilee River when that channel was cut in the years 1996 to 2001 to relieve flooding in Maidenhead, Windsor and Eton. The next channel is the original course of the river, to the east of Ray Mill Island. The third channel is the mill-stream for Ray Mill, the building of which was converted in 1950 into what is now the Boulter's Lock Hotel. The fourth (western) channel is the navigation channel that contains Boulter's Lock and lies between Boulter's Island and the Maidenhead-Cookham Road (A4094). Boulter's Lock Bridge crosses the tail of the lock to link the hotel with the road. A second bridge links Boulter's Island with Ray Mill Island.

Ray Mill existed in the 14th century and a flash lock had been made there before the end of the 16th century. The first pound lock was built on the Taplow mill-stream under an Act of 1771 (11 George 3, c. 45) and opened in 1772. It was replaced by a new lock, on the present site, in 1829 with a bridge immediately below. The lock and bridge were rebuilt in 1912.

1. The bridge of 1829 *(previous page)*

The first Boulter's Lock bridge had a cast-iron deck supported by stone abutments and provided with iron balustrades. It, and the lock gates, are shown in the best-known painting by Edward Gregory (1850-1909); he painted the picture in 1895 and, after it had been exhibited at the Royal Academy, was elected a Member.

Dimension
Span: 19ft 9in.

2. The bridge of 1912 *(below)*

A new bridge was provided for the rebuilt lock, with a stone arch and ornamental stone balustrades. The parapet now bears a plaque with the wording 'Royal Borough of Windsor and Maidenhead – RICHARD DIMBLEBY CBE 1915-1965 Journalist, war correspondent and television presenter Lived in Mill Head Boulters Island'.

Dimensions
Span: 31ft 6in; width: 20ft 4in.

11.7.76

COOKHAM LOCK CUT FOOTBRIDGE

Cookham Cut Footbridge spans the navigation channel from the south bank on Cookham Lock Island to the north bank on Sashes Island.

The waterways downstream of Cookham Bridge have always been complex and have on occasion been altered. There are now four streams – from north to south, they are:

(i) the Hedsor Channel. This is the former navigation channel around the north of Sashes Island (a name not seen on present maps). It contained wharves that for centuries had been used for handling important traffic, including timber, paper and coal;

(ii) Cookham Lock Cut, the navigation channel through the pound lock opened on 1 November 1830, between Sashes Island, to the north, and the artificial lock island;

(iii) the Odney Weir Stream, between the lock island and the north of Formosa Island; and

(iv) the Lulle Brook.

All these streams are crossed by bridges and (i), (iii) and (iv) necessarily have weirs.

The opening of Cookham Lock Cut to bypass the Hedsor Channel caused Lord Boston, owner of the Hedsor estate, to lose toll income and he succeeded in obtaining compensation from the Thames Commissioners and gaining the right to enjoy the Hedsor water as a private channel.

Cookham Lock has been altered a number of times, notably in 1892 and more recently in 1956-57, when a third pair of gates was provided to give alternative chamber lengths.

1. The bridge of c1830

Thacker (1920) refers to 'a timber structure with very narrow openings'.

2. The bridge of 1871 *(right)*

The present bridge was ordered in 1870 and opened in 1871. It has an arch of steel beams carrying a concrete deck and having lattice steel parapets. Brick abutments, set back from the banks, are built on concrete coping and piling.

Dimensions
Span: 61ft; width of deck: 10ft 10in.

7.11.76

COOKHAM BRIDGE

Cookham Bridge carries the A4094, which runs north from Maidenhead to Bourne End and a junction with the Oxford Road (A40) just beyond Beaconsfield. It was a toll-bridge until 1947. The appearance of one end of the bridge is known to admirers of Sir Stanley Spencer (1891-1959) from his painting of 1915-19, 'Swan Upping at Cookham', in Tate Britain.

1. The bridge of 1840

The first bridge was built for the Cookham Bridge Company under an Act of 1838 (1 & 2 Victoria, x) to replace a ferry. It was of wood, with 13 spans, and designed by George Treacher, Surveyor to the Thames Commissioners. He had succeeded his father, the younger John Treacher (1760-1836), in that office in 1835. Construction by a Mr Freebody was carried out between June and December 1839 and the bridge was opened on 1 January 1840. Construction cost £4,224 and the total cost, including the cost of obtaining the Act of Parliament and buying the ferry, was £8,274. An octagonal brick toll-house was built to the west of the road on the northern, Buckinghamshire, bank of the river.

Dimensions
Spans: nine of 24ft and four of 18 ft.

2. The bridge of 1867 *(overleaf)*

The present bridge, now a Grade II listed structure, was built in 1867 by Messrs Pease, Hutchinson & Co at Skerne Ironworks, Darlington. That company's estimate of £2,520 was accepted from the 37 received, which ranged from £1,900 to £27,000, and the work was carried out within the estimate.

The deck of the bridge has two longitudinal and about 45 equally spaced transverse wrought iron girders. Originally the girders carried

3-inch planking covered with asphalt, but when the bridge was strengthened in 1948 the planking was replaced with concrete-filled steel troughing. The deck is supported by red-brick abutments and seven intermediate piers, being fixed to the three central ones and carried by rollers on the other four and on the abutments. Each pier consists of two cast-iron pillars carried by two hollow wrought-iron screw piles screwed into the river bed and filled with concrete. The pillars and the upper portions of the piles are cross-braced.

The 1948 strengthening was carried out the year after the bridge had ceased to be a toll-bridge. The last toll-collector had paid the bridge-owners £350 a year, and further takings provided his income.

Additional strengthening was carried out in 1971. In 1985 a weight limit of 7.5 tonnes was imposed, and in 1998 single-lane traffic controlled by lights had to be introduced. The following year it was decided to repair the bridge thoroughly.

Dimensions

Two shore spans: 30ft; six intermediate spans: 40ft; overall length: 335ft; length between abutments: 300ft; width between parapets: 20ft; depth of main girders: 3ft 6in; spacing of transverse girders: 6ft 8in; diameter of wrought iron tubes of screw piles: 21in; diameter of cast iron pillars: 10½in.

3. The refurbished bridge of 2001   • *Grade II listed* •

In 2001 the bridge was extensively refurbished to enable it to carry loads of up to 17 tonnes. The main works carried were as follows.

In the superstructure the concrete deck was removed to expose the steel troughing, which, together with the crossbeams that carried it, were then removed in sections for cleaning, repair and painting; the repair of the crossbeams included strengthening with additional plates. The other metalwork, including the parapets, was repaired or replaced as necessary. Finally, a new concrete deck was constructed and waterproofed, and new wooden handrails were fitted to the repaired metal parapets.

In the substructure, the piers were cleaned and painted at the same time as the troughing and crossbeams. The original rolled iron columns were replaced with steel circular columns, and some missing ornamental spandrels were replaced. All the works cost a total of about £1.2 million.

The Royal Borough of Windsor & Maidenhead, the engineer (the Babtie Group), and the contractor (John Mowlem & Company PLC) received two awards for the refurbishment: a commendation in The Historic Bridge Awards 2001 made by the Institution of Civil Engineers, English Heritage, British Waterways, et al; and the Institution of Civil Engineers Chiltern Association Winning Merit Award for 2002.

20.11.76

BOURNE END RAILWAY BRIDGE AND FOOTBRIDGE

This railway bridge carries a line from Maidenhead to Bourne End that used to continue to High Wycombe. Now trains can only continue along a branch to Marlow, reached by reversing at Bourne End station. In the early 1990s a footbridge for the Thames Path was attached to the upstream side of the railway bridge.

The Wycombe Railway Company was formed under an Act of 1846 (9 & 10 Victoria, ccxxxvi) and authorised to build a 10-mile single-track broad gauge line from Maidenhead to High Wycombe. By an Act of 1847 (10 & 11 Victoria, ccxvi) it was given the power to amalgamate with the Great Western Railway (GWR). The line was not built at once and the Parliamentary powers had to be revived in 1852 (15 & 16 Victoria, cxlvii). The line was eventually opened on 1 August 1854 and was absorbed by the GWR in 1867 (29 & 30 Victoria, ccliv).

The branch from Bourne End to Marlow was opened on 28 June 1873. Almost 100 years later, on 4 May 1970, the northern end of the original line, between Bourne End and High Wycombe, was closed.

1. The railway bridge of 1854 *(below)*
The first Thames bridge was of timber and designed by T. H. Bertram with 13 openings between piers formed from piles. There were six spans over the river, formed of triangular trusses, and shorter spans on the banks, five on the Berkshire and two on the Buckinghamshire side. Each of the five river spans at the Buckinghamshire end was divided into two by additional piers.

As noted above, the bridge came into service on 1 August 1854. It was strengthened in 1870, just before the broad gauge (7ft 0¼in) track was converted to the standard (4ft 8½in) gauge between 23 August and 1 September of that year.

Dimensions
Six river spans: 42ft 6in (five at Buckinghamshire end halved by central piers); seven land spans: 32ft; angle of crossing river: 69 degrees.

2. The railway bridge of 1894 *(overleaf)*
The timber bridge was replaced with a bridge designed by J. C. Inglis and built by F. C. Caffin of Leamington. Work was started in July 1894 and it was opened for traffic on 28 October 1895. It has three wrought iron lattice girder spans supported between brick abutments by piers consisting of braced pairs of wrought iron cylinders extending into the river bed. Brick approach viaducts have five arches at the southern (Berkshire) end and two arches in Buckinghamshire, at the northern end.

Dimensions
Spans: 99ft 0in, 99ft 0in, 98ft 6in; span of five approach arches (Berks): 23ft 6in; span of two approach arches (Bucks): 16ft 3in.

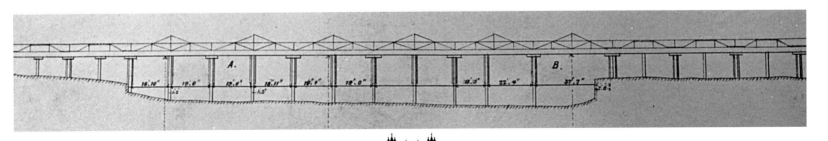

11.7.76

2a. The attached footbridge
(see page 10)

A footbridge to carry the Thames Path was attached with brackets to the upstream side of the railway bridge and opened on 14 July 1993.

Dimension
Width between parapets: 55in.

MARLOW BYPASS BRIDGE

The Marlow Bypass carries the A404 Watford to Maidenhead route past the eastern edge of the town and across the Thames downstream of Marlow Bridge and Marlow Lock. It runs south from a roundabout on the M40 motorway at Handy Cross, High Wycombe, to a roundabout just south of Bisham. From there the A404 continues southwards to the A4 at Maidenhead and on to join the M4. A survey for the bypass was carried out as long ago as 1929, but construction was not started until November 1970. The bypass, and the bridge, was officially opened on 20 December 1972.

The bridge was designed by Mr E. W. Davies, County Surveyor of Berkshire, with Courtney Theobald as consulting architect. It is a reinforced concrete box structure having cantilevers supporting a suspended span of pre-cast, pre-stressed concrete beams. The foundations of the piers and abutments are of reinforced concrete and were made within sheet-steel piling. The contractor was Fitzpatrick.

18.9.77

Dimensions
Central span: 190ft; two shore spans: 112ft; length of suspended span: 85ft; length between abutments: 414ft; width between parapets: 78ft 8in; width of each carriageway: 24ft.

MARLOW BRIDGE

Before the building of the Marlow Bypass, Marlow Bridge carried the A404 route between the Bath Road (A4) west of Maidenhead and the Oxford Road (A40) at High Wycombe. The road over the bridge is now classified as C8804.

1. The ancient bridge

The first Marlow Bridge was built of timber for the Knights Templar before 1227, the year in which Henry III gave an oak tree for its repair. It was downstream of the present bridge, on the line of St Peter Street, and there was a chapel dedicated to St Mary at the town end. During the Civil War it was partly destroyed by the Parliamentary Army, but the damage was repaired in 1642.

2. The bridge of 1789

The ancient bridge, like all timber bridges, needed continual repair, but by 1787 had become unsafe. A new timber bridge designed by Thomas Brettingham, and probably incorporating wood from the previous one, was opened in 1789. To meet the cost of £1,800, money had to be raised by public subscription because the ecclesiastical origin of the first bridge enabled Buckinghamshire to avoid having to pay.

3. The suspension bridge of 1832

By 1828 the timber bridge had become past economic repair and the Bridge Wardens were advised to build a new, shorter bridge upstream. They appointed a commission, which, in 1829, obtained an Act (10 George 4, xlv) for the work and approved a design for a suspension bridge by John Millington. Construction was started but it soon became evident that the design was unsatisfactory and Millington left Marlow and went to America.

The Commissioners now consulted William Tierney Clark (1783-1852), a distinguished engineer who had started his career as an apprentice to a millwright, then worked, in turn, at Coalbrookdale; under John Rennie (1761-1821); as engineer to the West Middlesex Water Works (1811); and as a consulting engineer. The first bridge he designed to cross the Thames was the original Hammersmith suspension bridge of 1824-27. When asked to design a bridge for Marlow, he offered a scaled-down version of the Hammersmith design, and this was accepted.

The new bridge was built between 1829 and 1831. It had a deck of planks, supported by oak crossbeams, which was stiffened at its edges, to some extent, by parapets formed of cast-iron standards connected by timber rails and cross-bracing. The deck was suspended from vertically arranged pairs of wrought iron eye-bar chains by wrought iron rods connected to the crossbeams. These chains were supported between anchorages at each end of the bridge by bearings near the tops of two masonry towers founded, not very deeply, in the Thames ballast. A pavement was cantilevered from each side of the deck beyond the line of the chains. The ironwork was supplied by W. Hazeldine of Shrewsbury, the stonework carried out by Corby & Clifford of Marlow, and the timberwork by W. Bond of Marlow. Building the bridge cost £22,000.

In 1860 the oak crossbeams were replaced with wrought iron girders, this work costing £3,300.

Dimensions

Spans: 71ft 0in (Bucks), 227ft 3in (main), 70ft 4in (Berks); width of carriageway: 20ft 9in (12ft in tower archways); width of footways: 12ft.

4. The reconstructed bridge of 1966 *(overleaf)* • *Grade I listed* •

In about 1928 the Buckinghamshire and Berkshire County Councils proposed replacing the bridge with one of reinforced concrete – a proposal defeated in 1930. A 5-ton weight limit was imposed, but failure of suspension rods in 1951 and 1957 led to the weight limit being reduced to 2 tons in 1958. Once again the County Councils considered replacing the bridge with a modern one, but a Bridge

18.9.77

Preservation Committee, formed in 1963, persuaded them to reconstruct it without changing the appearance and restore the 5-ton weight limit.

Drawings and documents for the reconstruction were prepared by Rendel, Palmer & Tritton. The mechanical engineering was carried out by the Horsley Bridge & Thomas Piggott Ltd, and the civil engineering was done by Aubrey Wilson Ltd. The work took from January 1965 to September 1966.

During the reconstruction the timber deck was replaced with a deck of stiffened steel plates coated with gritted epoxy resin and carried by steel cross-girders. Also, the wrought iron chains and suspender rods were replaced with steel equivalents, and this operation made it necessary to dismantle the tops of the masonry suspension towers so that new chain supports could be installed inside them. It was also necessary to strengthen the chain anchorages at each end of the bridge. The reconstruction cost £223,000.

TEMPLE FOOTBRIDGE

Temple Footbridge was built just above Temple Lock, at the site of a ferry closed in 1953, to carry the Thames Path across the river. It was built for Thames Water (now the Environment Agency) and Buckinghamshire County Council. The County Council built the sub-structure and Ekki Sarum Hardwood Structures, of Winchester, built the superstructure. The bridge cost about £360,000 and was opened on 24 May 1989. The Countryside Commission made a grant towards the cost and donations were received from various bodies including the Royal County of Berkshire, the Royal Borough of Windsor and Maidenhead, the Ramblers' Association, the Thames Heritage Trust and local authorities. There were also gifts from many individuals.

The deck is carried by a pair of laminated hardwood beams attached to concrete bank seats and supported in the river by two No 2 steel 'A' frames, which define a central main span with shorter spans at either side. The deck has timber handrails.

Dimensions
Central span: 46m (150ft); distance between abutments: 84m (275ft).

17.10.93

HURLEY LOWER AND UPPER TOWPATH BRIDGES

Hurley Lock is in the Thames where it flows from west to east at the northern edge of Hurley village. The Upper and Lower Towpath Bridges (sometimes called the East and West Horse Bridges) cross the navigation channel above and below the lock from the south bank of the river to an island north of the channel.

There are eight or more islands in the river at Hurley, and the island just noted is the easternmost of a chain of three, interconnected by bridges and weirs, which is linked at its upstream end by a long weir to the north bank of the river. All the islands were bought by the Thames Conservancy in 1932.

Hurley Lock was opened in 1773 and was the fifth of seven pound locks built for the Thames Commissioners under an Act of 1771 (11 George 3, c. 45).

1. Early bridges

Thacker (1920) refers to a footbridge above the pound lock, which, in the summer of 1827, was substituted for a swing bridge; presumably this is the timber bridge shown in Tombleson's 1834 view of Hurley. Thacker also refers to a crossing below the lock, which was rebuilt early in 1834. The bridges existing after 1834 were also of timber and each had six spans, three of them at one side of the navigation span and two at the other. In the lower bridge, the group of three spans was at the south side of the navigation channel, whereas in the upper bridge it was at the northern side.

Dimensions
(L = Lower (East) bridge, U = Upper (West) bridge, n = navigation span)
1834 (L) Spans: (i)-(ii) 14ft 0in, (iii) 23ft 8in (n), (iv) 13ft 9in, (v) 12ft 7in.
1827 (U) Spans: (i)-(iii) 13ft 9in, (iv) 21ft 6in (n), (v) 13ft 10in.

2. The bridges of 1884

The bridges above and below the lock were replaced in 1884 by an upper bridge of four spans and a lower bridge of five. The piers were wooden piles and the decks and balustrades were also of timber.

Dimensions

1884 (L) Spans: (i)-(iii) 25ft 0in (n).
1884 (U) Spans: (i)-(iii) 23ft 0in (n).

3. The bridges of 1934 *(opposite)*

The bridges above and below the lock were replaced in 1934 by those now in use. They differ slightly in their dimensions but are similar in construction and appearance. Unlike the preceding bridges, they are not entirely of wood: the decks of the navigation spans are supported by rolled steel joists encased in timber.

Dimensions

1934 (L) Spans: (i) 22ft 0in, (ii) 33ft 0in (n), (iii) 22ft 0in.
1934 (U) Spans: (i) 26ft 0in, (ii) 34ft 0in (n), (iii) 26ft 0in.

HENLEY BRIDGE

1. The mediaeval bridge

The first bridge was built to replace a ferry a few years after 1215, the year of the signing of Magna Carta by King John at Runnymede. The bridge and a chapel upon it, dedicated to St Anne, are both recorded in a patent of 1232. Later in its history there was a gate at its end and a granary on the bridge, which allowed grain to be loaded easily into barges.

In about 1530 Leland reported that the bridge was of timber on stone foundations, and considered, probably incorrectly, that it had

22.5.77

been entirely of stone. During the Civil War, in 1642, the bridge was damaged and the chapel destroyed. Finally, in March 1774, the bridge was swept away by a flood.

2. The bridge of 1786 *(previous page)*
The bridge to replace the mediaeval structure was to have been built by William Hayward (1740-82), a Shrewsbury architect, but he died before work started and his brother John was appointed in his place. John Townsend of Oxford was the contractor. An Act of Parliament was obtained in 1781 (21 George 3, c. 33) and the bridge was opened

in 1786. It is an elegant five-arched bridge of Headington stone and cost £10,000. The keystones of the central arch are decorated with heads of Isis (upstream) and Thamesis (downstream), carved by the sculptress Mrs Damer (1749-1828), a daughter of General Conway who lived at Park Place about a mile upstream. It was a toll-bridge until the end of February 1873.

Dimensions
Spans: Nos 1 and 5 34ft, Nos 2 and 4 38ft 6in, No 3 (central) 39ft 6in; pier thickness: Nos 1 and 4 7ft 6in, Nos 2 and 3 8ft; overall length: 292ft; width of roadway: 19ft 4in; width of footways: 4ft.

SHIPLAKE RAILWAY BRIDGE

The railway bridge at Shiplake carries the branch line north from Twyford (on the Great Western main line) to Henley.

The 4½-mile-long broad gauge Henley branch was built by the Great Western Railway (GWR) under powers granted by an Act of 1847 (10 & 11 Victoria, cxxxvi) and revived by an Act of 1853 (16 & 17 Victoria, cliii). The branch opened on 1 June 1857, and was converted to standard gauge between 9.30pm on Friday 24 March 1876 and 9.30am on the following day, the quickest gauge conversion to be carried out.

1. The bridge of 1857 *(below)*
The first Shiplake Railway Bridge across the Thames was of timber and had 17 spans, six in Berkshire and 11 in Oxfordshire. Spans 5, 6 and 7, in Berkshire, were main spans across the river, the remainder being shorter approach spans. The bridge was strengthened in the 1870s by adding central piers to halve the length of all the approach spans.

Dimensions (as built)
Three river spans: 39ft 9in, 40ft, 39ft 3in; approach spans 1-4 (Berks) and 8-13 (Oxon): average 32ft.

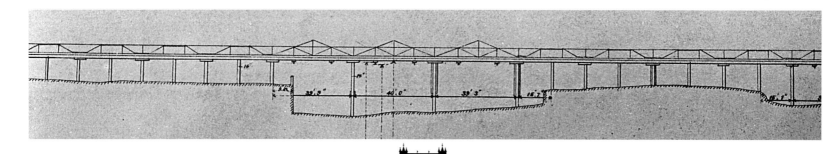

2. The bridge of 1897 *(right)*

When the branch was doubled in 1896-98, the timber bridge was replaced by an iron bridge designed by E. Olander (1834-1900) and built by E. Finch of Chepstow in 1897. The new bridge has 11 plate girder spans, the two longest being across the river. The remaining spans, three in Berkshire and six in Oxfordshire, are of varying length. Except between the river spans, where the pier is a line of three cross-braced concrete-filled cast iron cylinders, the piers are of brick, as are the abutments and approach viaducts.

The branch was made single-line in June 1961 and the upstream portion of the bridge was removed in 1965.

10.5.76

Dimensions

Two river spans: 71ft; other spans: one 45ft 0in, two 59ft 5in, two 60ft 2in, one 60ft 0in, two 43ft 0in; thickness of brick piers: 4ft 6in; diameter of iron cylinders: 6ft.

SONNING BRIDGE

The B478, which links the A4 route to Bath at Charvil with the A4155 Henley-on-Thames to Reading road, is carried over the Thames at Sonning by a series of four bridges. From east to west, these are: (i) the old brick bridge over the navigation channel; (ii) Mill Bridge and (iii) Hall's Bridge, which together cross an island bisected by a millstream; and (iv) New Bridge, which crosses a northern backwater.

Navigation channel
1. The early timber bridge

Some authors have referred to a bridge dating back to Saxon times, but the earliest authentic record of a timber bridge is that published by Leland in 1535. Phillips (1981) traced a complex chain of ownership of Sonning Manor (which included the bridge), starting with transfer from the Church to Queen Elizabeth I in 1574 and leading to conveyance of the bridge in 1654 to a merchant and parish freeholder, Thomas Rich, whose family retained it until 1795.

2. The bridge of c1770 *(overleaf)* • *Grade II listed* •

Phillips suggests that the present brick bridge was built in 1772 by John Treacher (1735-1802) of Sonning, whose firm carried out various works for the Thames Commissioners; later, in 1787, he was appointed their Surveyor. The bridge has 11 arches, and in 1907 it was strengthened with tie bars and plates to arrest cracking caused by the lateral pressure of the roadway. It is now a Grade II listed structure.

Dimensions

Clear spans and (widths of piers) from east to west: (23ft) 14ft (4ft) 15ft 6in (4ft) 18ft (4ft 6in) 20ft (7ft 6in) 28ft (8ft 6in) 20ft (4ft 6in) 17ft 6in (4ft) 15ft 6in (4ft) 13ft 6in (5ft) 21ft (5ft) 20ft 6in (5ft).

Mill, Hall's and New Bridges
1. The timber bridges

The earliest reference to Mill Bridge given by Phillips is dated 1453. At some time it will have become part of the complete crossing, and in its later years had 13 wooden trestle spans and a length of earth embankment. Hall's Bridge latterly had three trestle spans and four brick arches. New Bridge had 13 trestle spans.

Dimensions
Mill Bridge: Length of 13 trestle spans and embankment: 188ft
Hall's Bridge: Length of three trestle and four brick spans: 111ft
New Bridge: Length of 13 trestle spans: 139ft.

2. The bridges of 1904 *(below)*

An Oxfordshire proposal of 1902 to replace Mill, Hall's and New Bridges with a single lattice girder structure was rejected following strong public opposition, and in 1905 the existing trestle bridges were replaced with smaller iron bridges having lattice parapets. In about 1958 the spans of Mill and New Bridges were strengthened with intermediate piers.

Dimensions
Mill Bridge: Lattice spans: 51ft 2in, 47ft 9in, 50ft 4in; causeway: 41ft 3in (total 190ft 3in)
Hall's Bridge: Lattice span: 39ft; four brick arches of 10ft span (total 101ft 6in)
New (Backwater) Bridge: Lattice spans: 47ft 4in, 49ft 11in, 51ft (total 148ft 3in).

Mill Bridge, 19.10.72

READING BRIDGE

Reading Bridge is about half a mile downstream from the much older Caversham Bridge, and crosses the Thames from the centre of Reading, on the south bank, to Lower Caversham. The bridge carries the B3345, which links the A329 Wallingford road, to the south, with the A4155 Henley road to the north.

An Act of 1911 (1 & 2 George 5, cxlviii) authorised the widening or reconstruction of Caversham Bridge and the building of a footbridge downstream. Reading Corporation soon decided that a road bridge would be more useful than a footbridge, and in 1913 obtained a further Act (3 & 4 George 5, cvii) authorising the change of plan.

The bridge of 1923

The building of Reading Bridge was delayed by the First World War and did not start until 1922. The bridge was designed, in association with the Borough Surveyor, A. S. Parsons (1852-1908), by L. G. Mouchel & Partners Ltd according to the T-beam system of reinforced concrete construction devised by the famous French engineer Francois Hennebique (1842-1921) and patented by him in 1892. The contractors were Holloway Brothers (London) Ltd.

Reading Bridge has a single main arch with four ribs over the river, a smaller arch on each bank, and an arched southern approach. Its deck is a concrete slab supported by longitudinal and secondary beams, which, in turn, are supported by spandrel columns springing from the tops of the arched ribs. The abutments embody large stepped concrete blocks to counter the thrust of the arches and are faced with Portland stone, the material also used for the parapets.

The bridge itself cost £35,000, but the cost of the approaches (£32,000) and other expenditure made the total cost £76,000. The bridge was opened for traffic on 3 October 1923 by the Mayor of Reading, Alderman Frederick Alfred Cox JP.

Dimensions

Spans: 180ft (river), 12ft (towpaths), 19ft 6in (in south viaduct); length: 265ft (bridge), 260ft (south viaduct), 1,000ft (north approach); width between parapets: 40ft (27ft roadway and two 6ft 6in footways).

12.5.74

CAVERSHAM BRIDGE

Caversham Bridge links a roundabout south of the Thames on the A329 Wallingford road with a junction north of the river of the A4074 Oxford road and the A4155 road to Henley and Bourne End.

1. The 13th-century bridge *(below)*

The ancient Caversham Bridge was of brick, stone and timber and had a wayfarers' chapel (referred to in a close roll of 1231) dedicated to St Anne near its north end on an island in the Thames. In April 1643, during the Civil War, the Parliamentarians drove back a Royalist force, under General Ruven and Prince Rupert, that had come from Oxford and was attempting to cross the bridge and raise the siege of Reading.

2. The rebuilt bridge of 1830

The old bridge was rebuilt in motley fashion in 1830 and had, going north from the Berkshire to the Oxfordshire bank, two timber navigation spans (later replaced by metal ones), six brick arches, a filled arch adjacent to a waterman's house on the island in the river, and eight brick and stone arches.

3. The bridge of 1869 *(opposite top and middle)*

The rebuilt ancient bridge was narrow and plans to widen it were drawn up in 1855, but not implemented. However, an Act of Parliament to replace the bridge was obtained in 1868 (31 & 32 Victoria) and the work was carried out in 1868-69. In making room for the new bridge, the waterman's house on the island was jacked up whole and shifted 25 feet.

The replacement bridge was an ugly one formed of deep wrought iron lattice girders supported by pairs of concrete-filled cast iron pillars. The engineers were Nathaniel Beardmore and Henry Woodman, Borough Surveyor of Reading, and the contractors were Messrs M. T. Shaw and T. F. Howard. The cost of the bridge was £12,371.

Ireland

Dimensions

Spans: 63ft 9in, 61ft, 42ft, 61ft, 63ft 9in; width between parapets: 29ft (21ft roadway and two 4ft footways); depth of lattice girders: 6ft 5in; diameter of cast iron pillars: 2ft.

4. The bridge of 1926 *(bottom)*

The building of the fourth and present bridge was authorised by an Act of 1911 (1 & 2 George 5, cxlviii), then by a new Act of 1913 (3 & 4 George 5, cvii), but work was delayed by the Great War and did not start until 1924. Like Reading Bridge, the new Caversham Bridge was designed by L. G. Mouchel & Partners Ltd according to the

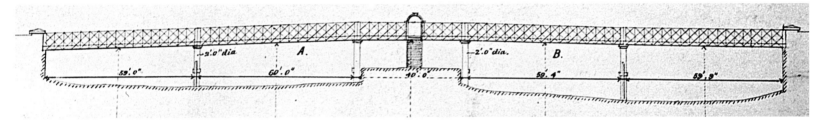

26.10.69

Hennebique system of reinforced concrete construction, and built by Holloway Brothers (London) Ltd.

The bridge crosses the river at an angle of 78 degrees and has two main spans separated by a massive central pier that includes upstream and downstream promenade bays. The balustrades are of Aberdeen granite, and the open spandrels are decorated with laurel wreath motifs. Of a total cost of £78,250, £67,000 was for the bridge, the remainder being for the approaches and other expenses.

It was originally intended for the bridge to be opened on 12 May 1926 by HRH The Prince of Wales (later King Edward VIII, 1894-1972). However, the General Strike prevented this, so although the bridge came into use on 8 May, the commemorative tablet was not unveiled by the Prince until 25 June.

Dimensions

Clear spans: 126ft 4in (Reading end), 106ft 4½in; length: 360ft (bridge), 200ft (south approach), 130ft (north approach); width of central pier: 34ft 9in; length of promenade bays on pier: 23ft 6in; length between abutments: 267ft 6in; width between parapets: 56ft (32ft roadway and two 12ft footways).

WHITCHURCH BRIDGE

This bridge carries the B471 across the Thames between Pangbourne and Whitchurch, linking the A329 at Pangbourne with the A4074 near Woodcote. It is one of the two remaining toll-bridges over the non-tidal Thames.

1. The bridge of 1793

For centuries the river had been fordable at Whitchurch and there had been a ferry. When a pound lock was built here in 1787 by the Thames Commissioners, just above where the lock now stands, the river could no longer be forded and the length of the ferry crossing was increased. A group of residents instructed John Treacher Senior (1735-1802) to prepare and submit a design to the Commissioners for approval. His design was approved, and an Act authorising construction was obtained in 1792 (22 George 3, xcvii).

The bridge was built of timber and opened in 1793. It had 24 spans and cost, with a toll-house, about £1,800; the rights in the ferry were bought for £350.

2. The bridge of 1852 *(left)*

The first bridge failed in 1850 and was replaced with a new timber bridge, having nine main spans and two short spans on each bank. It was built by a Mr Tredwell of Reading and cost just over £2.000.

Dimensions

Main spans: 25ft, 25ft, 25ft, 24ft 11in, 26ft, 23ft 3in, 26ft, 25ft 9in, 25ft.

18.9.74

3. The bridge of 1901 *(above)* • *Grade II listed* •

The second timber bridge was replaced with a four-span iron bridge built by the Cleveland Bridge & Engineering Co in 1901. The deck is supported by three pairs of iron columns and has iron lattice balustrades. The cost of construction was just under £6,000.

The bridge is currently owned by 50 shareholders and in 2003 some 2,000 cars crossed to provide a turnover of about £170,000. Money is set aside for possible future rebuilding.

Dimensions

Clear spans: 63ft 6in, 61ft 3in, 61ft 9in, 66ft 9in; width of three intermediate piers with protective piling: 6ft 6in; width of roadway between kerbs: 17ft 10in; width of sidewalk (west side): 4ft.

BASILDON (GATEHAMPTON) RAILWAY BRIDGE

Basildon Railway Bridge carries the Great Western main line from Reading to Didcot across the Thames between Pangbourne and Goring & Streatley stations. Because it lies between Lower Basildon village and Gatehampton Farm, it is sometimes called Gatehampton Railway Bridge.

Basildon is the second of the three brick bridges across the Thames designed by Isambard Kingdom Brunel (1806-59) for his broad gauge main line from London to Bristol, which was built under an Act of 1835 (5 & 6 William 4, cvii) and opened throughout in 1841. The 20-mile section including Basildon Bridge, from Reading to Steventon (just beyond Didcot), was opened on 1 June 1840.

1. The bridge of 1839

The contract for building Basildon Bridge was let in February 1838 and the work was completed by the end of August 1839. The bridge has four arches and crosses the Thames at an angle of 75 degrees. It is of red brick with Bath stone facings and originally carried two broad gauge tracks. The line was converted to mixed gauge on 22 December 1856.

2. The widened bridge of 1890 *(above)*

To allow quadrupling of the line from Taplow to Didcot, Basildon Bridge was widened by the engineer W. Armstrong (1846-1918) on the downstream (eastern) side. The work was started in 1890 and completed in 1892, in readiness for the final abolition of the broad gauge that year.

Dimensions

Spans: four arches of 62ft (measured square), 64ft 4in (measured skew); width between parapets: 29ft 6in (as built), 55ft 6in (as widened); length of piers: 45ft (as built), 73ft 3in (as widened); thickness of piers: 12ft.

GORING AND STREATLEY BRIDGES

These bridges, which meet on an island in the Thames, link the small town of Goring, on the east (left) bank, with the village of Streatley, on the west. Particularly since their rebuilding, the two bridges are effectively one structure, referred to by some as Goring Bridge, and by others as Streatley Bridge. The navigation channel is at the Goring side of the river, the lock being just upstream (north) of the bridge.

Goring Bridge is at the site of an ancient ford by which travellers along the Icknield Way and the Ridgeway crossed the river. For centuries a ferry was provided, and after the water level had been raised by the building of the first lock in 1797, this was the sole means of crossing. A ferry accident in 1810 led to the drowning of a number of people and an increasing demand for a bridge. Eventually, in 1837, a band of local gentry obtained an Act (7 William 4 & 1 Victoria, xcii) authorising construction.

1. The bridge of 1838 *(above right)*

The first Goring Bridge was of timber and had 23 spans from Goring to the intermediate island and 16 spans from there, westwards, to Streatley. It was opened as a toll-bridge in 1838, with the necessary toll-cottage and gates on the island.

Dimensions

Spans: 22 of 13-18ft and one of 29ft 3in (Goring section), 16 of 14-18ft (Streatley section); length: 755ft (Goring section 372ft, Streatley section 250ft).

2. The bridge of 1923 *(below)*

By the beginning of the 20th century the timber bridge had weakened and become subject to a 3-ton weight limit. In 1915 an Act (5 & 6 George 5, xxiv) was obtained to authorise rebuilding, but by then conditions during the First World War prevented the starting of work. In 1920 the Ministry of Transport agreed to contribute to the cost of a new bridge on condition that the Berkshire and Oxfordshire County Councils took over responsibility for the bridge from the commissioners and freed the bridge from toll. The transfer of authority took place on 28 February 1922 and removal of the old bridge soon commenced.

The new bridge was designed by the Trussed Concrete Steel Co Ltd in conjunction with A. E. Cockerton, County Surveyor of Oxford, and Lt-Col J. R. Hawkins, County Surveyor of Berkshire, who had been engineer to the bridge commissioners. It was built by A. Jackaman of Slough at a cost of just over £27,000.

The bridge looks distinctly like one of timber but is, except for oak balustrades, of reinforced concrete. It has fewer spans than the previous bridge: six for the Goring end and nine for the Streatley end. The Goring section was opened by Mrs Murrell on 29 April 1923 and the Streatley section was opened by Sir Henry Maybury (1864-1943), Director General of Roads, on 8 November of the same year.

Dimensions

Spans, from Goring: six of 38ft 8in, 26ft, four of 36ft, 64ft, 58ft, 44ft, 19ft; length: 587ft; width: 25ft (18ft carriageway and 6ft footway).

12.5.74

MOULSFORD RAILWAY BRIDGE

Moulsford Bridge carries the Great Western main line from Reading to Didcot across the Thames between Goring & Streatley and Cholsey & Moulsford stations. It is, in fact, a pair of bridges, close together, which cross the Thames at an angle of 45 degrees. The first bridge was built in 1839 to carry two broad gauge tracks, then the second was added upstream in 1892 to quadruple the line. The latter was built at a time when the Great Western Railway (GWR) was abolishing the broad gauge, so carried two standard gauge tracks.

1. The bridge of 1839

The 1839 Moulsford Bridge is the third of the brick railway bridges designed and built by Isambard Kingdom Brunel (1806-59) for his broad gauge (7ft 0¼in) main line from London to Bristol. This line was authorised by an Act of 1835 (5 & 6 William 4, cvii) and opened throughout in 1841.

A contract for building the bridge was made in February 1838 and construction started later that year. It was completed by the end of 1839, and the 20-mile section of line from Reading to Steventon, which crosses it, was opened on 1 June 1840. There was a station called Wallingford Road just west of the bridge, but this was superseded in 1892 by Cholsey & Moulsford, three-quarters of a mile further west

The bridge is of red brick, with four circular arches outlined in white with wedges ('voussoirs') of Bath stone. The original pair of broad gauge tracks were converted to mixed gauge on 22 December 1856.

2. The bridge of 1892 *(below)*

The quadrupling of the line across Moulsford Bridge was carried out by E. Olander (1834-1900). The new bridge, like the old, is of red brick but the arches are outlined by rings of brickwork instead of voussoirs. The piers of the 1839 bridge were lengthened to support the new bridge and small brick bridges, one above each pier, were built across the gap between the two structures.

In 1975 refuges for linemen were built, projecting beyond the parapets over the ends of the piers.

Dimensions (both bridges)
Spans: four arches of 62ft (measured square), 87ft 8in (measured skew); thickness of piers: 12ft; gap between bridges: 9ft 1½in; length of piers: 29ft (1839), 73ft (both); width between parapets: 29ft 11in (1839), 25ft 11in (1892).

WINTERBROOK BRIDGE (WALLINGFORD BYPASS)

Winterbrook Bridge takes the Wallingford Bypass (part of the A4130) across the Thames about a mile downstream of Wallingford Bridge, south of the town. It was placed so that its construction did not disturb a Bronze Age island site on the west bank of the river. The A4130 runs from a junction with the A404, west of Maidenhead, to a junction at Harwell with the road from Streatley to Cirencester (A417).

The bridge of 1992

The Winterbrook Bridge was designed by the Oxfordshire County Council Consultancy for the County Council (the County Engineer being D. H. Hook) and built by Galliford Midlands (Civil Engineering Contractors) of Wolvey, Hinckley, Leicestershire.

The bridge superstructure is carried by bank-seats and two piers. The bank-seats are of reinforced concrete and are supported by embankments of reinforced earth constructed on the undisturbed flood plain. The piers are also of reinforced concrete and are supported on the river banks by closely spaced small-diameter driven, cast-in-place, piles. The edges of the river banks are protected by sheet piles.

The bridge superstructure has three spans with a cast-in-situ reinforced concrete deck carried by four profiled steel plate girders. To protect these girders against rusting, they are enclosed within glass-reinforced polyester panels designed and made by ANMAC; these are attached to the girders with steel fittings and make the bridge look like a box girder structure. The deck is edged with aluminium-rail parapets and has a carriageway for two single lanes of traffic between a pair of footpaths.

Winterbrook Bridge cost about £1.6 million to build and was opened by Councillor John Jones, Chairman of Oxfordshire County Council, on 29 July 1993.

Dimensions

Spans: 38m (125ft), 55m (180ft), 38m (125ft); length: 131m (430ft); overall width: 14m (46ft), including 9.3m (30.5ft) carriageway and two 1.5m (5ft) footpaths.

4.8.03

WALLINGFORD BRIDGE

Until the construction of the bypass just south of the town, Wallingford Bridge carried the A4130 Henley-Didcot road.

1. Ancient bridges

It was held traditionally that the first bridge at Wallingford was built in AD600, but no documentary evidence supports this assertion. Almost certainly, timber bridges did exist at the crossing.

2. The bridge of c1240 *(below)*

The first stone bridge seems to have been built by Richard, Earl of Cornwall, brother to Henry III, in about 1240. It had 19 arches of which three – Nos 1, 10 and 14, counting from the town (western) end – survive with internal ribbing. There was a bridge chapel, named Mary Grace, at the town end. The bridge had to be repaired fairly frequently; for instance, in 1530 five land arches (Nos 8, 9, 12, 13 and 15), and possibly also No 7, were rebuilt incorporating stone from the dissolved Benedictine Priory Church.

During the Civil War Wallingford Castle was held for Charles I and four arches (Nos 2, 6, 11 and 16) were removed and replaced by drawbridges. These arches were reconstructed in brick and stone in 1751. The bridge was partly widened in 1770.

3. The bridge of 1813 *(below)*

• *Grade II listed/Ancient Monument* •

The river arches were destroyed by severe floods in 1809, and an Act of Parliament was obtained later in the year (49 George 3, cxliii) setting up a body of trustees and increasing the tolls that could be levied to pay for repairs. Three elliptical arches (Nos 3, 4 and 5), designed by John Treacher (1760-1836), were built to span the river, the total number of arches being unchanged. Also, the whole of the bridge was widened by 7 feet on the upstream side. These works were carried out between 1810 and 1813 and cost approximately £7,000.

In 1934 ownership of the bridge passed to Berkshire and Oxfordshire County Councils, and they strengthened the bridge without altering its appearance.

Dimensions

Spans (river arches): 25ft, 29ft, 25ft; width between parapets: 21ft 6in-23ft 6in; overall length: 825ft. The bridge has 20 spans.

Ireland

SHILLINGFORD BRIDGE

The bridge at Shillingford carries the A329 road northwards across the Thames between Wallingford and Shillingford.

1. The first bridge

Thacker refers to a document in the Patent Rolls for 1301 that names Shillingford Bridge as the lower limit for a leased fishery. He lists arguments for and against this reference, confirming the existence of a bridge at such an early date, and the arguments in favour seem to outweigh those against. The bridge, if it existed, did not have a long life because later documents refer to a ferry.

2. The bridge of c1785 *(below)*

In 1749 William Blackstone (1723-90), who was a lecturer on, and later a professor of, English Law at Oxford University, was made recorder of Wallingford. As a frequent traveller between those places, he became interested in improving the river crossing at Shillingford and was instrumental in obtaining an Act in 1765 (4 George 3, c. 42) setting up a turnpike trust for improving the Reading-Shillingford road

and replacing the ferry with a bridge. The works were not completed within the specified time, so a new Act had to be obtained in 1783 (24 George 3, c. 32). By about 1785 a timber bridge with stone abutments and piers had been completed.

3. The bridge of 1827 *(below)*   • *Grade II listed* •

The timber bridge did not last long, so an Act for replacing it with a stone bridge was obtained in 1827 (7 & 8 George 4, xi). The new bridge was completed the same year and has three main arches across the river, a small arch at each bank and a causeway at its northern (Oxfordshire) approach containing six flood arches. A toll-keeper's cottage was built at the north end of the bridge, but was demolished in 1937.

Under an Act of 1883 Oxfordshire and Berkshire took over the bridge from the Turnpike Trustees, each county agreeing to pay half the cost of maintenance. The bridge was repaired in 1906 and 1930.

Dimensions

Clear spans and (widths of piers) from north end: 15ft (25ft) 34ft 3in (9ft) 51ft 9in (9ft) 35ft 0in (?) 15ft; span of eight flood arches: 8ft; total length: 416ft; width: 48ft (20ft carriageway and two 14ft kerbs).

13.5.75

LITTLE WITTENHAM (DAY'S) FOOTBRIDGE

Little Wittenham Footbridge is in two parts, the eastern across the main stream, used as the navigation channel, to an island in the Thames, and the western across a backwater between the island and Little Wittenham. It is just downstream (south) of Day's Lock, and is therefore sometimes referred to as 'Day's Footbridge'.

The first pound lock, with the necessary weir, was built in the years 1788-89 and originally called Dorchester Lock. It later became known as Wittenham, or Day's Lock. The lock was reconstructed in 1871, a new weir was built in 1886, and the lock was rebuilt again in 1925.

The eastern footbridge
1. The timber bridge
In his book of 1869, J. M. Davenport refers to a succession of three wooden bridges, the first in Berkshire across a back stream, the second across the main river (at the centre of which was the Berkshire-Oxfordshire boundary), and the third across a navigable cut in Oxfordshire made about 1790 by the Thames Commissioners. The first two bridges were repairable by the owner of the Little Wittenham Estate. The third bridge belonged to the Thames Conservators, who, by an Act of 1866 (29 & 30 Victoria, c. 89), were required to maintain communication across the river and specifically empowered to take tolls at Little Wittenham Bridge, which they did. All the timber bridges referred to by Davenport were likely to have dated from 1789, but by the time his book was published were probably replacements. The bridge across the cut was a swing bridge.

The fact that the crossing is now provided by two bridges, instead of three, suggests that the works of 1871 and 1886 abolished a channel and re-sited at least some of the rebuilt structures.

Eastern footbridge, 13.5.75

2. The bridge of 1870 *(above)*
The present navigation footbridge was built for the Thames Conservancy in 1870, designed by their Engineer, Stephen Leach, and built by Cochrane, Grove & Co at a cost of £250. It has abutments of concrete and stone and a superstructure of two arched steel lattice girders supporting a concrete deck.

Dimensions
Span: 65ft 10in; width of deck: 6ft 0in.

3. The rebuilt bridge of 1981 (?)
The 1870 bridge was scheduled for repair in 1981 and rebuilt to the original design.

The western footbridge
1. The timber bridge
As suggested above, the timber bridge across the backwater referred to by Davenport was probably a replacement of a bridge dating from 1789.

2. The footbridge of 1870
The 1870 footbridge across the backwater to the island had a deck of concrete on plate and angle iron beams, which was supported, between

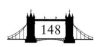

concrete and stone abutments, by three pairs of cast iron columns. The deck had steel railings at each side.

Dimensions
Four spans: 20ft; width of deck: 6ft 7in.

3. The vehicular bridge of 1981 (?)
The 1870 footbridge was replaced in 1981 (?) by a bridge wide enough for vehicles. This has a reinforced concrete deck, with steel handrails, supported by steel piles driven into the river.

CLIFTON HAMPDEN BRIDGE

• *Grade II listed* •

This bridge carries an unclassified road from Clifton Hampden village, on the A415, south to Long Wittenham and takes the Thames Path across the river at the point where the towpath used to change sides.

Originally there was a ferry where the bridge now stands, and cattle could no longer walk across. However, improvements for navigation increased the depth of the water so that cattle could no longer walk across.

Henry Hucks Gibbs, Lord Aldenham, succeeded to the Manor of Clifton Hampden in 1842 and set about improving the estate. In 1864 he obtained an Act of Parliament (27 & 28 Victoria, xliv) for building a toll-bridge to replace the ferry. The bridge was designed by a Mr Homfrey and George Gilbert Scott (1811-78), who was later to design famous Victorian Gothic structures, including the Albert Memorial (1872) and the St Pancras Station Hotel (1873). He received a knighthood in 1872.

Clifton Hampden bridge is of brick and has six four-centred arches between piers having both upstream and downstream triangular cutwaters that extend to the top of the balustrades to provide pedestrian refuges. A toll-house was built on the Berkshire shore. Tolls were charged until 1946 when the bridge was bought by the Berkshire and Oxfordshire County Councils.

Dimensions
Spans of arches and (pier widths): 23ft 9in (7ft 6in) 30ft (8ft) 31ft 6in (8ft 6in) 34ft 6in (8ft 6in) 31ft 6in (8ft 6in) 30ft; each arch has four 18in-wide ribs 2ft 9in apart; width between parapets: 13ft 4in.

24.2.73

CLIFTON CUT FOOTBRIDGES

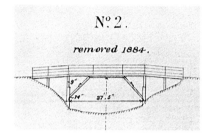

No. 2.
removed 1884.

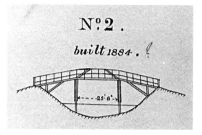

No. 2.
built 1884.

The pound lock at Clifton was completed in 1822 but has been rebuilt since then. It stands at the downstream end of Clifton Cut, which was dug to bypass a southward loop of the Thames that flows past the northern edge of Long Wittenham village.

Originally, the lock cut was spanned by two footbridges providing access to the island between the cut and river. The lower crossing, about a quarter of a mile above the lock, is still provided, but the upper crossing (about half a mile above the lock and near the upstream entrance to the cut) is not, the bridge having been removed in 1944.

The lower footbridges

At least three successive footbridges, each of three spans, have existed at the lower end of the cut: (i) built in the year of opening of the lock, 1822 (*top left*); (ii) built in 1884 (*top right*); and (iii) built in 1958 (*middle*).

Bridges (i) and (ii) were entirely of timber, while (iii) has a deck and handrails of timber carried by steel beams faced with timber. Each end of the bridge rests on a concrete bank seat and each of the two piers is a pair of concrete piles driven into the channel bed.

The upper footbridges

At least two three-span timber footbridges were provided at the upper end of Clifton Cut: (i) built in the year of opening of the lock, 1822 (*bottom left*), and (ii) built in 1884 and removed in 1944 (*bottom right*).

Dimensions

Lower footbridges: Central spans: (i) 37ft 5in, (ii) 25ft 6in, (iii) 31ft 10in (with side spans of 23ft 4in).
Upper footbridges: Central spans: (i) 19ft, (ii) 25ft 6in.

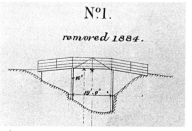

No. 1.
removed 1884.

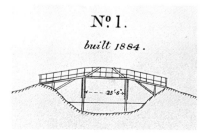

No. 1.
built 1884.

APPLEFORD RAILWAY BRIDGE

Appleford Railway Bridge takes the Great Western line running north from Didcot to Oxford across the Thames between Appleford and Culham stations.

In 1843 an Oxford Railway Company obtained an Act (6 & 7 Victoria, x) authorising construction of a broad gauge branch line from Didcot, on the Great Western Railway (GWR) main line from Paddington to Bristol, to Oxford, where a terminus was to be built in a field just south of the Thames, near Folly Bridge. In its 10-mile northward course, the line had to cross the Thames twice because, between Nuneham Park and Appleford village, the river flows round a western loop that skirts the eastern edge of Abingdon.

A few months after obtaining the 1843 Act the shareholders of the Oxford Company resolved to sell their company to the GWR. Construction of the branch was started in October 1843 and was rapid enough for the line to be opened on 12 June 1844, after due inspection by I. K. Brunel (1806-59) and the Government Inspector of Railways. The Didcot-Oxford line amalgamated with the GWR under an Act of 1844 (7 & 8 Victoria, iii). By the year 1852, under two Acts of 1848 (11 & 12 Victoria, lix and cxxxiii), the branch had been extended across the Thames to a new station at Oxford (on the present site) and on, through Banbury, to Birmingham.

1. The bridge of 1844
For rapid construction and economy, the first Appleford Railway Bridge was built of timber.

2. The bridge of c1850
After a few years the timber bridge was replaced with an adjacent pair of wrought iron bridges, one for each track, each having seven spans of wrought iron girders carrying timber floors with Barlow rails, and supported by cast iron columns sunk into the river bed. The two broad gauge tracks were converted to mixed gauge on 22 December 1856 and to standard gauge on 26 November 1872. In 1877 the bridges were strengthened by replacement of the wooden floors with steel decks.

3. The bridge of 1927 *(below)*
Because of a progressive increase in the weight of steam locomotives, the pair of wrought iron bridges was replaced in 1927 with a single steel bridge designed by J. C. Lloyd. It has a main span comprising three Whipple arch-trusses carried by brick abutments. There are five segmental brick arches in the northern approach.

Dimensions
1850 bridge: Spans: five of 43ft 4in (river), two of 32ft (land); depth of wrought iron main girders: 5ft; diameter of cast iron columns: 2ft.
1927 bridge: Main span: 167ft; land arches: four of 18ft, one of 14ft.

13.5.74

CULHAM LOCK AND SUTTON BRIDGES

Sutton Bridge, and Culham Lock Bridge just to the north, are on a minor road that links the B4016 at Sutton Courtenay with the A415 at Culham. Sutton Bridge crosses the original course of the Thames, now a weir stream, and Culham Lock Bridge crosses a navigation channel, Culham Cut. Culham Lock is at the eastern end of the cut, and the Lock Bridge is just downstream of the lock.

Culham Lock Bridge

For centuries, navigation round a southward loop of the Thames through Sutton Pools, north of Sutton Courtenay, was awkward and expensive There were mills with flash weirs to provide the necessary head of water, but whenever a weir was opened to allow passage of a vessel, the water level was lowered and milling had to stop until it rose again. The millers therefore made the navigators pay dearly for their passage. The great loss of water caused by the use of flash weirs was avoided when a pound lock was provided in about 1638, but that was not trouble-free because the upper lock gates were just below a mill floor. In 1801 the surveyor of the Thames Commissioners recommended construction of a cut, and a scheme of 1808 (the third to be proposed) was agreed upon and resulted in the building of Culham Cut and Lock, and their opening the following year.

1. The bridge of 1810

Culham Cut and Lock were built by the Thames Commissioners under Acts of 1795 (35 George 3, c. 106) and 1803 (43 George 3, c. 59), and opened in 1809, just after Sutton Bridge had been completed. In building Culham Lock Bridge, the Commissioners therefore had to cut through the northern approach to Sutton Bridge. The lock bridge had a single brick arch and was opened in 1810.

2. The bridge of 1906 *(above)*

The bridge of 1810 was rebuilt in 1906, in stone with a concrete arch.

Dimensions
Span: 24ft (1810), 23ft (1906); width: 23ft (1810), 20ft (1906).

Sutton Bridge *(above right)*   • *Grade II listed* •

For centuries inhabitants of Sutton Courtenay who wished to go north from the village had first to cross a long sequence of footbridges, then cross the main stream of the Thames by ferry. In 1807 a group of local gentlemen obtained an Act (47 George 3, xliii) that made them proprietors of a company empowered to raise money for, and build, a bridge, the money to be repaid from tolls. The company chose Edward Clarke, a Gloucestershire man, as contractor and he built an arched stone bridge, with three main spans and a flood arch on each bank. He also built causeways at the approaches.

Sutton Bridge was opened as a toll-bridge in 1808, the toll-house

being on the Berkshire (south) bank. In 1938 Berkshire and Oxfordshire County Councils each paid £1,448 to buy the bridge from the proprietors and it was freed from toll in January 1939.

Dimensions
Main spans: 30ft, 40ft, 30ft;
pier width: 8ft; width: 20ft 6in;
length: 117ft.

CULHAM CUT LOWER AND UPPER FOOTBRIDGES

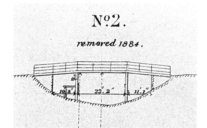

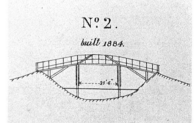

Culham Cut has been described in the previous entry, and Culham Lock Bridge crosses the eastern (downstream) end of the cut just below the lock. Lower and upper occupation footbridges across the cut were provided when the cut was opened, the lower a quarter of a mile, and the upper half a mile, above the lock. The upper footbridge was subsequently removed, but the lower remains to carry a footpath southwards from the towpath (now the Thames Path) to the lock island, then across weirs at Sutton Pools to the village of Sutton Courtenay.

The lower footbridges

At least three successive footbridges have been built across the approximate mid-point of Culham Cut: (i) of three spans, built in 1809, the year of opening of the cut (*above left*); (ii) of five spans, built in 1884 (*above right*); and (iii) of three spans, built in 1935 (*right*).

Bridges (i) and (ii) were entirely of timber, while the present bridge

(iii) has a concrete deck carried by steel beams, faced with timber, and has timber handrails. Each end of the bridge rests on piled bank seats and each of the two piers is a cross-braced pair of timber piles driven into the bed of the cut.

Dimensions
Central span: (i) 23ft 2in, (ii) 25ft 6in, (iii) 34ft 1in (with side spans of 24ft 7in); deck width 9ft 10in.

The upper footbridges
At least two timber footbridges were built across the western end of Culham Cut: (i) built in 1809, the year of opening of the lock, with three spans (*right*); and (ii) built in 1883 with five spans and removed in the 1940s (*far right*).

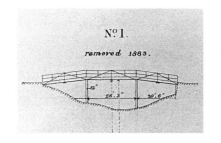
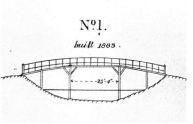

Dimensions
Central span: (i) 26ft 3in, (ii) 25ft 4in.

ABINGDON BRIDGES

On its journey from Oxford to Wallingford the Thames flows round a semi-circle between points upstream and downstream of Abingdon. The land within the semi-circle is Andersey Island, formed in the early Middle Ages by cutting a navigation channel running from north-east to south-west along the diameter. Roughly half-way round the semi-circle, opposite the town, the Thames is divided by a small island into north and south streams. It was therefore necessary, in providing a northward Thames crossing at Abingdon for the Burcot to Witney Road (now the A415) to build three bridges: Culham Bridge, across the southern end of the navigation channel; Burford Bridge, across the south stream; and Abingdon Bridge, across the north stream.

The navigation channel, about a mile long, was dug by the monks of the Benedictine Abbey of Abingdon, and was originally known as the 'Swift Ditch'. After 1590 it was no longer used, because the main course of the Thames had been dredged, and eventually it became known as the 'Back Water'.

The three bridges of the Abingdon crossing, and a causeway linking Culham and Burford Bridges, originated in the 15th century as follows. When the English wool and cloth industries were developing, Cotswold merchants had to travel to and from London. When doing so they preferred to use the road through Wantage, which crossed the Thames by Wallingford Bridge, rather than use the shorter road through Abingdon, which crossed both the Thames and the Swift Ditch by dangerous fords. A guild of Abingdon merchants, the Fraternity of the Holy Cross, decided to replace these fords with bridges to encourage the Cotswold merchants to use the Abingdon road, and also to ease the transport of cloth woven in Abingdon.

Two members of the Fraternity petitioned Henry V for a licence to carry out the work and were granted letters patent on 23 June 1416. Local stone for the project was given by Sir Peter Bessils and substantial donations were made by other important inhabitants, including Jefforye Barbur and John Howchion. The bridges and

causeway were completed by 1422 and had the hoped-for effect of reducing traffic through Wallingford.

Culham Bridge   • *Grade II listed/Ancient Monument* •
1. The bridge of 1416 *(above)*

The old Culham Bridge has five pointed arches. It was doubled in width in about 1790 by the addition of semi-circular arches at the upstream side. A portion of the bridge collapsed in 1925, and after Christ's Hospital in Abingdon had disclaimed responsibility for repair, Oxfordshire County Council carried out the work.

Dimensions
Spans and (widths of piers): (40ft 6in) 20ft (11ft 4in) 16ft (11ft 4in) 16ft 6in (30ft 8in) 16ft 6in (31ft 9in) 15ft 4in (9ft); total length: 280ft; width: 12ft, later increased to 24ft.

2. The bridge of 1928

To relieve the ancient bridge of traffic, Culham New Bridge was built a few yards upstream. It is of reinforced concrete faced with Forest of Dean stone and has a main arch and one smaller arch at each side. The design was by A. E. Cockerton and construction was by Messrs Aubrey Watson Ltd.

Dimensions
Spans: 15ft, 51ft, 15ft; total length: 181ft; width: 22ft plus two 7ft 6in footways.

Burford Bridge
1. The bridge of 1416

As built, Burford Bridge (the name from 'Borough Ford') had seven pointed arches. In 1790 the second and third of these, counting from the south bank, were replaced with a roughly elliptical navigation arch. Later, in about 1828, the bridge was widened on the upstream side, the pointed arches being lengthened with semi-circular additions.

Dimensions
Spans and (widths of piers): (50ft) 7ft 9in (11ft 6in) 20ft 6in (10ft 9in) 16ft 3in (11ft 6in) 16ft 2in (9ft) 13ft 9in (11ft 6 in) c8ft.

2. The bridge of 1929 *(overleaf above)*

In 1927 the Berkshire and Oxfordshire County Councils decided to rebuild Burford Bridge. The new bridge, of stone-faced reinforced concrete, was designed by the joint engineers, J. F. Hawkins (Berkshire) and A. E. Cockerton (Oxfordshire), and the work was carried out by James Byrom Ltd. During the rebuild the navigation arch and the two pointed arches north of it were replaced with a new navigation arch, with a span almost three times that of the 1790 arch, and a smaller arch matching that on the south bank. The bridge was also widened upstream.

The causeway linking Culham and Burford Bridges was rebuilt at

25.2.73

25.2.73

the same time as Burford Bridge, so three flood arches forming part of Maud Hales Bridge, dating from 1453 and named after the widow who paid for it, were reconstructed.

Dimensions
Spans: 8ft 6in, 60ft, 8ft 6in, 15ft, 15ft 6in; width: 24ft, plus two 6ft 6in footways. Maud Hales: three spans of 9ft.

Abingdon Bridge   • *Grade II listed/Ancient Monument* •
The bridge of 1416 *(left)*
Like Burford Bridge, Abingdon Bridge was built with seven pointed arches and widened upstream in about 1828 by extension of the arches with semi-circular portions. However, it was not further widened and the downstream face retains its ancient appearance. It is linked to Burford Bridge by a section on the intermediate island having three arches.

Dimensions
Spans and (widths of piers): 15ft 6in (10ft 10in) 16ft (11ft) 15ft 4in (12ft 8in) 15ft 4in

NUNEHAM RAILWAY BRIDGE

13.5.74

Nuneham Railway Bridge carries the Great Western main line north from Didcot to Oxford across the Thames between Culham and Radley stations, about a mile downstream of Nuneham Park.

The story of the broad gauge Didcot to Oxford branch is briefly told in the account of Appleford Railway Bridge. The branch was opened on 12 June 1844, and by 1852 had been extended to provide a main line to Birmingham.

1. The bridge of 1844
For rapid and cheap construction, the first Nuneham Railway Bridge was made of timber.

Dimensions
Timber spans: 40ft.

2. The bridge of c1852 *(below)*
In about 1852 the timber bridge was replaced with an adjacent pair of

seven-span wrought iron bridges, one for each railway track. Each bridge had deep plate girders at either side of a timber deck. These girders were supported by piers consisting of cross-braced pairs of cast iron cylinders sunk into the river bed and filled with concrete.

The two broad gauge tracks were converted to mixed gauge on 26 November 1856, and to standard gauge on 26 November 1872. In 1877 the timber decks were replaced with ones of steel.

Dimensions
Clear spans: 35ft 6in, 38ft, 38ft, 40ft, 40ft, 40ft, 35ft 6in; length between abutments: 287ft 9in; pier cylinder diameter: 2ft 0in.

3. The bridge of 1908 *(above)*
The present Nuneham Railway Bridge was built in 1907-08. It has two main spans supported by brick abutments and a central brick pier pierced by two arches, one under each track. Each main span has a Whipple arch truss (a bowstring girder with vertical and diagonal bracing) at each side, and a truss of similar type, but with steel plate substituted for the bracing, in the middle, between the two tracks. The bridge crosses the river at an angle of 75 degrees and the northern approach includes a brick viaduct with three arches.

Work, presumably strengthening, was carried out on the bridge in 1930.

Dimensions
Two spans: 82ft 9in (square), 86ft 0in (skew); width: 39ft 0in; spans of arches in northern viaduct: two of 27ft 6in (square), 28ft 0in (skew), and one of 23ft 6in (square), 24ft 0in (skew).

KENNINGTON RAILWAY BRIDGE

Kennington Railway Bridge carries a line that initially provided an alternative Great Western Railway (GWR) broad gauge route from Oxford to London (Paddington) via High Wycombe and Maidenhead, but now extends only to the former Morris Cowley car factory, now owned by BMW, a few miles south-east of Oxford.

The new Oxford to London route was provided by building from Maidenhead, on the GWR main line from Paddington to Bristol, the following three sections of line: (i) from Maidenhead to High Wycombe, opened on 1 August 1854; (ii) from High Wycombe through Princes Risborough to Thame, opened on 1 August 1862; and (iii) from Thame to Oxford, opened on 24 October 1864. Section (i) was built under Acts of 1846 (9 & 10 Victoria, cxxxvi) and 1852 (15 & 16 Victoria, cxlvii) and crosses the Thames using Bourne End Railway Bridge. Sections (ii) and (iii) were built under Acts of 1857 (20 & 21 Victoria, clviii) and 1861 (24 & 25 Victoria, lxxxvii), section (iii) crossing Kennington Railway Bridge, westwards, immediately before joining the line south from Oxford to Didcot at Kennington Junction. The bridge and junction are named after Kennington Island (also known as Rose Island) just south of the railway, adjacent to Kennington village on the right bank of the river.

The gauge of the whole 37-mile line was converted from broad to standard gauge between 23 August and 1 September 1870.

Passenger services over the complete Kennington Junction to Princes Risborough line were withdrawn on 7 January 1963 and goods services on 1 May 1967.

1. The bridge of 1863 *(below)*

The original broad gauge single line was carried across the Thames by a five-span wrought iron girder bridge. This was designed by E. F. Murray (1818-82) and had piers consisting of cross-braced pairs of cast iron screw piles between brick abutments.

In 1914 some of the piles settled, so each pile was supported by wooden trestles resting on concrete laid, in cloth bags, on the bed of the river.

Dimensions

Three central spans: 48ft 6in, 61ft 0in, 49ft 3in; pile diameter: 2ft 0in.

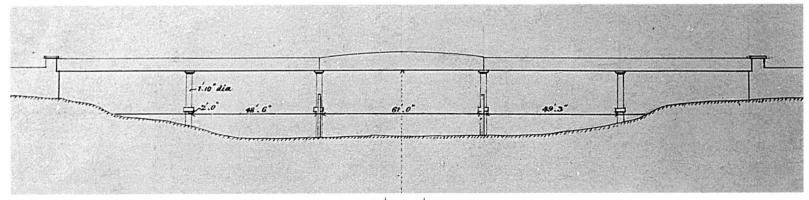

2. The bridge of 1923 *(right)*

In anticipation of heavy traffic to and from the Morris Cowley motor works, which was being enlarged, a bridge was built in 1922-23 immediately downstream of the failing one. The old bridge hindered the construction of its replacement and was removed as soon as that had been completed.

The new bridge was designed by A. C. Cookson and built by George Palmer. It has three Whipple arch trusses supported by brick abutments and two piers, each a pair of steel cylinders sunk into the river bed. It crosses the river on a curve, the pier cylinders being parallel to the centre line of the river and giving the central arch a skew angle of 29 degrees. The bridge cost just over £22,000.

Dimensions
Clear spans: 77ft 6in, 79ft 6in, 77ft 6in; truss length: 83ft; maximum depth of truss: 11ft; width: 21ft 0in.

17.5.74

ISIS (OXFORD SOUTHERN BYPASS) BRIDGE

Isis Bridge takes the Oxford Southern Bypass (A423) across the Thames between Kennington Railway Bridge, a quarter of a mile to the south (downstream), and Iffley Lock, a quarter of a mile to the north.

The Southern Bypass (A423) is part of a Ring Road surrounding Oxford. The northern section is provided by the A40, and the portion skirting the east is part of the A4142, which runs south from a roundabout on the A40, at Headington, to just beyond the Cowley motor works. Here the A4142 turns west, and the portion of the Ring Road skirting the south of Oxford is formed by the west-facing end of the A4142 and the Southern Bypass (A423) proper, which join about three-quarters of a mile east of Isis Bridge. The remainder of the Ring Road is a section of the A34, known as the Western Bypass, which joins the Southern Bypass west of Isis Bridge and, some 4½ miles to the north, crosses the Thames by Thames Bridge, just upstream of Godstow Bridge, before reaching a junction for the A40 and A44 a mile further on.

The bridge of 1965

Isis Bridge was built for the Ministry of Transport with a deck designed by the British Constructional Steelwork Association and substructures designed by Oxfordshire County Council. It was built by John Mowlem & Co Ltd, at a cost of £180,000, and opened in the autumn of 1965.

The bridge has a reinforced concrete deck cast in situ on ten continuous steel girders supported at their ends on reinforced concrete abutments and at the river banks by reinforced concrete piers. These are sited to provide a central span across the Thames and the Thames Path, here on the west bank, and two land spans. The bridge deck carries two carriageways separated by a central reservation, and at each side a footpath and verge, and additionally at one side a verge and a cycle track.

Dimensions

Spans: 62ft, 135ft, 62ft; length between abutments: 259ft; width between parapets: 112ft (footpath/verge 13ft 3in, carriageway 24ft 0in, reservation 15ft 0in, carriageway 24ft 0in, verge 15ft 0in, cycle track 12ft 0in, footpath/verge 8ft 9in).

DONNINGTON ROAD BRIDGE AND FREE FERRY FOOTBRIDGE

Donnington Road Bridge crosses the Thames (or Isis) just over half a mile below Iffley Lock. It carries a secondary road, the B4495, which links the A4144, a mile south of Folly Bridge, with the A4158, to the east. Both these A roads link south Oxford with roundabouts on the Ring Road.

Donnington Road Bridge *(below)*

Donnington Road Bridge was built as a replacement for the Free Ferry Footbridge (see below), which used to stand 100 yards north of it, upstream. The City of Oxford Rowing Club has its clubhouse a few yards to the south, on the east bank of the river.

The bridge was built for the Oxford City Engineer by the Cementation Co Ltd at a cost of £120,000. It was designed by R. Travers Morgan & Partners in 1955, but construction work did not start until 1960 and the bridge was not opened until late in 1962.

The Donnington Road Bridge comprises ten portal frames, each

consisting of a pre-stressed concrete beam, profiled as a shallow arch, having at each end a triangular support formed of outer and inner legs converging at an angle of 40 degrees to a joint at their lower ends. The outer legs are of pre-stressed concrete and the inner legs are of reinforced concrete. The beams were made by stressing together on site pre-cast central and end sections. The triangular supports, and bearings for them, are housed in abutment-shaped reinforced concrete casings clad with pre-cast slabs of mixed Blue Shap and Criggion Green aggregates.

Once the portal frames were in position, their beams were connected by casting concrete around steel reinforcement near their ends to form transverse diaphragms, and throughout their length to form a superimposed deck. Fascia plinths of pre-cast units were then attached to each side of the bridge to decorate the beams with vertically ribbed white calcined flint aggregate and to edge the deck in readiness for balustrades. Those fitted have mild steel vertical rods carrying a bronze-sheathed hardwood rail.

Dimensions
Distance between housings of beam supports: 145ft; distance between support bearings: 170ft; deck width: 55ft (30ft roadway, two 10ft footways and two 2ft 6in upstand verges).

Free Ferry Footbridge
This bridge was built by McAlpine for Oxford Corporation, and had a single shallow arch of elegant shape made of reinforced concrete with metal handrails. The footbridge was spoilt aesthetically in 1955 when L. G. Mouchel & Partners was employed to fit two large pipes, one for water and the other for gas, below its arch. The bridge was removed following completion of the Donnington Road Bridge in 1962.

Dimensions
Clear span: 151ft 11in; width: 13ft 8in.

FOLLY BRIDGE (GRANDPONT)

This bridge carries the A4144 southwards from the city to join the bypass.

It is commonly supposed that a timber bridge had been maintained at the southern approach to Oxford since Saxon times.

1. Grandpont ('Folly Bridge') of 1085 *(below)*
The first bridge for which there is definite information was the stone bridge known as 'Grandpont', which was built in 1085, during the reign of William I, by Robert D'Oyley. The name referred not only to the bridge of 18 arches but also to the causeway on 42 arches that carried the road 2 miles southwards from St Aldate's to the bottom of Hinksey Hill. At the south end of the bridge proper, there was a small chapel to St Nicholas at which money was collected for maintenance of the bridge.

In 1142 King Stephen built a gateway and drawbridge after capturing the city from Queen Matilda. In the following century the Franciscan friar Roger Bacon studied astronomy there (so it was believed) and after about 1600 the tower became known as 'Friar Bacon's Study'. Some 50 years later, the City leased the building to a citizen named Welcome who repaired it and added a storey. The

Folly Bridge south

building then acquired a new name, 'Welcome's Folly', and the bridge accordingly became known as 'Folly Bridge'. The folly was demolished in 1779 to allow widening of the roadway.

The bridge seriously hindered navigation and at the end of the 18th century the main arch, of only 14-foot span, was reconstructed. The work weakened the bridge, and despite repairs in 1797 and 1803 it became necessary to build a replacement.

2. The bridge of 1827 *(below)* • *Grade II listed* •

An Act for removing and replacing Folly Bridge was obtained on 28 June 1815 (55 George 3, xciv). Ebenezer Perry was chosen as architect and the new bridge was built between 1824 and 1827. It has four arches and crosses an island on which are several interesting houses. One of these was built in 1849 for Joshua Cardwell, an eccentric accountant, and is of brick with battlements and statues. Originally it was North Hinksey House, but now is No 5 Folly Bridge. The three main arches of the bridge are north of the island. The southern arch is south of those and crosses a channel in which, from 1821 until 1884, there was a pound lock just downstream of the bridge.

Dimensions
Clear spans: three of 30ft 9in, southern 21ft; width between parapets: 28ft 6in (including 19ft roadway and two 4ft 7in footways); length of roadway on island: 65ft.

Folly Bridge north, 24.9.05

OXFORD GAS WORKS BRIDGES

Since the removal of the gas works, these bridges have come to link the Thames Path, on the south bank of the river, with the City of Oxford on the north bank.

The Oxford Gas, Light & Coke Company was founded in 1818 and, after building a gas works at a 2-acre site on the north bank of the Thames, started to supply gas for street lighting in 1819. The works was progressively enlarged to cover 5 acres, and in 1882 an Act (45 & 46 Victoria, cxxvii) was obtained authorising construction of an additional gas works on the south bank of the Thames. The Act also approved construction of a railway system that would connect the two works together and connect them both to the Great Western Railway (GWR) main line south of the river; the latter connection was opened in 1886.

In 1930 the gas company took over the Abingdon gas works and changed its name to the Oxford & District Gas Co. Following nationalisation under an Act of 1948, the company became part of the Southern Gas Board, which closed the works in 1960.

Gas Works Footbridge
1. The bridge of 1927

This footbridge was built in 1927 by Head Wrightson & Co Ltd of Thornaby-on-Tees to link the north and south gas works. The footway is supported by two steel trusses resting on brick abutments. Originally the footway was approached by cast iron steps, but when it was decided to lay gas pipes across the bridge these steps were removed.

2. The bridge of 1972 *(above right)*

After the gas works had been closed and dismantled, the City bought the bridge and it was adapted by the then City Engineer, A. T. Morris,

18.9.74

for use as a footbridge once more. A concrete approach ramp of 1-in-10 slope was built on each bank, and a new deck, of concrete and fitted with handrails and safety mesh, was provided. This work was carried out between late 1971 and the summer of 1972.

Since then, the south bank has been improved by the Sir Geoffrey Archer Building of the University and a nature park established just upstream. The north bank has also been improved by residential development.

Dimensions
Span: 120ft; clear span: 116ft 6in; deck width: 10ft.

Gas Works Railway Bridge
The bridge of 1886 (right)
The railway bridge built to link the gas works on opposite sides of the river was designed by Thomas Hawkesley and constructed by Vernon & Co. It carried a standard gauge railway track, a narrow roadway and, below the latter, five gas mains. A second railway track was added later. The deck is supported by two wrought iron lattice girder spans,

the outer ends of which rest on brick abutments and the inner ends on a pair of decorated cylindrical cast iron piers. The ironwork cost just under £4,000.

The whole of the deck is now covered by a smooth road surface.

Dimensions
Spans: two 73ft 6in girders; clear spans: two of 65ft; pier diameters: 5ft 6in (upper part), 8ft 6in (lower part); deck width: 22ft.

24.9.05

OXFORD (ISIS) RAILWAY BRIDGES

The first railway to reach Oxford was a 10-mile branch, built to Brunel's broad gauge (7ft 0¼in), running north from Didcot, on the Great Western Railway (GWR) main line from London to Bristol. It was built under an Act of 1843 (6 & 7 Victoria, x) and opened to a terminus south of the Thames near Folly Bridge on 12 June 1844.

12.8.77

By an Act of 1846 (9 & 10 Victoria, ccxxxvii) a Birmingham & Oxford Junction Railway Company was formed and the London & North Western Railway (LNWR) attempted to gain control of it to prevent competition with its own Birmingham line. In 1848 the GWR successfully defeated this attempt and was empowered to take over the new company. The GWR then built a broad gauge single line from Millstream Junction, south of its Oxford terminus, across the Thames (Isis) by a wrought iron and timber bridge, and on to Banbury. The line opened on 2 September 1850. Inconveniently, trains between the Oxford terminus and Banbury had to reverse at Millstream Junction.

When the Banbury line was built, room for a second track was provided, so the GWR could more readily lay the whole of its Oxford to Birmingham route with double mixed-gauge track. When this route was opened on 1 October 1852 a new Oxford station, north of the Thames and west of the city centre, was inaugurated so that trains calling at Oxford no longer had to reverse at Millstream Junction. The line from there to the old terminus was retained for goods traffic for 20 years, closing on 26 November 1872.

The downstream (goods line) bridge of 1887 *(left)*

When a railway system was built for the Oxford Gas, Light & Coke Co under its Act of 1882 (45 & 46 Victoria, cxxvii), a junction was made with the GWR main line south of the Thames in 1886. In 1887 the GWR built a bridge across the Thames (Isis), immediately downstream of the one carrying the main line, to connect the gas works sidings with its own sidings north of the river. The bridge was designed by A. H. Baylis and has three plate girder spans with brick abutments and piers of twin cast iron cylinders. In 1958 this bridge was strengthened so that it could be used to carry freight trains.

Dimensions

Clear spans: 44ft, 58ft 6in, 27ft; width: 17ft; depth of girders: 3ft (towpath span), 6ft (river spans); distance between girder centres; 15ft 6in.

The upstream (main line) bridge
1. The bridge of 1850

The first GWR main line bridge across the Thames at Oxford carried the single broad gauge track to Banbury, but, with foresight, was built wide enough to carry double track. It crossed the river at an angle of 75 degrees on three wrought iron girders, the lower flanges of which supported the deck and were themselves supported by brick abutments and two intermediate piers. Originally each pier was a row of six timber piles, but these were replaced later with groups of cast iron cylinders.

Dimensions

Clear spans: 28ft, 60ft, 28ft; depth of main girders: 7ft 6in, reduced near abutments to 5ft 6in; distance between main girder centres: 33ft 6in.

2. The bridge of 1898 *(below)*

The 1850 bridge was replaced in 1898 by a steel plate girder bridge

13.5.75

designed by E. Olander (1834-1900). This had a single long span across the river and a shorter span across the towpath along the south bank (now the Thames Path). The girders were supported by brick abutments and an intermediate brick pier.

Dimensions
Clear spans: 87ft, 24ft 7in; width: 35ft.

3. The bridge of 1981 *(below)*
The spans of the 1898 bridge were replaced in 1981 with twin new spans each formed of steel box girders connected by a composite deck of steel cross-members and reinforced concrete. The original brick pier between the Thames Path and the river was lowered to accommodate new intermediate bearings The downstream and upstream edges of the new spans were fitted with steel handrails.

Dimensions
Clear spans (measured square): 88ft, 25ft.

OSNEY BRIDGE

Osney Bridge carries the A420 Oxford-Swindon road westward across the Thames from near the railway station on Osney Island to the east end of Botley Road; that road crosses the flood plain of the river on a mile-long causeway.

1. Ancient bridges
An Augustinian priory was founded on Osney Island in 1129 and was raised to abbey status in 1154. The name Osney derives from Osa's Island, which is bounded by the old navigation channel to the east, now called the Castle Mill Stream, and the present-day navigation channel to the west, the Thames (or Isis) itself. The Botley Road carried by Osney Bridge was an important route and the Abbey built a stone bridge of three arches across the river, almost certainly to replace an earlier timber structure.

2. The bridge of 1769 *(below)*
In 1764 the great lawyer Sir William Blackstone (1723-90) had obtained an Act (4 George 3, c. 42) establishing a turnpike trust that repaired the road from Reading to Shillingford, and replaced Shillingford ferry with a bridge. After the death, in debt, of Lord

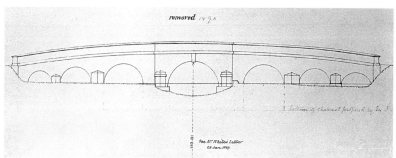

24.9.05

13.5.75

Abingdon in 1760, Blackstone encouraged the fourth Earl to substitute a toll-bridge for Eynsham ferry, to provide himself with an additional source of income, and on 24 February 1767 obtained the necessary Act of Parliament (7 George 3, c. 63). The Botley causeway, at the eastern end of the road that would cross the proposed bridge on its way to Witney, was in a poor state. Blackstone therefore obtained a second Act (7 George 3, c. 66), which received the Royal Assent on the same day as the first, for establishing a turnpike trust for improving the road and rebuilding the causeway and its seven under-bridges. The ancient Osney Bridge was replaced with a new stone bridge similar in style to the Swinford toll-bridge but having one, instead of three, central arches, and three arches of diminishing spans at each side. There was a toll-house at the Oxford end. Toll collection ceased on 31 December 1868.

On 2 December 1885 part of one of the piers and the central arch of the bridge collapsed, precipitating three people into the stream – one of them, an 11-year-old girl, was drowned.

3. The bridge of 1888 *(above right)*

The bridge to replace the collapsed stone one was designed by W. H. White and built by Horsley Bridge & Thomas Piggott Ltd of Tipton, Staffordshire. It has a main arch of six cast iron ribs that carry rolled steel trough plates and are supported between stone-faced abutments and approaches. There are two smaller arches under the western approach. When built in 1888 it provided an 8ft 9in headway, but a change in the river level caused by the removal of Medley Weir in 1930 reduced this to only 7ft 6in.

Dimensions
Span of main arch: 60ft; depth of cast iron ribs: 22in at springing, 18in at crown; width between parapets: 30ft (20ft roadway and two 5ft footways).

MEDLEY FOOTBRIDGES

After Osney Bridge, the next Thames crossing for vehicles is at Godstow, about 2½ miles north-west of Oxford. Half-way between those crossings is the lock island of the former Medley weir, a flash lock built in the 18th century and removed in 1937. This narrow island divides the river into two streams: the west stream is the present navigation channel, while the east stream splits, a little to the south of the lock island, into the Castle Mill Stream, the former navigation channel, and a stream that accompanies the present navigation channel almost all the way to Osney Bridge.

In passing upstream through Oxford, the Thames Path runs along the west bank of the river to Osney Bridge, which it crosses, then follows the east bank to reach the land between the navigation channel and the accompanying stream. This land is a charming rural causeway leading to a footbridge across the water south of the lock island. After crossing this bridge, the path continues along the lock island, then returns to the west bank of the river across a footbridge, originally called Binsey Bridge after a ford at the site, but now called the 'Rainbow Bridge', because of its shape.

The Thames Path can be reached from Port Mead by means of a footbridge that crosses the stream east of the lock island and so completes the Medley crossing.

The 'Rainbow Bridge'
1. The bridge of 1865 *(below left)*
The 'Rainbow Bridge', otherwise known as Medley or Binsey Bridge, has a single lattice arch carrying a timber deck. It carries a plate bearing the words 'City of Oxford – This bridge was erected by public subscription, through the exertion and during the Shrievalty of Henry Grant, Esquire AD 1865 J. Pinchbeck, Engineer, The Reading Iron Works Limited, Manufacturers'.

Dimensions
Span: 69ft 2in; headway: 10ft; width of deck: 4ft 7in.

2. The rebuilt bridge of 1997
The 1865 bridge was refurbished in 1996-97 without changing its appearance, and formally re-opened as a Grade II listed structure. It now carries a second plate, bearing the words 'Environment Agency Rainbow Bridge Restored 1997 Engineer Chris Marr 1949-2000'.

The bridge to the old lock island
The present footbridge to the lock island at Medley is a prefabricated lattice steel structure.

25.9.74

GODSTOW AND WOLVERCOTE BRIDGES

The Godstow crossing carries the Wytham to Wolvercote road across three channels of the Thames about 2 miles north of Oxford city centre. From west to east the first channel is the navigation channel cut in the 18th century, which is crossed by Godstow Navigation Bridge; the second channel is the original course of the river, crossed by Godstow Ancient Bridge; and the third channel is a loop of the river passing through Wolvercote village, which is crossed by Wolvercote Bridge, often referred to as 'Airmen's Bridge'.

Godstow Navigation Bridge
1. The bridge of c1790

In 1783 the Thames Commissioners recognised the need to improve navigation from Oxford to Lechlade in readiness for traffic generated by the opening of the Thames & Severn Canal. Godstow was one of the places where improvement was required; accordingly, a navigation channel was cut there in about 1790, which was provided with a pound lock at its lower end and, near its upper end, a single-arched bridge.

The towpath of the navigation channel, now the Thames Path, is along the west bank of the river and passes the ruins of Godstow Abbey, the Benedictine nunnery where stood, until two years after his death in 1189, Henry II's memorial to his fair mistress Rosamund. The nunnery had been consecrated in 1138 and dedicated to the Virgin Mary and St John the Baptist.

Dimension

Span: 16ft 2in.

18.5.74

2. The 1920s bridge *(above)*

The 18th-century bridge was replaced by the Thames Conservancy in the 1920s with a brick bridge of arches.

Dimensions

Spans (pier): 26ft (4ft 6in) 26ft; width: 10ft 7in.

3. Godstow Bridge *(overleaf)* • *Grade II listed* •

The ancient bridge at Godstow probably dates back to the early days of the nunnery in the 12th century. It is of stone with two arches, the one nearer to the left bank (and the Trout Inn) being the older and pointed like the outer arches of the oldest surviving Thames bridge, Radcot Bridge, further upstream. The other arch has been rebuilt to have a rounded shape. The pier between the two arches has a cutwater upstream, and a weir for the lock backwater partly obscures the downstream face of the bridge.

Dimensions

Spans (pier): 12ft 2in (north) (6ft) 12ft 9in (south); width: 10ft 6in.

10.10.76

Wolvercote Bridge
1. The 12th century bridge
The first Wolvercote Bridge was probably built in the 12th century at the same time as the nunnery (consecrated in 1138) and bridge at Godstow. It was of stone and had five pointed arches.

2. The bridge of 1796
In 1796 the central arch of the ancient bridge was replaced by a rounded arch, John Henry Long being the engineer. This work, and numerous minor repairs, were paid for by the Third Duke of Marlborough.

Dimensions of both bridges
Length of parapet walls: 135ft; width between parapets: 14ft.

3. The bridge of 1876 ('Airmen's Bridge') *(below)*
• *Grade II listed* •
The 1796 bridge was rebuilt by Roland Green of Cassington at a cost of £2,558 for the County of Oxford. The new bridge has three segmental arches and is of Gibraltar stone with copings and arch rims of Milton stone. The soffits are of hard brick.

At the eastern end of the bridge is a memorial to Lt C. A. Bettington and 2/Lt E. Hotchkiss of the Royal Flying Corps, who were killed on 10 September 1912 when their monoplane crashed a hundred yards away. For this reason the bridge is often referred to locally as 'Airmen's Bridge'.

Dimensions
Spans: 24ft, 28ft, 24ft; width: 16ft; length: 135ft.

25.9.74

OXFORD WESTERN BYPASS BRIDGES

Thames Bridge, just above Godstow Bridge, carries the section of the A34 known as the Oxford Western Bypass across the main stream of the Thames. About half a mile north-west of Thames Bridge, the bypass crosses the loop of the Thames through Wolvercote by a plain modern bridge that can be reached on foot from the Thames Path via King's Weir and a footpath across Pixey Mead.

Thames Bridge *(below)*
Thames Bridge is not a single bridge but a pair of adjacent bridges that share abutments. Each bridge is similar in design to Donnington Road Bridge in south Oxford. The bridges were built for the Ministry of Transport by Berkshire County Council, the consulting engineers being R. Travers Morgan & Partners and the contractors Higgs & Hill Ltd. The cost of construction was about £110,000, and the bridges were completed in 1961.

Each bridge has six pre-stressed (post-tensioned) concrete portal frames, cast in situ, joined by diaphragms of the same construction, and carrying a reinforced concrete deck slab. Each deck carries a dual carriageway, a footpath and two verges. The 'V' legs at the ends of the portal frames are of reinforced concrete with the concrete of the outermost legs pre-stressed. The lower extremities of the legs are supported by bearings on slabs of concrete, cast in sheet steel piling, which provide the necessary foundations. To enhance the appearance of the bridge and protect the ends of the portal frames against the weather, the 'V' legs are housed in abutment-shaped casings clad with pre-cast units of exposed Menheniot Granite aggregate.

Dimensions
Clear spans: 116ft (east), 114ft (west); distance between bearings of portal frames: 140ft; width of each carriageway: 24ft; width between upstream and downstream parapets: 75ft.

Bridge over Wolvercote loop
The bridge across the loop of the Thames passing through Wolvercote, upstream of Airmen's Bridge, is a plain modern structure of reinforced concrete having a single rectangular opening spanning the waterway and a footpath at the southern side closed by a gate at the Wolvercote end.

12.10.98

SWINFORD (OR EYNSHAM) BRIDGE

Swinford Bridge carries the B4044 (previously the A4141 and, before that, the A40) road from Oxford to Eynsham across the Thames between Swinford and Eynsham. It has quite often been referred to as Eynsham Bridge and is now one of only three toll-bridges across the river (the others being at Whitchurch and Dartford).

In the 18th century there were alternative roads linking Oxford and Witney for use by travellers between London and Gloucester. Heavy traffic chose the longer, northern, road through Campsfield (using what are now the A44 and A4095) because this avoided the serious disadvantages of the shorter, southern, road through Eynsham – the worse condition of the roadway, especially across the Botley causeway; the need to climb over Wytham Hill; and the need to cross the Thames by ferry at Eynsham.

In 1757 William Blackstone (1723-90) was appointed by the third Earl of Abingdon to act as legal and financial advisor for his estate. The Earl died in 1760, heavily in debt. Blackstone decided to provide the young fourth Earl (1740-99) with a good source of income by establishing a turnpike trust to improve and manage the shorter Oxford to Witney road, and by building a toll-bridge across the Thames between Swinford and Eynsham. He obtained authorisation for his plan by two Acts of Parliament dated 24 February 1767 (7 George 3, c. 63 & 66).

Improvement of the road westward from Oxford to Witney required reconstruction of the Botley causeway and its seven bridges, including Osney Bridge. Building Swinford bridge required buying the ferry and the land on each bank of the Thames needed for the bridge approaches.

The bridge of 1769   • *Grade II listed/Ancient Monument* •

It is not known for certain who designed Swinford Bridge, but it was probably Sir Robert Taylor (1714-88). He had designed Maidenhead Bridge, which is similar in style, and was associated with Sir William Blackstone, in 1769 and later, in connection with improvements to St Peter's Church at Wallingford.

The bridge was built of local stone and has nine arches, three over the river and three in each approach. It cost more than £4,000, and buying the ferry and the land on the river banks cost a further £10,000.

In the Act Blackstone obtained for the bridge, the Earl was exempted from paying all future new taxes, hence the then unknown income tax on the toll revenues! The bridge was sold in the late 1960s, following the death of the eighth Countess, and since then has been sold at least twice (in 1981 and 1986).

Dimensions

Spans of arches: 16ft, 20ft, 24ft, 30ft, 36ft, 30ft, 24ft, 20ft, 16ft; width over river: 20ft (16ft roadway and two 2ft footways); overall length: 310ft.

18.5.74

SKINNER'S FOOTBRIDGE

Skinner's Bridge was a footbridge built across the Thames when Skinner's weir and two picturesque thatched cottages, including the Fish Inn, were removed. They had been in the possession of the Skinner family for many years, and Joe Skinner was the last proprietor of the inn. Taunt described the new footbridge as a gallows bridge. It was removed by the Thames Conservancy during the 1930s, but a replacement is being considered.

HART'S WEIR (OR RIDGE'S) FOOTBRIDGE

Hart's Weir Footbridge carries a footpath across the Thames between Northmoor and Netherton.

The first footbridge at this site was built in 1879 following removal of Ridge's weir, and both Taunt (1886) and Thacker (1920) refer to it as Ridge's Bridge. The name Hart's Weir (or simply Hart's) Footbridge was applied later, not without causing some confusion because Eaton Hastings weir, near Kelmscott, was often called Hart's weir from the name of the family that kept it for at least a hundred years.

1. The bridge of 1879 *(above right)*
The footbridge photographed by Taunt was of timber with six piers, each a pair of piles. The balustrades consisted of timber railings, those above the river being of lattice construction.

Dimension
Main span: 38ft 9in.

2 & 3. Bridges of the inter-war years and of 1965 *(below right)*
It is reasonable to assume that the 1879 bridge was replaced before the Second World War. The present 1965 bridge has abutments of steel piling and concrete and two piers of converging concrete piles supporting an arched deck of pre-stressed concrete beams. The deck is provided with timber handrails.

Dimensions (1965 bridge)
Spans: three of 28m (91ft 10in); width of deck: 6ft 5in.

H. Taunt

28.9.74

NEW BRIDGE

• Grade I listed/Ancient Monument •

New Bridge (spelled Newbridge by some authors in accordance with the name of the place where it stands) is on the A415 Abingdon to Witney road between Kingston Bagpuize and Brighthampton. It crosses from the Mayflower public house, on the south bank, to the Rose Revived Inn on the north. Until the end of March 1974 the Berkshire-Oxfordshire border was on the bridge, but since then the bridge has been wholly in Oxfordshire.

22.9.74

New Bridge was built in about 1250, in the reign of Henry III, and was probably called 'New' to distinguish it from Radcot Bridge 10 miles upstream. It is a stone bridge of six arches, the northernmost being across the River Windrush, not the Thames. The piers have cutwaters upstream, which extend to the top of the parapet to provide refuges for pedestrians. It was largely rebuilt in the middle of the 15th century by John Golafre, and in about 1793 the ribs of all but two of the arches were cut away to increase clearance for river traffic.

In 1644, during the Civil War, there were battles at the bridge when the Parliamentarians attempted to cross it to reach the Royalists in Oxford. Thacker recounts how Sir William Waller was so angry at failing to cross on 27 May that he retired to Abingdon and destroyed the beautiful market cross there. Later in the same year the bridge was partly destroyed by the Parliamentarians, and was not repaired until several years later.

Dimensions
Spans (from left bank): 13ft, 16ft, 19ft 6in, 17ft, 13ft 6in, 11ft 9in (piers all approximately 8ft.wide); width between parapets: 15ft; overall length: 148ft 6in; lengths of causeways at approaches: 300yds (northern), 373yds (southern).

SHIFFORD BRIDGES

These footbridges carry the Thames Path between the south bank of the Thames below Shifford Lock and the north bank of Shifford Lock Cut upstream of the lock.

Between Chimney and Shifford the Thames flows round a southern loop, at the lowermost point of which is Duxford ford. A ferry was established here in 1827, and until 1869 there was a flash weir a little downstream. Later, to improve navigation, a cut was made joining the northern arms of the loop, and Shifford Lock was built at its eastern end. The land enclosed by the loop became the lock island and the loop became a backwater. Weirs were provided at the west end of the loop and adjacent to the lock to control the water levels and flows in the backwater and navigation cut. The lock and cut were opened for traffic in 1898.

Shifford Lock Cut Bridge *(below)*

The present bridge across the lock cut was built for the Thames Conservancy and opened in 1955. It has concrete abutments and two piers, consisting of twin concrete supports carrying four rolled-steel joists to which a deck and timber handrails are attached.

Dimensions

Distance between abutments: 86ft 3in; width of deck: 10ft 6in.

Shifford Island Footbridge *(below)*

This modern bridge was built for the Countryside Agency to carry the Thames Path. It was designed by Oxfordshire County Council and constructed in 1994 by Dyer & Butler of Southampton for an approximate cost of £80,000. The bridge is now maintained by the County Council.

The bridge superstructure rests on bank seats carried by caps for twin piles, all these components being of concrete, cast in situ. The superstructure has two curved steel beams braced together by five steel cross-members and carrying timber steps, decking and handrails. The steps are of constant height and so vary in front-to-back width according to changes in the inclination of the supporting beams. Although the bridge looks symmetrical, it is not: the centre of the arch is not exactly half-way between the bank seats and there are 17 steps on the east side of the bridge and 19 on the west.

Dimensions

Clear span (distance between bank seats): 19m (62ft 4in); apex of arch: 0.26m (10in) east of mid-point; width of footway: 1.5m (4ft 11in); overall width of deck: 1.86m (6ft 1in); variation in step width (front to back): 300-977mm (12-38in).

TENFOOT BRIDGE

Tenfoot Bridge is between Shifford Lock and Tadpole Bridge and carries the Thames Path from south of the river to its north bank. The south end of the bridge can be reached using a footpath from Buckland.

Tenfoot Bridge stands at the site of an old flash weir, which had a 10-foot opening and was removed, in 1869 or 1870, because of its dangerous condition.

1. The bridge of 1869 *(below)*

The first Tenfoot Bridge was built by the Thames Conservancy. It had three spans of timber, the central span being horizontal and the outer spans sloping upward from the river banks to a level below that of the central span; the accompanying drawing suggests that the outer spans were ramps leading to steps up to the level of the horizontal span. The bridge was removed in 1890.

Dimensions
Central span: 15ft 7in: outer spans: 13ft 2in.

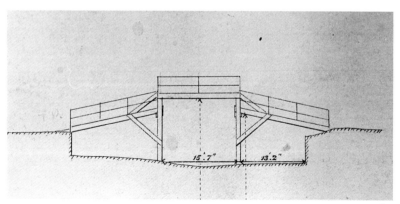

2. The bridge of c1890 *(below)*

Dredge gives 1894 as the year of construction of the second footbridge, but the long delay following removal of the first bridge seems unusual.

This bridge was of timber with three spans, a horizontal central section being reached by ramps at either side. These ramps were supported by concrete abutments and, towards their upper ends, by trestles. To make the bridge appear less angular, the handrails were arched at its centre.

Dimensions
Central span: 30ft; overall length: 62ft 8in.

20.10.72

3. The bridge of c1994

The second bridge was replaced by the National Rivers Authority with a bridge of closely similar design at some time before 1994.

TADPOLE BRIDGE

Tadpole Bridge carries a road north from near Buckland, on the Oxford to Faringdon road (A420), to a junction in Bampton with the road from Eynsham (B4449). Just south of the bridge, on the eastern side of the road, stands the Trout Inn.

Little is known about the origin and construction of Tadpole Bridge. Phillips (1981) gives an interesting account of relevant local history that includes the fact that the road carried by the bridge was improved by local landowners under an Act of 1777. He deduces that the bridge was almost certainly built in 1789, but is unable to identify the designer. The bridge failed soon after completion and the year 1802, given by Jervoise (1930) as that of its building, may be the year in which it was rebuilt after failure.

The bridge of c1789 • *Grade II listed* •

Tadpole Bridge is of stone and has a single segmental arch decorated with raised circles in the spandrel walls. The roadway is slightly humped to provide increased headway for navigation.

Dimensions

Span of arch: 42ft; overall length: 72ft; width between parapets: 15ft.

13.5.75

OLD MAN'S FOOTBRIDGE

This bridge carries a footpath across the river just below Radcot Lock.

1. The bridge of 1868 *(below left)*

The first footbridge was built in 1868 to replace a weir traversed by a footway variously known as 'Old Man's', 'Harper's' or 'Clark's' weir. It was a timber bridge of five openings, the widest being at one end.

Dimensions

Spans: 17ft 6in, 11ft 3in, 14ft 2in, 14ft 2in, and one other.

2. The bridge of 1890 *(bottom left)*

This was a timber bridge of a symmetrical design similar to Tenfoot Bridge.

Dimensions

Main span: 30ft; distance between abutments: 59ft; deck width: 3ft to 6ft 3in.

3. The mid-1980s replacement bridge *(below)*

The 1890 bridge was replaced during the 1980s by a bridge of the same design.

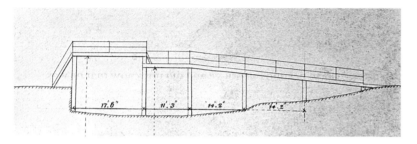

RADCOT BRIDGES

On its way north from Faringdon to Clanfield, the A4095 road passes successively over three bridges at Radcot. The first, Radcot Bridge, crosses the main stream of the Thames, now a backwater, and is the oldest surviving Thames bridge; the second, Radcot Navigation Bridge, crosses an artificial cut; and the third, Pidnell Bridge, crosses a northern loop.

In 1770 a turnpike trust was established to improve the Faringdon to Burford road. A toll-gate was placed south of Pidnell Bridge and this was not pulled down until 1878. The boundary between Berkshire and Oxfordshire used to be half-way across Radcot Bridge, but since 1 April 1974 this part of the Thames has been entirely in Oxfordshire.

Originally there were timber bridges where the present bridges stand, but these were replaced by stone bridges fairly soon after 1154 when Henry II succeeded Stephen to the throne. Radcot became important in the Middle Ages because it was the most convenient place on the river for loading stone from Taynton quarry, near Burford, for transport downstream. The quarry was already famous in 1086, when it was recorded in the Domesday survey, and Taynton stone was used abroad, for instance in the Abbey of Denis in Paris, as well as in England. It is also to be found in the crypt of St Paul's Cathedral, presumably from the ruins of Old St Paul's, burned in the Great Fire of 1666.

An important battle was fought at Radcot Bridge on 20 December 1387. Robert de Vere, Earl of Oxford and Duke of Ireland, attempted to reach London with a force raised in Chester to free Richard II from the power of rebel barons, the 'Lords Appellant'. His force was stopped at Radcot Bridge by the forces of Henry Bolingbroke (Lord Derby and later King Henry IV, 1367-1413), which had broken down the central arch. De Vere was prevented from retreating by the forces of the Duke of Gloucester, which had followed south down the causeway from Clanfield. Perceiving the trap, de Vere rode away and,

after failing to cross Newbridge, which was held by archers, forded the river at Bablockhythe and ultimately escaped to France.

There was military action at Radcot Bridge more than once during the Civil War. In November 1644 Charles I made Faringdon House his headquarters. In April the following year Cromwell (1599-1658) unsuccessfully attempted to take the house. Having heard that a Royalist attack on his own headquarters in Faringdon was being prepared, Cromwell sent 23 cavalry under Major Bethel to make sure that all was well with the men guarding Radcot Bridge. Major Bethel led his men north beyond the bridge and did not know that he was observed in the moonlight by 18 Royalist cavalry who had arrived from Lechlade. The Royalists hid by the road and each killed one returning Roundhead, the Major being spared. The bridge was then easily taken.

Radcot Bridge *(below)*   • *Grade II listed/Ancient Monument* •
Radcot Bridge was built soon after 1154, in the reign of Henry II. It was made of Taynton stone with three arches, which were originally all of the pointed Gothic shape, but when the central arch was rebuilt, at

6.5.76

the end of the 14th century, it was given a more rounded Tudor form. The downstream parapet has a socket believed to have held a cross.

In 1871 William Morris (1834-96) bought Kelmscott Manor, 2 miles upstream of Radcot Bridge, and six years later founded the Society for the Protection of Ancient Buildings. His daughter May (1862-1938) was a keen member and it was her campaigning from 1910 onwards that led to the ancient bridge being restored in 1914 by R. Redfern. It is now scheduled as an ancient monument.

Radcot Navigation Bridge
1. The bridge of c1154
The second stone bridge was built at the same time, and presumably in the same style, as the surviving ancient bridge. Baskerville, writing in 1692, noted that it had two arches.

Dimensions
Spans: 9ft, 12ft, 9ft; width between parapets: 12ft.

2 & 3. The 18th century bridges *(below)*
The ancient stone bridge north of Radcot Bridge was replaced in the 18th century by a crude wooden bridge. Then in 1787, in anticipation of traffic to be generated by the opening of the Thames & Severn Canal, the Thames Commissioners improved navigation at Radcot.

The timber bridge was replaced by the present Navigation Bridge, and the channel it crossed was widened to enable barges to avoid the small arches of Radcot Bridge. The new bridge cost just under £400.

The Navigation Bridge is of Taynton stone and has a single semi-circular arch. It crosses the enlarged channel on the skew and that fact, with the curvature of the channel, makes the bridge difficult to negotiate.

Dimensions
Span: 15ft 3in; width between parapets: 12ft 8in.

Pidnell Bridge
1. The bridge of c1154
Thanks to the existence of a watercolour by Mrs Davenport, we know that the ancient bridge across the northern loop of the Thames at Radcot was similar in style to the surviving Radcot Bridge, with four arches all of the pointed Gothic shape but, latterly at least, with railings rather than stone parapets. This beautiful bridge was replaced in 1863.

2. The bridge of 1863 *(below)*
The present Pidnell Bridge is formed of girders carried by three stone piers, the parapets consisting of iron railings supported by stone-capped brick columns.

EATON FOOTBRIDGES

There are now two Eaton Footbridges, one across the Thames to an island, and the other across a channel south of the island. Together they carry a footpath northwards from Eaton Hastings, south of the river, to the Thames Path along the north (left) bank, and on to Kelmscott. The second bridge used to provide access to the Anchor Inn, sadly destroyed by fire.

The Eaton Footbridges are at the site of a flash weir known as Eaton or Hart's weir. A photograph of this weir, taken in about 1865, is reproduced by Wilson in his 1987 book on Thames navigation, which also contains a description of flash weirs (or locks) and their operation. The sketch map in Thacker (1920) shows an island with the weir at its eastern end crossing the whole river.

In a flash weir there was a sill on the river bed with slots about 2 feet apart and 4 inches wide on the upstream side and, above the water, a footway next to a beam with holes through which 4-inch posts, called rymers, could be lowered from the footway by the weir-keeper so that their ends engaged the slots. Paddles 2 feet wide on poles were then lowered to rest against the sill and rymers and hold back the water. At the navigation section of the weir (at the right end of Hart's weir in the photograph) the channel was opened by removal of the paddles and rymers to allow the water levels above and below the weir to equalise; additional paddles could be removed to speed the process. Then, to allow passage of a sizeable craft, the footway was swung to the side. In wet weather the channel was sometimes left open.

Thacker (1909) described Hart's weir as 'the one real adventure of River life'. A boat going down river 'shoots through, guided by a pole from the bank, with an exhilarating swirl that sweeps you far away before you can get your sculls out.' Hart's weir was removed in 1937 but a rymer and paddle weir can still be seen upstream at Buscot, across a non-navigable channel south of the pound lock.

Eaton Footbridge (north)
1. The weir footbridge
The first footbridge across the channel of the Thames to the north of the island was the footway of the northern section of Hart's weir.

2. The footbridge of 1937 *(below)*
When Hart's weir was removed in 1937, the stream north of the island was widened to become the navigation channel. The present three-span

13.5.74

footbridge was built across this channel with abutments, piers of cross-braced piles, and superstructure, other than the timber handrails, of concrete. The centre of the deck is fixed between overhanging approach ramps.

Dimensions

Deck spans: 21ft 4in, 18ft, 21ft 4in; central clear span: 24ft; width between parapets: 8ft 6in.

Eaton Footbridge (south)

1. The weir swing span

Dredge describes 'a swing span from the left bank for traffic, only a few feet wide, counterbalanced with a box containing stones'. This is the span to the right of his 1865 photograph and suggests that Dredge should have written 'from the right bank'.

2. The bridge to the former Anchor Inn

This bridge has a deck supported by a central pier and strengthened by truss-like handrails.

BLOOMER'S HOLE FOOTBRIDGE

This footbridge is named after Bloomer's Hole, a bend in the River Thames about a quarter of a mile below St John's Bridge, Lechlade. It carries the Thames Path – which follows the old towpath upstream from Buscot to Lechlade – from the north to the south bank.

In 1992 the Countryside Commission and the *Architect's Journal* launched a competition for a design for a footbridge at Bloomer's Hole. However, there were objections to the winning design, which led to construction being delayed until the year 2000.

In 1999 Oxfordshire County Council, in agreement with Gloucestershire County Council, made a Scheme under the Highways Act 1980 (c. 66) to build a footbridge between Buscot and Lechlade for the Thames Path National Trail. A bridge was designed for the Countryside Agency by Charles Benner, of Oxfordshire County Council. A modification of the scheme was confirmed in February 2000 (S. I. 2000/298) and the bridge was built by Isis Accord Ltd and opened later that year. The total cost was about £175,000.

30.7.03

The Bloomer's Hole Footbridge has two curved 'H'-section steel beams supported at each end by concrete bank seats founded on twin concrete piles. Each beam is 27metres (86 feet) long and weighs 8 tonnes. Because of the soft ground on each side of the river, it would have been difficult to get a large crane to the site for lifting the beams into position, so they were transported by air, one at a time, from Brize Norton using a Chinook helicopter.

The beams are connected by six steel bracing members and carry timber decking, which includes 20 steps from each bank seat to the summit of the bridge, timber fascias and timber handrails. The path is gated near each end of the bridge.

Dimensions
Clear span: 23m (74ft 9in); overall length: 26m (84ft 6in); overall width: 1.8m (5ft 10in); width of footpath: 1.5m (4ft 11in); minimum headway over width of 7m (22ft 9in): 3.3m (10ft 8in); widths of steps (20 each side) from ends to centre of bridge: 330-1,978mm (13-78in); spacing of handrail posts (14 each side): 1,935mm (76in).

ST JOHN'S BRIDGE, LECHLADE

St John's Bridge carries the A417 Faringdon to Cirencester road across the Thames just below St John's Lock, less than a mile below the 'Halfpenny Bridge' at Lechlade. It is in two parts: the lock cut bridge across the navigation channel, and the main bridge across the river, immediately to the north.

The lock cut bridge
1. The bridge of 1791
In preparation for traffic using the Thames & Severn Canal, the Thames Commissioners engaged William Jessop (1745-1814) to survey the river above Oxford. He proposed building locks at Buscot and St John's and suggested alternative routes for the navigation channel at the latter location. The preferable, more expensive, route, requiring a new bridge over a southern channel, was chosen. The Commissioners obtained an authorising Act in 1788 (28 George 3, c. 51) and Josiah Clowes (d1795) completed the new channel and bridge in 1791. The bridge failed almost immediately, in 1795, and had to be repaired.

2. The bridge of 1879
The repaired bridge itself failed in 1879 and was replaced by the County Council with a single arch of blue brick.

3. The rebuilt bridge of 1920 *(below)*
Anderson (1970) noted that this bridge was restored and rebuilt in 1920.

Dimensions
Span of arch: 21ft 1in; headroom: 13ft 10in.

7.5.76

The main bridge
1. The timber bridge
A wooden bridge, possibly the first at the site, was swept away by floods in 1203.

2. The 13th-century bridge
The date of construction of the first stone bridge is not known, but the earliest reference to it is in a licence on the Charter Rolls of 1229 authorising Peter Fitzherbert, the second husband of Isabella Ferrers, heiress of the manor of Lechlade, to build a gate at its foot. Isabella founded a religious house nearby, which, with the bridge, she granted to the Brothers of St John at Lechlade; her grant was confirmed by Henry III in 1245. The religious house became the Priory of St John,

and its ownership, together with that of the bridge, changed from time to time. Subsequent owners included Richard, Duke of Cornwall (confirmed as Patron in 1270); Hayles Abbey (from 1300); the Duchess of York, mother of Edward IV (from 1471); and the Dean of St Nicholas College at Wallingford (from 1508). He was held to be responsible for repair of the bridge even after his college had been abolished by Henry VIII in 1540!

The cost of repairs was not always borne by the owner because the king sometimes made grants of pontage authorising the owner to collect tolls. For example, Edward III made such grants in 1338 and 1441, and Richard II made a grant in 1387 after the bridge had been broken by the Duke of Gloucester.

Details of the structure are somewhat uncertain. The bridge seems to have had two large and one lesser arch, with eight small arches towards the ends. A long causeway at the southern (Berkshire) end leading to Buscot contained a further 15 arches.

3. The repaired bridge of c1830
Soon after 1831 the bridge was altered when Peter Cox removed the two large pointed arches and the pier between them and built a single semi-circular arch between the remaining pier and abutment.

4. The rebuilt bridge of 1886 *(left)*
• *Grade II listed* •
Peter Cox's work did not last well and his arch and the remainder of the mediaeval bridge were replaced with a single segmental arch in 1886 by the County Council.

Dimension
Span of main arch: 35ft.

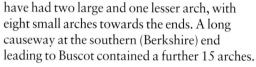

13.5.75

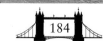

LECHLADE TOWN BRIDGE ('HALFPENNY BRIDGE')

• *Grade II listed* •

Lechlade Town Bridge is at the southern edge of the town and carries the A361 Burford to Swindon road southward across the Thames. The road and bridge were built for a turnpike trust established by an Act of 1792 (32 George 3, c. 153). The bridge made it unnecessary to use a ferry or to make a detour including St John's Bridge downstream.

The bridge was designed by Daniel Harris and built by James Hollinsworth of Banbury. It is of stone and has a segmental main arch of 50-foot span and two land arches on each bank. The stones between the main arch and the balustrades taper radially, like the stones ('voussoirs') forming the arch.

Until 1839 pedestrians had to pay a toll of one halfpenny, hence the bridge's nickname. The bridge was restored and strengthened in 1973.

Dimensions
Main span: 50ft; width of side arches: 9ft; width between parapets: 17ft 2in; overall length: 164ft; headway: 16ft 3in.

4.5.76

INGLESHAM ROUNDHOUSE FOOTBRIDGE

Three-quarters of a mile above Lechlade are the remains of Inglesham Lock at the entrance to the former Thames & Severn Canal. This was constructed under an Act of 1783 (23 George 3, c. 38) between that year and 1789. A watchman's house in the form of a circular tower was built in 1890 at the south side of the lock; this still exists and is known as Inglesham Roundhouse. The Thames Conservancy built a footbridge across the Thames just upstream of the canal entrance.

The canal was closed in 1933, but a society now known as the Cotswolds Canal Trust was formed in 1972 and, after 2001, when the Waterways Trust and British Waterways announced a commitment to restore the Cotswold Canals, joined the Cotswold Canals Partnership, formed to fund and steer restoration of these canals.

1. The Thames Conservancy footbridge *(overleaf)*
Until 1962, when it collapsed, a timber Thames Conservancy

4.5.76

3. The footbridge of 1996 *(below)*

The 1973 bridge deteriorated and was therefore replaced in 1996 with a steel footbridge designed by Halcrow and built by Nusteel Structures Ltd. The new bridge is closely similar in appearance to the 1973 bridge because its steel arch is clad in timber.

Dimension

Overall span: 17.57m (57ft 8in).

footbridge spanned the Thames immediately upstream of its junction with the former canal, close to Inglesham Roundhouse.

Dimensions

Three spans: 18ft, 19ft 6in, 18ft 6in; each pier formed of two 10in square piles; width: 4ft 6in.

2. The footbridge of 1973 *(above right)*

Replacement of the Thames Conservancy bridge was delayed by controversy as to where the new bridge should be built. Ultimately it was decided to build it just downstream of the canal entrance.

The bridge's main components were two curved beams of laminated wood, each weighing a ton, which rested at each end on stepped concrete abutments and carried a deck and handrails of hardwood. The structure was designed by Mr A. J. Summerel of Gloucestershire County Council and was opened on 9 October 1973 by Councillor Elizabeth, Lady Clarke.

Dimensions

Clear span: 17m (55ft 9in); deck width: 1.2m (4ft).

17.6.06

HANNINGTON BRIDGE

Hannington Bridge takes an unclassified road across the Thames between Kempsford, north of the river, and Hannington Wick and Hannington to the south. The Gloucestershire-Swindon boundary is mid-stream, but the bridge is now wholly owned by Gloucestershire.

Oak planks and piles were found when the river was dredged at the site of the present bridge, indicating that the Romans had built a bridge here.

1. The bridge of wood and stone

Baskerville (1692), quoted in Thacker (1920), describes a bridge '...about 120 yards over the river & is built of partly stone piers partly timber posts between 4 great stone piers and 4 timbers 8 arches besides to vent water in time of floods 16 in all.'

Tombleson (1855) describes the bridge as 'constructed of wood, with three arches on stone piers, the centre of which is considerably the largest.'

2. The bridge of 1841 *(right)*
• *Grade II listed* •

The present Hannington Bridge is a three-arched skew bridge of stone, but with brick soffits,

which, like its predecessor, is part of a long structure. This includes a northern approach viaduct with 11 arches and, at the southern end, an intermediate section with a bridge of two arches and a short approach.

Dimensions

Northern approach viaduct: 12 arches of 4ft span; length: 627ft; main bridge: three arches of 15ft 6in span; length: 61ft 3in; width between parapets: 18ft 9in; length of intermediate section: 154ft 6in; southern bridge: two arches of 10ft 6in span; length: 28ft 6in; length of southern approach: 45ft.

20.10.72

CASTLE EATON BRIDGE

Castle Eaton Bridge carries an unclassified road across the Thames at the north-west corner of the village. The road links villages in the area south of the RAF airbase at Fairford with a road (B4019) running south-west from Faringdon (east of Castle Eaton) to the primary route (A419), which runs south-eastwards from Cirencester to Swindon along the line of the Roman Ermine Way.

1. The bridge of wood and stone *(below)*

The old bridge had stone piers supporting a timber deck and was approached from the north-west along a stone causeway. Differences between the description of it by Baskerville (1692) as 'a bridge of 2 arches. Postes between them make 8 arches' and the bridge photographed by Taunt suggest that it was altered in the course of its long life.

The bridge of the photograph had five stone piers between stone abutments with a deck, slightly humped, and handrails of timber. It was beautiful, in complete contrast to the hideous structure with which it was replaced.

Dimensions

Causeway about 73yds long over 34 arches.

H. Taunt

2. The bridge of 1893 *(below)*

In 1893 the Swindon District Board replaced the old bridge with a bridge of twin flanged girders supported by brick abutments. The lower inside flanges of these girders were riveted to the ends of transverse flooring troughs, which were then filled with concrete to provide a level deck. A builder's plate reads 'E. Finch & Co Ltd Engineers & Ironfounders Chepstow 1893'. At one time the girders were painted vermilion but more recently they have been painted a more appropriate green.

Dimensions

Length of main girders: 64ft 0¾in; clear span: 59ft 6in; depth of main girders: 5ft; width: 23ft; width of carriageway: 18ft; flooring trough section: 8in x 11in.

WATER EATON FOOTBRIDGE

Sometimes referred to as Horse Bridge, Water Eaton Footbridge is an occupation bridge near Water Eaton House that carries the Thames Path from the south to the north bank of the river on its way upstream. The southern end of the bridge can be reached by a footpath running from a road between Castle Eaton and the A419 about a mile south-east of Cricklade.

12.5.74

Dimensions
Distance between abutments: 50ft; dimensions of 'H' girders: 5in x 12in; overall width: 4ft 1in; diameter of pier cylinders: 6in.

1. The first bridge *(above right)*
The bridge described by Dredge had a deck of planking supported at each edge by an iron girder of 'H' section and centrally by a wooden beam. The ends of this deck rested on brick abutments and its centre rested on a pier consisting of a row of three cylindrical iron piles, cross-braced and capped with a wooden beam.

2. The rebuilt bridge of 1995
The first bridge was renovated in August 1995 without significantly changing its appearance. The original girders were replaced with rolled steel joists and new parapets, of oak, were fitted. Now there is a gate at only one end of the bridge.

EYSEY FOOTBRIDGE

The footbridge just south of Eysey (or Eisey) carries the Thames Path from the north to the south bank of the river on its way upstream to Cricklade. Two footpaths from Eysey lead to the north end of the bridge.

1. The 18th century bridge *(right)*
In what may be a somewhat rare illustration of a minor Thames bridge, Ireland (1792) shows a slightly humped timber footbridge across the river having two main spans and short spans at each end under flights of four steps. There is a two-rail fence on the downstream side.

Ireland

2. The 19th century bridge *(left)*

The footbridge described by Dredge was a timber trestle bridge of three spans fitted with a handrail at each side. The central span was slightly shorter than the ones on either side.

Dimensions
Spans: 21ft 6in, 17ft 0in, 21ft 6in; width between parapets: 2ft.

3. The bridge of 1962 *(left)*

The deck of the present bridge is carried by two gently arched segmental 'T' beams of post-tensioned reinforced concrete, and is fitted with outwardly inclined timber post-and-rail parapets. Originally the ends of the beams rested on abutments of set bags of cement, but in 1989 those were replaced with concrete walls faced with white brickwork.

Dimensions
Span: 60ft; length of main beams: 65ft 10in; width between handrails: 3ft.

13.5.74

CRICKLADE BYPASS (ISIS) BRIDGE

The Isis Bridge across the Thames carries a section of the Cirencester to Swindon primary route (A419) east of Cricklade, which serves as a bypass for the town.

The bridge of 1975

The Bypass Bridge was built for the Department of the Environment to the design of the Wiltshire County Surveyor, C. R. Chadwick, by C. Bryant & Sons of Birmingham. The bypass and bridge were opened in 1975, and the bridge is maintained by DBFO for Wiltshire County Council.

The bridge has concrete abutments supporting composite pre-stressed concrete beams on which a reinforced concrete deck was cast in situ. There are aluminium horizontal post-and-rail parapets at each side.

Dimensions
Span: 75ft 3in; width: 89ft 6in.

CRICKLADE TOWN BRIDGE

Until the completion of the Cricklade bypass in 1975, this bridge carried the A419 Swindon to Cirencester road across the Thames at the north end of the town.

By an Act of 1866 (29 & 30 Victoria, c. 89) Cricklade was made the upper limit of the jurisdiction of the former Thames Conservancy, the lower limit being at Teddington.

1. The 17th-century bridge

Thacker (1920) quotes an account of Cricklade bridges written by Baskerville in 1692 that seems to indicate that a 17th-century timber bridge approached by stone causeways then existed at the present site.

2. The bridge of 1854 *(right)*
• *Grade II listed* •

Cricklade Town Bridge is of stone and carries the north end of the High Street across the Thames. From upstream, the bridge appears to have only one arch, but from downstream a second, smaller, arch can be seen spanning a narrow stream parallel to the Thames. The words 'Rebuilt by the Feoffees of the Cricklade Waylands AD 1854' are cut in the stone above each end of the main arch, and also given on a plate attached to the west parapet.

The Cricklade Waylands Estate largely arose from a bequest of Lord Hungerford in 1449 for an annual mass for the good of his soul to be said in the Hungerford, or Our Lady, Chapel of St Sampson's. In 1566 the bequest was diverted by the Lord Chancellor towards road maintenance.

The bridge was strengthened with a saddle of reinforced concrete in January 1970. It is a Grade II listed structure and is now maintained by the Department of the Environment using Wiltshire County Council as agents.

Dimensions
Spans of arches: southern (across Thames) 10ft (east) to 11ft (west), northern 6ft; width of deck between parapets: 40ft (south) to 37ft 6in (north).

30.7.03

CRICKLADE FARM BRIDGE (THAMES PATH)

This bridge carries the Thames Path from the south to the north bank of the river on its way upstream from Cricklade.

The 1 inch Ordnance Survey map of 1968 (revised to 1967) shows no bridge at this point, but the map in *Nicholson's Guide to the Thames* (1969), based on the Ordnance Survey, does. These facts indicate that the farm bridge now used for the Thames Path was built in about 1968. The bridge connects Cricklade North Meadow, famous for its wild flowers, with Mill Lane, a road leading south to Stone's Farm.

The bridge is strong and wide enough for vehicles. It has concrete abutments supporting a reinforced concrete deck with metal post-and-wire mesh fencing at each side and a metal gate across its north end.

Dimensions
Approximate length of deck: 35ft; width of deck: 13ft 6in; height of metal posts: 5ft.

15.5.74

CRICKLADE NORTH MEADOW FOOTBRIDGE

This footbridge was built at the site of Latton aqueduct, which carried the North Wiltshire Canal across the Thames a mile and a half upstream of Cricklade Town Bridge. The canal used to connect the Thames & Severn Canal, a few hundred yards north of the aqueduct, with the Wiltshire & Berkshire Canal at Swindon, about 7 miles south-south-east of it. The Thames & Severn Canal was built under an Act of 1783 (23 George 3, c. 38) and opened in November 1789; the Wiltshire & Berkshire Canal opened towards the end of 1810.

The North Wiltshire Canal was built under an Act of 1813, opened on 2 April 1819, and merged with the Wiltshire & Berkshire Canal two years later. Its junction with the Thames & Severn Canal was at Weymoor Bridge, Latton, where there was a lock and a basin for handling traffic for Cricklade. The basin and the aqueduct were the property of the Thames & Severn Canal and their construction was supervised by the highly competent John Denyer (1780-c1842). For more than 38 years he was Manager at Brimscombe, 2 miles south-east of Stroud, the focal point and administrative centre of the canal.

The last boat on the Thames & Severn Canal passed through Sapperton Tunnel, at the summit level, on 11 May 1911. Abandonment of the canal from Lechlade to Whitehall Bridge, west of the tunnel in the Golden Valley, was authorised by an Act of 1927.

Latton aqueduct
The North Wiltshire Canal crossed the Thames, at an oblique angle, on a masonry aqueduct at the base of which were three culverts. Thacker (1920) includes a sketch of the structure.

Dimensions
Length: 78ft; width: 28ft; width of canal bed: 20ft; width of towpath: 6ft; depth of water in canal: 4ft 6in.

1. The footbridge of c1927
The footbridge at the site of Latton aqueduct was built on the line of the abandoned North Wiltshire Canal at some time after 1927, the year in which the Thames & Severn Canal was abandoned. It had abutments and a single, off-centre, pier of brick, which carried three parallel girders supporting a deck and railings of timber.

Dimensions
Spans (measured square): 8ft 10in (north), 16ft 5in (south); distance between abutments (measured square): 37ft 9in; angle of skew: 63 degrees.

2. The rebuilt footbridge of 1998 *(below)*
In 1998 the brickwork of the bridge was repaired and the steel and timber superstructure was replaced to the original design.

CRICKLADE RAILWAY BRIDGE

Cricklade Railway Bridge now carries a bridleway from Hailstone Hill, about a mile north-west of Cricklade, to South Cerney, 2 miles further in the same direction. It used to carry the Midland & South Western Junction Railway (M&SWJR) across the Thames between Cricklade and Cerney & Ashton Keynes stations.

A railway linking the Midlands with the South Coast had been promoted as early as 1846, but it was not until 1873 that an Act (36 & 37 Victoria, cxciv) for building part of such a route was passed. It formed the Swindon, Marlborough & Andover Railway Company, which opened from Swindon to Marlborough on 27 July 1881 and from there to a junction, near Andover, with the London & South Western Railway on 5 February 1883. The route was continued north from Swindon to Cheltenham by a Swindon & Cheltenham Extension Railway Co (formed by 44 & 45 Victoria, cxlvi), which opened via Cricklade to Cirencester on 18 December 1883. The two companies were amalgamated (by 47 & 48 Victoria, lxiv) on 23 June 1884 to form the M&SWJR, which completed the link with the Midland Railway by opening a line from Cirencester to Andoversford Junction, near Cheltenham, on 1 August 1891.

At the grouping of 1923 the M&SWJR was absorbed by the GWR. When the line was nationalised on 1 January 1948 the British Transport Commission split it between the Southern and Western Regions of British Railways. On 11 September 1961 passenger services were withdrawn, but some goods services continued until 24 March 1969.

1. The railway bridge
The railway through Cricklade was built by the contractors Watson, Smith & Watson, and was opened for goods traffic on 1 November 1883 and for passenger traffic six weeks later, on 18 December.

The railway bridge was built with brick abutments and a brick pier on the north bank of the river. These supported a main span over the Thames and a smaller span over a track along the left bank. The main span was formed of flanged, deep plate girders, and the bottom flanges carried a timber deck. The land span was similarly formed using lighter girders. The abutments and pier were built wide enough for a double-track bridge, and girders were provided to support two tracks; however, only the girders for one track were fixed in position and when it had become clear that a second track would not be laid, the unused girders were removed.

Dimensions

Spans: 35ft (over Thames), 11ft 6in (over track); depth of girders of river span: 3ft 6in; thickness of pier: 5ft; width of abutments: 28ft 9in.

2. The bridleway bridge *(below)*

After the railway track had been removed in 1965, little work was needed to make the bridge suitable for carrying a bridleway.

13.5.74

HAILSTONE FOOTBRIDGE

Hailstone Footbridge is a little upstream of Cricklade Railway Bridge and carries a footpath that drops down to the Thames from the top of Hailstone Hill, about a mile north-west of Cricklade, and crosses the river to join a path along its north bank, a permissive way at the edge of a private meadow.

1. The old bridge

Henry Taunt's map of 1886 shows a bridge at this site, and Thacker (1920) describes it as being of wood with stone piers. Until the rebuild of 1998 there were three stone piers, and these may date from before the 19th century.

2. The bridge of 1965 *(below left)*

The timber superstructure of the old bridge was replaced in 1965.

Dimensions

Spans between pier centres: 10ft 2in, 11ft 0in, 12ft 0in, 8ft 4in; width of piers: 1ft 11½in, 2ft 8in, 1ft 11½in; width of deck: 4ft 7in.

3. The rebuilt bridge of 1998 *(below)*

The footbridge was rebuilt in 1998, and the three stone piers were replaced with a single central concrete pier faced with natural stone. As in the earlier bridge, a timber deck is supported by two wooden beams and provided with balustrades of timber railing.

Dimensions

Spans: 22ft 2in (west), 19ft 8in (east); overall length: 44ft 6in; width of deck: 4ft 11in; height of handrails: 4ft 1in; width between handrails: 4ft 4in.

MANOR BROOK BRIDGE

Manor Brook Bridge and Waterhay Bridge are the only public bridges for vehicles between Cricklade and the village of Ashton Keynes, 3 miles to the west. Waterhay Bridge carries a minor road that runs slightly south of east from Ashton Keynes to a crossroads on the B4040 Malmesbury to Cricklade road. Manor Brook Bridge carries a lane that branches north from that minor road, at a point three-quarters of a mile east of Waterhay Bridge, passes between Brook and Manor Farms, then crosses the river to give access to artificial lakes, including Manor Brook Lake (No 59) and Thamesmead Lake (No 72), at the southern edge of the Cotswold Water Park.

The bridge of c1996

Manor Brook Bridge was built to carry 30-tonne gravel lorries used during the excavations that created the artificial lakes. The private

bridges at Manor and Brook Farms were too weak to carry these, so the much stronger new bridge was built between the old ones in about 1996.

The bridge superstructure is of steel and spans the river between reinforced concrete abutments. The deck is supported by two 'H'-section steel girders. The deck surface is provided by steel plates, except at the upstream side where a footway is formed of steel mesh. Both sides of the bridge have steel handrails.

Dimensions
Clear span: 7.8m (25ft 7in); overall length: 9m (29ft 6in); width of roadway: 3.1m (10ft 1in); width of footway: 0.61m (24in); height of handrails: 0.87m (34in).

WATERHAY BRIDGE

Waterhay Bridge carries a road south-eastwards from the village of Ashton Keynes to a crossroads on the B4040 road from Cricklade to Minety.

Henry Taunt (1886), without quoting any reference, but noting 'existing vestiges of several weirs at and above Cricklade' states, 'In all probability the Thames was once navigable to this point [Waterhay Bridge] for boats of seven tons burden.'

1. The old bridge
Tombleson (1855) refers to '...a small bridge, called *Water Hayes*'. 'This rustic bridge is composed of five small stone arches, and is the first elliptical arch that the Isis glides beneath.'

2. The bridge of 1895 *(right)*
Thacker (1909) describes Waterhay Bridge as 'a white level crossing, iron railed now, but with clear evidence of having once been fenced with wood.' Dredge (1896) gives 1895 as the date for the bridge and describes the structure as having six 'I'-section longitudinal beams, equally spaced across its width. These are supported at their ends by abutments and centrally by a pier with cutwaters, all of brickwork and stone. The road metalling is on buckled floor plates carried on the bottom flanges of the beams, and above each outer beam two courses of 4-inch masonry form a kerb.

Dimensions
Clear spans: two of 17ft; thickness of central pier: 2ft; width: 15ft; 'I' cross-section of girders: 12in x 6in x ½in; approach lengths: 55ft (north), 10ft (south).

3. The bridge of 1970 *(above right)*
The present Waterhay Bridge was designed for Wiltshire County Council by the County Surveyor, C. R. Chadwick, and built by Denward Construction of Painswick, Gloucestershire, for an approximate cost of £13,000.

Wiltshire County Council

19.10.72

The bridge has a single span, supported by concrete abutments, formed of composite pre-stressed concrete beams with a cast-in-situ concrete deck. The parapets are of vertical infill steel railings.

Dimensions
Clear span: 36ft; width: 36ft (including 20ft road and two 6ft 9in pavements)

ASHTON KEYNES BRIDGES

The village of Ashton Keynes, just inside the northern boundary of Wiltshire, is remarkable for the number of Thames bridges it contains – there are at least 41, 26 across the main stream of the river, six across a west loop, and at least nine across a loop to the east.

The Thames approaches the north of Ashton Keynes from the west. Shortly before reaching the village, it feeds the west loop, which flows south from Flood Hatches Copse to Three Bridges (where the Swill Brook joins from the west), then east to rejoin the main stream above Waterhay Bridge.

Beyond Flood Hatches Copse, the main stream continues east, passing under Manor House (or Pound) Bridge, a footpath, and Rectory Road Bridge (all used by the public) to reach the north end of Ashton Keynes High Road. Some water passes beyond this, under Ashton Keynes Bridge, to feed the east loop, which flows east to Kent End, then south-east to rejoin the Thames just below Waterhay Bridge.

Ashton Keynes High Road runs from north to south through the village and continues south to High Bridge to cross the west loop. On reaching the High Road, the Thames turns south and flows down its west side under 23 bridges. These, with their variety of design, and, of course, the river itself, add much to the charm and interest of the village. Only five of the 23 bridges carry thoroughfares: (i) the northernmost, Gumstool Bridge, carries Church Walk; (ii) the eighth carries Gosditch; (iii) the 16th carries a public footpath; (iv) the 22nd carries The Derry; and (v), the 23rd and last, Oaklake Bridge, carries the southern continuation of the High Road. The remaining 18 bridges are all private and lead to houses in the village.

At the western side of Oaklake Bridge, a stream from between Three Bridges and High Bridge, on the west loop, joins the Thames, which then continues east under the bridge to flow via Ragman's Lane Bridge and the junction with the west loop to reach Waterhay Bridge.

RAGMAN'S LANE FOOT-BRIDGE, ASHTON KEYNES

Going up the main stream of the Thames from Waterhay Bridge, Ragman's Lane Footbridge is the next bridge to be encountered. It stands beside a ford.

1. The old bridge described by Dredge (1896-98)

Dredge described a bridge having abutments and a central pier, all of un-cemented masonry, and a deck of two planks spiked down on baulks of timber let into the masonry. A wooden handrail fixed to six wooden posts was fitted to the downstream side.

Dimensions
Two clear spans: 10ft; thickness of central pier: 3ft 6in; deck: two 12in x 3in timber planks.

2. The present bridge *(below)*

The present bridge has abutments and a central pier of cemented masonry and a reinforced concrete deck. The deck is fitted with six concrete posts having, at the top, bores holding a steel tube as a handrail.

Dimensions
Two spans: 10ft 2in; thickness of central pier: 24in; deck: reinforced concrete slab 8½in thick, 26in wide; handrails (downstream only) held by 41in posts with 2in diameter steel tube 3ft above deck, timber rail 19in above deck.

19.10.72

OAKLAKE BRIDGE, ASHTON KEYNES

Oaklake Bridge carries the southern continuation of Ashton Keynes High Road across the main stream of the Thames immediately after its junction, at the west end of the bridge, with a stream from the west loop.

1. The old bridge described by Dredge (1896-98)

Dredge described the bridge as being of stone and having three round arches, the voussoirs of which continued down to form the piers. The construction can still be seen in two surviving bridges further north in the village that carry The Derry and Gosditch. Because the span of each arch was only a quarter of the width of the road, Dredge considered the arches to be culverts. Each side of the road had wooden handrails.

Dimensions
Three clear spans: 5ft: width between handrails: 22ft; pier thickness: 2ft.

2. The post-Second World War bridge *(below)*

The post-war replacement for the old Oaklake Bridge has mass concrete abutments and a central pier supporting a filler beam deck using reinforced concrete joists. The original parapets were tubular rails supported by 'T'-section steel posts, but by 1997 these needed replacement.

Dimensions
Two clear spans: 8ft; width between handrails: 22ft; width of roadway: 15ft 7in.

13.5.74

THE DERRY BRIDGE, ASHTON KEYNES

This bridge carries a road westward from Ashton Keynes High Road across the Thames to The Derry at the south-west corner of the village.

1. The old bridge described by Dredge (1896-98) *(right)*

This bridge was described by Dredge as having three round masonry arches small enough, in relation to the width of the road, to be considered as culverts. It had post-and-rail parapets.

Dimensions
Clear spans: 5ft, 5ft 4in, 5ft 4in; width between parapets: 19ft 5in.

2. The reconstructed bridge of 1979

In 1979 the old bridge was reconstructed without changing its appearance. The arches were replaced with three concrete pipes and the parapets were replaced with steel posts and rails.

Dimensions
Diameter of concrete pipes: 5ft; width between parapets: 19ft 9in.

30.4.76

FOOTPATH BRIDGE, ASHTON KEYNES

This bridge across the Thames carries a footpath west from Ashton Keynes High Road, about half-way between The Derry and Gosditch, to connect with other footpaths in the village.

The bridge has a pair of reinforced concrete beams that rest on stone abutments and carry a deck of concrete slabs. It is provided, on the upstream side, with a simple balustrade consisting of a tubular steel handrail supported by four timber posts.

Dimensions
Length: 22ft; width of deck: 41in.

6.8.06

GOSDITCH BRIDGE, ASHTON KEYNES

This carries the road Gosditch from almost opposite the White Hart Inn, at the top of Ashton Keynes High Road, across the Thames westward to join Ashton road (B4696), which skirts the eastern edge of the village.

1. The previous bridge *(below)*

The Gosditch Bridge had two segmental arches close together, the arches and spandrel walls being of masonry. At each side of the road there were simple balustrades of four angle-steel posts holding pairs of steel rails. At the High Road end, the rails at each side of the road were bent to be parallel with the river, and held in place by the first two of the posts provided.

Dimensions

Two skewed spans: approx 5ft 6in (square), 6ft 6in (skew); width between parapets: 16ft 6in.

2. The reconstructed bridge of 2005 *(below)*

The bridge was rebuilt in January 2005. To make the rebuild look similar to the old bridge, half-cylindrical fibreglass formers were placed where the masonry arches had been and embedded in reinforced concrete. Masonry ends to the arches, spandrel walls and low parapets were then built across them, using some original stone. The painted steel post-and-tube handrails of the old bridge were not re-used but were replaced with rails of galvanised larger-diameter steel tubing. The dimensions were little changed.

GUMSTOOL BRIDGE, ASHTON KEYNES

• *Grade II listed* •

Gumstool Bridge crosses the Thames at the north of Ashton Keynes where the river changes direction of flow from eastward to southward to pass down the west side of the High Road. It carries Church Walk.

Gumstool Bridge is of stone and possibly dates from the 18th century, when some of the fine stone houses in the High Road were built. It stands near the base and column of a mediaeval stone cross.

The bridge has two arches separated by a narrow pier and surmounted by stone parapets that slope in at the top to shed water. It has been strengthened by saddling the arches with concrete. Both upstream and downstream, the arches are flanked by straight wing walls, at 45 degrees to the roadway, which extend the parapets.

Dimensions

Two clear spans (measured square): 4ft 6in; thickness of pier: 1ft 6in; distance between parapets: 15ft.

RECTORY ROAD BRIDGE, ASHTON KEYNES

Rectory Road Bridge carries Church Lane, which connects Church Walk – just south of the Thames – with a parallel lane just north of it. The bridge has two masonry arches with steel post and rail parapets.

Dimensions

Two clear spans: 5ft 8in; length between abutments: 16ft 11in; width between parapets: 25ft 42in.

4.5.76

4.5.76

CHURCH PATH FOOT-BRIDGE, ASHTON KEYNES

Between Manor House Bridge and Rectory Road Bridge, the Thames flows eastwards under the garden of a house. The water is shared between two parallel culverts, the exit from the northern, longer, one being east of that from the southern. The Church Path Footbridge crosses the southern stream as it emerges from beneath the garden and is at the eastern side of a stone garden wall that serves as an upstream parapet.

The footbridge is a stone slab that rests on dry stone walls edging the banks of the river.

POUND (MANOR HOUSE) BRIDGE, ASHTON KEYNES

Pound Bridge takes the B4696 road across the Thames at the western edge of Ashton Keynes village. The alternative name, Manor House Bridge, was used by Dredge (1896-98).

1. The old bridge
The former Pound Bridge had three circular arches of masonry with pointed cutwaters upstream. The parapets consisted of timber posts with top rails of iron.

Dimensions
Three semi-circular arches of clear span: 5ft; width of roadway: 18ft.

2. The bridge of 1961 *(right)*
The old bridge was replaced in 1961 by a structure designed by W. S.

Payne, the County Surveyor of Wiltshire. The new bridge has concrete abutments supporting a deck formed of post-tensioned reinforced concrete 'T'-beams laterally post-tensioned with reinforced concrete edge beams. The parapets consist of dwarf natural stone walls surmounted by timber posts carrying timber guard and top rails. There is a pavement at one side.

The bridge was strengthened to take heavier lorries in 2002. A new filler beam and concrete slab was built into the downstream side, carrying a deeper hardened verge.

Dimensions
Single span: 27ft 3in; overall width: 28ft 2in; width of roadway: 19ft 2in.

13.5.74

LOWER MILL FOOTBRIDGE

This footbridge is downstream of Lower Mill Farm, Somerford Keynes. It was included by Dredge in his illustrated survey of Thames bridges (as was a private bridge to the farm), but was derelict when photographed by the author in October 1972. By 1985 it had been rebuilt to carry the Thames Path. Since then, the Lower Mill Estate has been built south of the Thames, and a second private bridge constructed downstream of the first.

1. The footbridge described by Dredge

This bridge had abutments of dry masonry and a timber pile driven into the bed of the river, at its centre, to support a deck plank. A slack wire above one edge of the plank was provided as a hand support.

Dimensions

Distance between abutments: 21ft 6in; cross-section of footway plank: 3in x 12in; cross-section of central pile: 4in x 12in.

2. The first replacement footbridge *(below left)*

The bridge that replaced the earlier footbridge had abutments of set bags of concrete. These supported two timber beams spaced apart and transversely planked to provide a deck. Timber uprights fixed to the edge of the beam on the downstream side of the bridge, at its ends and centre, supported a steel tube handrail.

3. The footbridge of 2003 *(below)*

The footbridge was replaced again in July 2003 by ABC Bridges and the Gloucester County Council rights of way team. The new bridge was designed by John Gibson, Managing Director of ABC Bridges, Cirencester.

The bridge consists of a steel sub-frame formed of three lattice modules and having a top tube to which 'Expamet' walkway mesh has been welded. Two sections of welded tubular steel rails are bolted to each side of the bridge as parapets. All the steelwork is galvanised and the cost of the actual structure was £2,900.

Dimensions

Overall length: 8m (28ft); width: 1.2m (48in); height of parapets: 1.09m (43in).

SOMERFORD KEYNES BYPASS BRIDGE

The village of Somerford Keynes in Gloucestershire is at the intersection of two routes. The first (class 3 county road No 181) runs south from Cirencester to Minety, on the B4040 Cricklade to Malmesbury road; the second (class 3 county road No 183) runs west from North End, Ashton Keynes, in Wiltshire, to the A429 Cirencester to Malmesbury road between Kemble and Crudwell. The first route crosses the Thames at Somerford Keynes using Neigh Bridge at the south end of the village. Until the opening of a bypass in 1976, the second route did this also, but the bypass was provided with a bridge of its own, just below Neigh Bridge, which now carries the traffic.

The bridge of 1975

The bypass bridge was designed and built by Gloucestershire County Council, and completed in 1975. The bypass was opened in the following year. The bridge has concrete abutments supporting a reinforced concrete deck. Its upstream and downstream faces are finished with stone, which is also used for capping the parapets.

Dimensions

Span: 20ft (6.1m) (measured square), 20ft 4in (6.194m) (measured on the skew); angle of skew: 10 degrees; height of opening: 5ft 11in (1.8m); width between parapets: 47ft 8in (14.6m); height of parapets: 2ft 7½in (0.8m); thickness of parapets: 12in (0.305m).

9.8.77

NEIGH BRIDGE, SOMERFORD KEYNES

Neigh Bridge carries the Cirencester to Minety road (class 3 county road No 181) across the Thames at the southern end of Somerford Keynes in Gloucestershire. It gives its name to the nearby Country Park south-west of the village.

1. The original bridge of c1850

Neigh Bridge was built in about 1850. It is of grey stone and has two segmental arches of brick. Parapets were provided by extending the spandrel walls upward.

Dimensions

Two clear spans: 7ft 6in; thickness of pier: 2ft; width: 13ft 6in; approx length of abutments: 25ft.

2. The widened bridge *(below)*

In the 1960s the two brick arches were extended with concrete arches.

Dimension

Width between outside faces of parapets: 34ft.

10.10.76

NEIGH BRIDGE COUNTRY PARK FOOTBRIDGE

This footbridge carries the Thames Path from the east bank of the river to the Neigh Bridge Country Park, on the west bank, at a point about a quarter of a mile upstream of Neigh Bridge.

The present wooden footbridge came into service between the publication of the March 1990 edition of the Ramblers' Association guide *The Thames Walk*, by David Sharp, and the first (1996) edition, by the same author, of the National Trail Guide *The Thames Path*.

The bridge has a timber deck fitted each side with nine vertical handrail supports, those at the ends being about half as far apart as those in between. There are three steps up to the deck at each end. A small aluminium plate inside the downstream parapet reads 'Walford Ross on Wye Sawmills'.

Dimensions

Length of handrails: 38ft 9in; distance between handrails: 29½in; height of handrails above deck: 39in.

KEMBLE MILL FOOTBRIDGE

Above Neigh Bridge the Thames flows past three former mills; in upstream order, they are Kemble Mill, Old Mill and Upper Mill. Footbridges span the river near all of them.

North of Kemble Mill a millstream branches west from the Thames to flow through the mill building and rejoin the river downstream. Above where the millstream enters the building, a small footbridge used to carry a public footpath leading west to Somerford Keynes. A second bridge carried the path over the main stream.

In about the year 2002 the Kemble Mill property was enclosed so that the two footbridges could no longer be used by the public. The path was therefore moved away from the mill building and a new footbridge was built further upstream. These changes were desirable because after 1996, when the Thames Path was inaugurated, the number of walkers gaining access to the Path from the west increased.

1. The mill footbridge *(below)*

The small wooden footbridge above the millstream was close to the wall of the mill building, so only needed a handrail on the upstream, northern, side.

2. The upstream footbridge *(left)*

The new footbridge upstream is longer and more substantially built than the old and has a slightly humped deck approached at the east end by two steps.

Dimensions

Length of handrails: 36ft 4in; height of handrails: 45in.

OLD MILL FARM BRIDGE

This bridge spans the Thames immediately east of Old Mill Farm and originally led to a footpath running south-east to near the church at Somerford Keynes. It now crosses to the Thames Path, and the footpath to Somerford Keynes has been re-routed to start from further south along the Path, a little way above Kemble Mill.

The bridge has a semicircular concrete arch with, downstream, stone spandrel and wing walls. On the northern, upstream, side the river is channelled into the arch by parallel masonry walls on either side of a sluice. The top of the bridge is a roughly square slab of concrete that is gated at the farm end.

Dimensions

Span of arch: approx 6ft; top slab: approx 10ft square.

POOLE KEYNES FOOTBRIDGE

This footbridge carries a footpath from a point on the Thames Path upstream of Old Mill Farm to join a lane, providing access to that farm, which crosses the lane between Neigh Bridge Country Park and Ewen and continues to Poole Keynes. The footbridge is a more convenient alternative to Old Mill Farm Bridge. It is of timber, and its west end is reached from its northern side across a style.

Dimensions
Length of deck: 40ft; width between parapets: 29½in; height of parapets: 40in.

15.6.06

UPPER MILL FARM FOOTBRIDGES

Two footbridges cross the Thames as it flows south past Upper Mill Farm. The upstream bridge is small and crosses the old mill-race close to the farmhouse. The downstream bridge is more than three times longer and crosses the millstream 25 yards below the mill-race. The history of these bridges is closely related to that of the Thames Path and its precursor, the Thames Walk.

The first guide to the Thames Walk was published in 1981 by the Ramblers' Association. In the second edition, of 1985, the Walk was described as crossing the river by a flimsy footbridge (since removed) a quarter of a mile above Upper Mill Farm, but by the time of the 1990 edition the Walk crossed the small upstream bridge. This was still the case in 1996, when the Thames Path was designated a National Trail

and the first official guide to it was published. When a revised edition of the National Trail Guide was published in 2001, it described the Path as crossing the longer, downstream, bridge; in fact, either bridge could still be crossed. This was the case until August 2006 when the footpath that used the drive to the farm and the small bridge was legally diverted to a route south of the drive leading to the downstream bridge.

The lower (Thames Path) footbridge
1. The bridge of c1997
The first downstream footbridge was entirely of timber, and was similar in dimensions and appearance, but not in structure, to the bridge of 2005 described below.

2. The bridge of 2005 *(overleaf)*
This steel and timber footbridge was designed by John Gibson, Managing Director of ABC Bridges, and built by that company.
The deck is of grooved hardwood supported by a sub-frame of three

15.6.06

modular sections formed from galvanised steel tube and lattice. The sides of the subframe are clad with sapele hardwood from sustainable forest, and this wood was also used for the post-and-rail parapets. The structure cost £2,900, and was installed for Gloucestershire County Council by a sub-contractor in four days during June 2005.

Dimensions
Length of deck: 9m (29ft 5in); width of deck: 1.2m (47in); height of handrails: 1.11m (43¾in).

The upper footbridge
1. The rustic bridge *(see page 5)*
This was a small, single-span timber footbridge across the tail of the

mill race. It had a rustic appearance because parapet rails at each side of it were made of small logs.

2. The replacement bridge *(below)*
The original frail structure was replaced with the present more substantial timber bridge at some time after 1974. In 2006 the public footpath that crossed the bridge was diverted away from it and the drive to Upper Mill Farm.

Dimensions
Length of deck: 106in; depth of supporting beams: 10in; distance between handrails: 32in; height of handrails above deck: 36½in.

EWEN BRIDGE

Ewen Bridge carries Gloucestershire Class 3 county road No 184 across the Thames on the way south from the centre of Ewen village to the Neigh Bridge Country Park.

1. The old bridge described by Dredge (1896-98) *(above right)*
This was a masonry bridge with three small spans and a chain-and-post fence at each side. It was washed away in March 1947.

2. The bridge of 1947 *(below)*
The present Ewen Bridge was designed by Gloucestershire County Council and opened in December 1947. It has mass concrete abutments supporting a single reinforced concrete skew span edged with stone wall parapets.

Dimensions
Single clear span: 15ft 11in (square), 18ft 0in (skew); angle of skew: 28 degrees; width between parapets: 24ft.

PARKER'S BRIDGE

Parker's Bridge takes Gloucestershire Class 3 county road No 179 across the Thames between the villages of Kemble and Ewen. The river approaches the bridge from the north and, after passing beneath, turns east towards Ewen.

1. The old bridge
Mr and Mrs Hall in *The Book of the Thames* (1884) name this 'The First Bridge which crosses the Thames' and comment that it is 'level with the road, the river flowing through three narrow arches; it is without parapet.' This does not fit the present bridge.

2. The present bridge *(below)*
The description given by Dredge (1896-98) does fit the present bridge. This has two arches with the central pier having a small cutwater on the upstream (north) side. The bridge is of stone with metal post-and-rail parapets.

Dimensions
Two clear spans: 10ft (square); thickness of central pier: 2ft; overall width: 19ft 6in.

14.6.06

CLAYFURLONG BRIDGES

Clayfurlong Bridge carries the A429 Malmesbury to Cirencester road across the Thames at a point just north of the village of Kemble. It takes its name from Clayfurlong Farm immediately to the south. The bridge is much wider than might be expected because at one time it supported a railway bridge carrying the branch line from Kemble to Cirencester.

1. The pre-1841 road bridge
It must be assumed that a bridge existed to carry the Cirencester-Malmesbury road over the infant Thames before the Cirencester branch was built, even though Mr and Mrs Hall (1884), in their

description of the river near its source, refer only to 'that part of the field where the railway-arch crosses the Thames'.

2 & 3. The road bridge and the superimposed railway crossing of 1841 *(below left and right)*
In 1836 the Cheltenham & Great Western Union Railway Company was formed by Act of Parliament (21 June 1836) to build a broad gauge line from Cheltenham to near Swindon, on the Great Western main line from Paddington, and also a branch line from Kemble to Cirencester. Train services over these lines were to be operated by the Great Western Railway (GWR). The new company expected to be leased by the GWR, but was absorbed by it on 1 July 1843.

It was decided to make the branch line cross the Thames at the site of the bridge carrying the Cirencester to Malmesbury road. There, the

river flows from north-west to south-east and the new road and railway bridges both needed to run towards the north-east. The railway company therefore constructed a two-layer crossing of fairly complicated geometry.

The old road bridge was replaced with a wide bridge carrying an earth embankment for the railway, and this embankment was pierced with a skewed brick arch for the road. To reduce the angle of skew required, the road was made to curve slightly towards the arch entrances. To prevent earth slipping from the embankment, masonry walls were built into each side, around the arch openings. The tops of these walls were ornamented with stone copings, and steel rails were fitted across the centre of the bridge at both sides of the railway track. Because the road bridge was so wide, the Thames flowed underneath through twin tunnels with offset entrances, roughly parallel to the railway line, connected by straight central sections parallel to the arch.

The line to Cirencester was opened on 31 May 1841, and until 12 May 1845, when the route from Kemble to Cheltenham was opened throughout, Cirencester was a terminus of the Great Western broad gauge system from Paddington.

The Cirencester branch closed in 1964, the last night of passenger operation being Sunday 5 April. Track lifting was begun in 1966, and in 1973 the section of embankment, and the bridge it contained, were removed. The embankment ends at each side of the gap were tapered down to allow the road to be straightened.

Dimensions

1841 road bridge: Approximate width of each tunnel: 11ft; height of each tunnel above centre of concave tunnel bottom: 7ft; lengths of tunnel sections, measured along line between tunnels from Kemble side upstream: 42ft (Kemble section, inclined from SE to NW), 73ft (central section, at 20 degrees clockwise to Kemble section), 29ft (source section, at 30 degrees, anticlockwise, to central section). 1841 railway bridge: Width of arch: 23ft (measured square), 25ft (measured on the skew); height of arch: 12ft 6in (from road surface to springing of arch).

FOSSE WAY CULVERT

The Source of the Thames is in Trewsbury Mead, some 3½ miles south-west of Cirencester. If there has been enough rain, the river flows about half a mile through the meadow to the entrance of a culvert (ie an arched channel) under the Cirencester to Tetbury road (A433). At this point the road is following the line of the Fosse Way, the famous Roman road from Axemouth, near Exeter, to Lincoln. On emerging from the culvert, the river continues through fields to Clayfurlong Bridge, just north of Kemble, which is the first true bridge across the Thames. The Fosse Way Culvert cannot have this distinction because the Highways Act (1980 Ch. 66 ['Interpretation']) states that the word 'bridge' 'does not include a culvert'. Presumably this is because the job of a culvert is to contain and direct a flow of water, not to support a structure that crosses it.

The Fosse Way Culvert is a narrow tunnel with masonry portals, each consisting of a circular arch of wedge-shaped stones ('voussoirs') surrounded by a small section of stone walling.

Dimensions

Diameter of culvert: 3ft 6in; length of culvert: 29ft.

14.5.74

APPENDIX 1
LIST OF CROSSINGS WITH MILEAGES AND MAP REFERENCES

FB = Footbridge; Rly = Railway; TP = Thames Path

Crossing name	Miles above PLA boundary	Grid reference	Left (N) bank authority	Right (S) bank authority
			Essex	Kent
Dartford	-38.24	TQ 570 764	Thurrock	Dartford
			Greater London	
Tower	-19.01	TQ 337 803	Tower Hamlets	Southwark
London	-18.45	TQ 328 805	City of London	
Cannon Street Rly	-18.27	TQ 325 805		
Southwark	-18.16	TQ 324 806		
Millennium FB	-17.94	TQ 320 807		
Blackfriars (St Paul's) Rly	-17.76	TQ 317 807		
Blackfriars Rly	-17.76	TQ 317 807		
Blackfriars	-17.71	TQ 316 806		
Waterloo	-17.15	TQ 308 805	Westminster	Lambeth
Hungerford, Golden Jubilee, and Charing Cross Rly	-16.92	TQ 305 802		
Westminster	-16.55	TQ 305 797		
Lambeth	-16.09	TQ 304 789		
Vauxhall	-15.60	TQ 304 782		
Victoria (Grosvenor) Rly	-14.64	TQ 288 778		Wandsworth
Chelsea	-14.52	TQ 286 778		
Albert	-13.77	TQ 274 775	Kensington & Chelsea	
Battersea	-13.51	TQ 270 773		
Battersea Rly	-12.86	TQ 265 765	Hammersmith	
Wandsworth	-12.16	TQ 260 755		
Putney Rly	-11.19	TQ 244 756		
Putney (Fulham)	-11.03	TQ 242 757		
Hammersmith	-9.29	TQ 230 781		Richmond
Barnes Rly	-7.47	TQ 214 763	Hounslow	
Chiswick	-6.70	TQ 203 763		

Crossing name	Miles above PLA boundary	Grid reference	Left (N) bank authority	Right (S) bank authority
Kew Rly	-5.83	TQ 195 765		
Kew	-5.42	TQ 190 778		
Richmond Lock	-2.95	TQ 169 750	Richmond	
Twickenham	-2.77	TQ 172 748		
Richmond Rly	-2.73	TQ 173 748		
Richmond	-2.39	TQ 177 745		
PLA boundary obelisk	**0.00**	**TQ 163 719**		
Teddington FB	0.39	TQ 167 714		
Kingston Rly	1.86	TQ 177 696		Kingston
Kingston	2.03	TQ 177 694		
Hampton Court	4.86	TQ 154 684		Surrey
Sunbury Lock Cut FB	8.00	TQ 108 684	Surrey	
Walton	9.60	TQ 092 665		
Desborough Channel (E)	9.93	TQ 089 661		
Desborough Channel (W)	10.43	TQ 079 660		
Chertsey	12.88	TQ 054 666		
Chertsey (M3)	13.26	TQ 054 772		
Staines Rly	16.51	TQ 036 712		
Staines	16.83	TQ 032 715		
Runnymede (M25)	17.68	TQ 020 719	Windsor & Maidenhead	Windsor & Maidenhead
Ham (Old Windsor Lock Cut)	20.92	SU 992 751		
Albert (Datchet)	21.51	SU 984 756		
Datchet (removed)	22.46	SU 985 769		
Victoria (Datchet)	23.00	SU 979 775		
Black Potts Rly	23.39	SU 975 780		
Windsor (Town)	24.18	SU 967 772		
Windsor Rly	24.60	SU 960 773		
Windsor & Eton Bypass	24.90	SU 957 773		

Crossing name	Miles above PLA boundary	Grid reference	Left (N) bank authority	Right (S) bank authority	Crossing name	Miles above PLA boundary	Grid reference	Left (N) bank authority	Right (S) bank authority
Summerleaze FB	28.47	SU 916 787	Buckingham	(Windsor &	Kennington Rly	90.96	SP 524 027		
Maidenhead (M4)	29.00	SU 913 795		Maidenhead)	Oxford S Bypass (Isis)	91.22	SP 525 032		
Maidenhead Rly	30.51	SU 901 810			Donnington Road	92.24	SP 524 044		
Maidenhead	30.71	SU 901 813			Free Ferry FB	92.29	SP 524 045		
Boulter's Lock	31.35	SU 903 824			Folly Bridge (Grandpont)	92.99	SP 514 055		
Cookham Lock Cut FB	33.55	SU 904 856			Oxford Gas Works FB	93.19	SP 511 056		
Cookham	33.95	SU 898 856			Oxford Gas Works Rly	93.35	SP 509 050		
Bourne End Rly	35.00	SU 892 970			Oxford Rly (Isis)	93.61	SP 507 056		
Marlow Bypass	37.31	SU 859 859			Osney	94.08	SP 503 062		
Marlow	37.90	SU 852 861			Medley FBs	94.47	SP 497 074		
Temple FB (TP)	39.55	SU 835 843			Godstow	96.45	SP 484 092		
Hurley, Lower Towpath	39.92	SU 829 843			Godstow (Wolvercote)	96.51	SP 486 094		
Hurley, Upper Towpath	40.17	SU 825 942			Oxford W Bypass	96.61	SP 482 093		
Henley	45.81	SU 764 847		Wokingham	Swinford (Eynsham)	100.20	SP 443 086		
Shiplake Rly	49.33	SU 779 787			Skinner's FB	101.80	SP 438 067		
Sonning	52.16	SU 755 757	Oxford		Hart's Weir (Ridge's) FB	106.45	SP 420 010		
Reading	55.25	SU 718 741	Reading	Reading	New Bridge	107.61	SP 403 014		
Caversham	55.76	SU 711 746			Shifford Island FB (TP)	110.39	SP 371 009		
Whitchurch	61.64	SU 636 738	Oxford	West Berkshire	Shifford Lock Cut FB (TP)	110.70	SP 367 007		
Basildon Rly	64.54	SU 606 795			Tenfoot FB	111.94	SU 353 996		
Goring and Streatley	65.76	SU 596 808		Oxford	Tadpole	113.76	SU 334 004		
Moulsford Rly	68.41	SU 595 847			Old Man's FB	116.89	SP 299 002		
Winterbrook (Wallingford Bypass)	71.29	SU 608 881			Radcot	117.76	SP 286 994		
Wallingford	71.71	SU 610 894			Eaton FB (Kelmscott)	120.96	SP 247 985		
Shillingford	74.20	SU 597 920			Bloomer's Hole FB (TP)	123.20	SU 225 988	Gloucester	
Little Wittenham (Day's)	76.83	SU 567 934			St John's, Lechlade	123.42	SU 222 989		
Clifton Hampden	79.44	SU 547 934			Lechlade Town (Halfpenny)	124.10	SU 213 913		Swindon
Clifton Cut (Lower FB)	80.12	SU 545 944			Inglesham Roundhouse FB	124.74	SU 205 988		Gloucester
Clifton Cut (Upper FB)	80.34	SU 542 942			Original FB nearer canal	124.80	SU 204 988		
Appleford Rly	81.41	SU 526 942			Hannington	128.25	SU 174 961		Swindon
Culham Lock (Sutton)	82.63	SU 509 949			Castle Eaton	130.95	SU 144 985	Swindon	
Culham Cut (Lower FB)	82.44	SU 504 947			Water Eaton FB (TP)	133.49	SU 124 929	Wiltshire	Wiltshire
Culham Cut (Upper FB)	82.58	SU 501 947			Eysey FB (TP)	134.24	SU 113 941		
Abingdon: Culham	83.90	SU 501 957			Cricklade Bypass	134.59	SU 108 938		
Abingdon: Burford, Abingdon	84.80	SU 499 969			Cricklade Town	135.18	SU 101 938		
Nuneham Rly	86.65	SP 526 970			Cricklade Farm (TP)	135.71	SU 095 941		
					Cricklade North Meadow FB	136.19	SU 085 947		

Crossing name	Miles above PLA boundary	Grid reference	Left (N) bank authority	Right (S) bank authority	Crossing name	Miles above PLA boundary	Grid reference	Left (N) bank authority	Right (S) bank authority
Cricklade Rly	136.66	SU 083 947	Gloucester	(Wiltshire)	Lower Mill FB (TP)	141.24	SU 027 942	Gloucester	Gloucester
Hailstone FB	136.90	SU 079 945			Somerford Keynes Bypass	141.91	SU 019 946		
Manor Brook	138.11	SU 067 934	Wiltshire		Neigh	141.99	SU 019 948		
Waterhay	138.67	SU 060 932			Neigh Country Park FB (TP)	142.21	SU 014 949		
Ragman's Lane FB	139.12	SU 053 933			Kemble Mill FB (private)	142.42	SU 013 951		
Ashton Keynes:					Kemble Mill FB (to TP)	142.44	SU 013 952		
Oaklake	139.67	SU 049 935			Old Mill Farm (to TP)	142.69	SU 012 957		
The Derry	139.79	SU 048 937			Poole Keynes FB (to TP)	142.89	SU 011 959		
Ashton Keynes FB	139.91	SU 047 939			Upper Mill Farm FB (TP)	143.18	SU 012 962		
Gosditch	140.04	SU 046 940			Upper Mill Farm FB (private)	143.20	SU 012 962		
Gumstool	140.18	SU 045 942			Ewen	144.27	SU 004 973		
Rectory Road	140.23	SU 044 942			Parker's	144.89	ST 996 974		
Church Path FB	140.26	SU 044 842			Clayfurlong	145.47	ST 991 979		
Manor House (Pound)	140.44	SU 041 942			Fosse Way Culvert	146.27	ST 984 989		
					Source of the Thames	146.74	ST 980 995		

APPENDIX 2
AUTHORITIES RUNNING PASSENGER TRAIN SERVICES ACROSS THAMES RAILWAY BRIDGES

There have been four periods of peace-time ownership covering virtually all the railways in Britain:

1. Ownership by the private companies that built the lines. These companies either ran passenger services themselves or arranged for other companies to run them
2. Ownership by one of four large companies produced by amalgamation of 123 companies under the Railways Act, 1921 (11 & 12 George 5, c. 55)
3. Ownership by the state following nationalisation of the railways, and other transport concerns, by the Labour Government's Transport Act, 1947 (10 & 11 George 6, c. 49)
4. Ownership by private companies formed under the Conservative Government's Railways Act 1993 (c. 43).

During the privatisation of British Rail, an Office of Passenger Rail Franchising (OPRAF) divided the passenger businesses (Intercity, Network SouthEast and Regional Railways) into 25 Train Operating

Units (TOUs) and, from 1 April 1994, sold these as franchises so that they became Train Operating Companies (TOCs).

Passenger train services were provided on the lines crossing the Thames by the authorities shown in the tables below. These give, where possible, the dates of introduction of the services and the dates when the authorities (companies or national bodies) ran their first passenger services anywhere.

Table 1 Southern bridges (i)

1 Charing Cross, 2 Cannon Street

Bridge	Services	Starting date
1	Charing Cross-Kent Coast main lines, and South London and Kent suburban lines	11.1.1864
2	Cannon Street-Kent Coast main lines and South London and Kent suburban lines	1.9.1866

Authorities	First services
South Eastern Railway	26.5.1842
South Eastern & Chatham Railway	1.1.1899
Southern Railway	1.1.1923
British Railways (Southern Region)	1.1.1948
British Rail (London & South East Business Sector)	4.1.1982
British Rail (Network SouthEast) SE Subsector	10.6.1986
South Eastern (TOU)	1.4.1994
Connex South Eastern	13.10.1996
South Eastern Trains (SRA) (Connex on LC map)	9.11.2003
Southeastern	1.4.2006

Table 2 Southern bridges (ii)

1 Blackfriars, 2 St Paul's (Blackfriars)

Bridge	Services	Starting date
1	South London and Kent services from Ludgate Hill	21.12.1864
2	St Paul's (Blackfriars), Holborn Viaduct, Moorgate	10.5.1886
	Brighton etc to Luton or Bedford (Thameslink)	11.5.1988

Authorities	First services
London, Chatham & Dover Railway	(new name) 1859
South Eastern & Chatham Railway	1.1.1899

Authorities	First services
Southern Railway	1.1.1923
then as Table 1 but with the following additions:	
Thameslink (TOU)	1.4.1994
Thameslink (TOC)	30.1.1997
First Capital Connect	1.4.2006

Table 3 Southern bridges (iii)

1 Grosvenor (Victoria) (original), 2 Grosvenor (Victoria) (widened)

Bridge	Services	Starting date
1	Victoria 'Brighton' (north) station, Sussex Coast main lines, South London, Surrey and Sussex suburban lines	1.10.1860
	Victoria 'Chatham' (south) station	3.12.1860
2	Kent Coast main lines, South London and Kent suburban lines	20.12.1866

Authorities	First services
'Brighton' station:	
London, Brighton & South Coast Railway	(new name) 1846
Southern Railway	1.1.1923
British Railways (Southern Region)	1.1.1948
British Rail (London & South East)	4.1.1982
British Rail (Network SouthEast)	10.6.1986
Network South Central (TOU)	1.4.1994
Connex South Central (TOC)	26.5.1996
South Central	25.5.2003
Southern (new name for South Central)	31.5.2003
'Chatham' station:	
London, Chatham & Dover Railway	(new name) 1859
South Eastern & Chatham Railway	1.1.1899
Southern Railway	1.1.1923
then as Table 1	

Table 4 Southern bridges (iv)

1 Barnes, 2 Richmond, 3 Kingston, 4 Staines, 5 Black Potts (Windsor)

Bridge	Services	Starting date
2, 4	Waterloo to Staines, Ascot and Reading	4.6.1856
2, 5	Waterloo to Windsor	1.12.1849
1, 2	Waterloo, Hounslow loop, Waterloo	22.8.1849
2, 3	Waterloo, Kingston loop, Waterloo	1.7.1863

Authorities	First services
London & South Western Railway	(new name) 1839
Southern Railway	1.1.1923
British Railways (Southern Region)	1.1.1948
British Rail (London & South East)	4.1.1982
British Rail (Network SouthEast)	10.6.1986
South West Trains (TOU)	1.4.1994
South West Trains	4.2.1996

Table 5 Great Western bridges

1 Maidenhead, 2 Basildon, 3 Moulsford, 4 Appleford, 5 Nuneham, 6 Oxford, 7 Windsor, 8 Bourne End, 9 Shiplake, 10 Kennington, 11 Clayfurlong

Bridge	Services	Starting date
Great Western services:		
1	Paddington to Twyford	1.7.1839
1, 2, 3	Paddington to Steventon (later to Bristol and Wales)	1.6.1840
1-5	Paddington to Oxford	12.6.1844
1-6	Paddington to Oxford and beyond	2.9.1850
7	Slough to Windsor & Eton	8.10.1849
8	Maidenhead to Marlow branch	1.8.1854
9	Twyford to Henley-on-Thames branch	1.6.1857
10	Oxford to High Wycombe (closed 7.1.1963)	24.4.1864
11	Kemble Junction to Cirencester (closed 5.4.1964)	31.5.1841
Cross-country services:		
2-6	Scotland and the North to Penzance and South Coast	
1-6	Scotland and the North to Paddington	

Authorities	First services
Great Western services:	
Great Western Railway (original)	4.6.1838
Great Western Railway	1.1.1923
British Railways (Western Region)	1.1.1948
British Rail (Network SouthEast)	10.6.1986
Great Western Trains (TOU)	1.4.1994
Thames Trains (TOU)	1.4.1994
Great Western Trains (TOC)	1.4.1994
First Great Western (new name for Great Western Trains) (i)	1999
First Great Western Link (TOC) (ii)	4.2.1996
Greater Western (from (i) (ii) and Wessex Trains)	1.4.2006
Cross-country services:	
British Rail (Intercity Cross Country)	
Cross Country Trains (TOU)	1.4.1994
Virgin Trains (Cross Country) (TOC)	1.4.1994

Table 6 London Transport Bridges

1 Putney, 2 Kew

Bridge	Services	Starting date
1	Putney Bridge to Wimbledon (a)	3.6.1889
2	Mansion House to Richmond (a)	1.6.1877
	Moorgate to Richmond (b)	1.10.1877
	Broad Street to Richmond (c)	1.1.1869
	North Woolwich to Richmond (c)	13.5.1985

Authorities	First services
(a) Metropolitan District Railway	29.7.1864
(b) Metropolitan Railway	10.1.1863
(b) London Passenger Transport Board	1.7.1933
(c) North London Railway	(new name) 1853
London & North Western Railway	(new name) 1846
London, Midland & Scottish Railway	1.1.1923
British Railways (London Midland Region)	1.1.1948
Network SouthEast (North London Lines)	10.6.1986
North London Railways (TOU)	1.4.1994
Silverlink (TOC)	2.3.1997

APPENDIX 3
AUTHORITIES RUNNING ELECTRIC TRAMS AND TROLLEYBUSES ACROSS THAMES BRIDGES AND AROUND LONDON

An American, George Francis Train (b1829), introduced the first London trams in 1861. There were three routes operated with horse-drawn vehicles running on rails that projected above the road surface. These rails interfered with other traffic so seriously that the Metropolitan Board of Works ordered Train to remove all his tramways within months of their opening.

From the year 1869 onwards, a number of companies were formed to construct horse tramways in and around London. The Tramways Act, 1870 required the new lines to be built using grooved rails flush with the road surface. The House of Lords rejected, from 1872 onwards, all Parliamentary Bills for the construction of horse, and later electric, tramways entering central London. This ban prevented South London lines from reaching the City or West End by crossing the Thames. It was not until 1906, five years after London United Tramways (LUT) had started running electric trams north of the Thames, that the LCC managed to overcome the ban and obtain authority to build electrified lines across Vauxhall and Westminster Bridges.

The dates between which electric trams first crossed these and other Thames bridges are summarised in the accompanying table. The routes are all London County Council except for Kingston Bridge, which was LUT; the latter was converted by LUT to trolleybus operation on 15 June 1931. That company, and many other concerns, became part of London Transport on 1 July 1933, when the London Passenger Transport Board was formed under the London Passenger Transport Act, 1933 (23 & 24 George 5, c. 14). Although the Board came to replace trams on a number of routes, none of those crossed the Thames, so Kingston was the only bridge to carry London Transport trolleybuses.

Bridge	Section or route across the bridge	Service dates
Kingston	Hampton Wick to Surbiton	1.3.1906 to 14.6.1931
Vauxhall	Victoria Station to Vauxhall	5.8.1906 to 3.1.1952
Westminster	From Stangate via Victoria Embankment to north end of Blackfriars Bridge (John Carpenter Street)	15.12.1906 to 5.7.1952
Putney	From Hammersmith across Putney Bridge to Lower Richmond Road	23.1.1909 to 11.9.1937
Blackfriars	From north end of bridge to Southwark Bridge Road	14.9.1909 to 5.7.1952
Battersea	From Battersea Park Road to King's Road, Chelsea	22.6.1911 to 30.9.1950
Southwark	From south end of bridge to The City	14.7.1925 to 5.7.1952

APPENDIX 4
THE PROPOSED THAMES GATEWAY BRIDGE

Plans for a bridge downstream of Tower Bridge were drawn up by the Greater London Council in 1969, but the idea for such a bridge was not pursued until 1979, when a Conservative Government decided to revitalise the Docklands. On 8 October 1981 *The Times* described a bridge, 1,200 feet long, which would cross the Thames at Gallions Reach, between the Blackwall and Dartford Tunnels, and carry a 5-mile link road from Beckton, on the north bank, to Thamesmead, on the south. An artist's impression showed a cable-stayed design. However, these plans did not materialise.

In 2006 it seems certain that a twin dual-carriageway road will be constructed from the A13/A406 junction at Beckton, across a Thames Gateway Bridge and on to join the A2016 in Thamesmead. The design work, by Halcrow Group Ltd for Transport for London, has largely been completed. The bridge is to be of spine beam form, with a pair of reinforced concrete box girders, one under each carriageway, formed integrally with the deck. In addition to the carriageways, it is to carry two segregated lanes for public transport, and a combined cycleway/footway. It is expected that construction will commence during the summer of 2009 and the bridge will be open in the winter of 2012/13. Tolls will be levied.

Probable dimensions

Navigation channel: 100m with minimum headway of 46.35m; main span: 270-290m; side spans: c135m; depth: c17m above main piers to c6m mid-span. Widths of items supported by deck, west to east: Parapet: 500mm; paved verge: 1000mm; combined footway/cycleway: 4000mm; carriageway: 7300mm; dedicated public transport corridor: 7110mm; central reserve: 2250mm; paved verge: 1700mm; carriageway: 7300mm; concrete barrier; 650mm; paved verge: 1000mm; parapet: 500mm.

REFERENCES

Bagust, H. (2006) *The Greater Genius? A biography of Marc Isambard Brunel* (Hersham: Ian Allan)

Baker, R. (1976) *New & Improved. Inventors and Inventions that have changed the modern world* (p99) (London: British Museum Publications – for the British Library)

Basa, A. K. (1991) 'Construction of a Cable-stayed Bridge near Dartford in England' (New Delhi: Indian Roads Congress Journal 52-3 546-569 (November 1991))

Benskin, J. (1933) 'The Bridges of London – Past, present, and future' (*Royal Society of Arts Journal* 81 280-296)

Bradescu, R., Weld, F., & Mackworth-Praed (1973) 'Thames Bridge at Chertsey' (*Proceedings of the Institution of Civil Engineers* 54 307)

Bray, N. (1998) *The Cirencester Branch* (Usk, Monmouth: Oakwood Press)

British Library (1999) Social Policy Information Service 3: *Legislation of the United Kingdom*

British Rail (1965-85) *Greater London Network* and *Passenger Network* maps

Brown, D. & Jackson, A. A. (1990) *Network SouthEast Handbook* (Harrow Weald: Capital Transport)

Brown, D. J. (1993) *Bridges – Three Thousand Years of Defying Nature* (p132) (London: Mitchell Beazley)

Buckton, E. J. & Fereday, H. J. (1937-38) 'The Reconstruction of Chelsea Bridge' (*Journal of the Institution of Civil Engineers* 7 383)

Callender-Hamilton bridge design: see UK patents 423,926 and 423,996 of 1935 and C. O. Boyne *Structural Engineer*, October 1938

Chaplin, P. H. (1982) *The Thames: from source to tideway* (Weybridge: Whittet Books)

Chapman, W. G. (1939) *Track Topics*, 3rd ed (GWR/(1987) Newton Abbot: David & Charles)

City of London (1973) *The Story of Three Bridges: the history of London Bridge* (London)

Civil Engineering, etc (1961, July) M4 Maidenhead (*Civil Engineering & Public Works Review* 56 897)
(1962, January) Oxford Western Bypass (*Civil Engineering & Public Works Review* 57 55)

Colourmaster (undated) *Read about London's Bridges*

Colourmaster (undated) *Read about Thames Bridges*

Concrete Society (1967) 'Some Recent Concrete Bridges' (Oxford Southern Bypass and Eton-Windsor Relief Road) (*Concrete*, March 1967 97-103)

Connelly, B. (1964) *The London United Tramways* (Worthing: The Tramway and Light Railway Society)

Connor, J. E. (1997) *North Woolwich to Palace Gates* (London: Connor & Butler)

Connor, P. (1993) *Going Green – the story of the District Line* (Harrow Weald: Capital Transport)

Cookson, Brian (2006) *Crossing the River* (London's bridges) (Edinburgh: Mainstream Publishing)

Council for the Preservation of Rural England (1929) *The Thames Valley from Cricklade to Staines* (London: University of London Press)

Counsell, J. H. W. & Nossiter, P. A. *Widening & Strengthening of Kingston Bridge* (LOBEG website)

Cove-Smith, C. (1996) *The River Thames Book* (St Ives: Imray, Laurie, Norie & Wilson)

Cracknell, D. W. (1963) 'The Runnymede Bridge' (*Proceedings of the Institution of Civil Engineers* 25 325-344)

Croad, S. (1983) *London's Bridges* (London: HMSO)

Dallard, P., Fitzpatrick, A. J., Flint, A., Le Bourva, S., Low, A., Ridsdill Smith, R. M. & Willford, M. (2001) 'The London Millennium Footbridge' (*Structural Engineer* 79 17-33)

Dalton, W. H. (1794) *The New and Complete English Traveller* (London: Alexander Hogg)

Daniels, G. & Dench, L. (1980) *Passengers No More* 3rd Ed (Shepperton: Ian Allan)

Davenport, J. M. (1869) *Oxfordshire Bridges*

Day, J. R. (1979) *London's Trams and Trolleybuses* (London: London Transport)

Dendy Marshall, C. F., rev Kidner, R. W. (1968) *History of the Southern Railway, Vols 1&2* (London: Ian Allan.)

Dredge, J. (1896-98) *Thames Bridges from the Tower to the Source* (London: *Engineering*)

Ellson, G. (1921) 'Cannon Street Strengthening' (*Minutes of the Proceedings of the Institution of Civil Engineers* 211, 305-322)

Elmes, James (1830) *Metropolitan Improvements* (drawings by Thomas H. Shepherd) (London: Jones)

Engineer (1890, 25 July) Battersea (*Engineer* 70, 64)
(1901, 5 April) 'Kew Bridge' (*Engineer* 91 352)
(1906, 30 March) 'New Vauxhall Bridge' (*Engineer* 101 315)
(1926, 25 June) 'New bridge over the Thames at Caversham' (*Engineer* 141 656)
(1933, July Supp) 'Three reinforced concrete bridges' (Scott, W. L. [Twickenham], Gueritte, T. J. [Hampton Court], Scott, W. L. [Chiswick]) (*Concrete and Constructional Engineering* 28 1-49)
(1939, 21 April) 'Wandsworth' (*Engineer* 167, 506-508)

Engineering (1923, 28 September) 'Reinforced Concrete Bridge across the Thames at Reading' (*Engineering* 116 385-386)
(1951) 'Engineering in the Festival of Britain IV – The Temporary Bridges at the South Bank Exhibition' (*Engineering* May 11, 1951 555)
(1960, 23 December) 'M4 Maidenhead' (*Engineering* 190 855)

Environment Agency (2002) *River Thames – a user's Guide*, Edition 3 (Reading)

Falkoner, J. (1995) *What's Left of Brunel* (Shepperton: Dial House, Ian Allan)

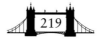

Glover, J. (2003) *London's Underground*. 10th ed (Hersham: Ian Allan)
(1996) *National Railways – a guide to the privatised railway* (Shepperton: Ian Allan)

Godfrey, H. (1988) *Tower Bridge* (London: John Murray)

Goslin, G. (1997) *Steam on the Widened Lines, Vol 1* (London: Connor & Butler)

Grant, M. J. (1982) 'Remedial Works to Cannon Street Railway Bridge' (*Institution of Civil Engineers Premium Papers* 1982-84)

Granter, E. (December 1952) 'Presidential Address' (*Structural Engineer* 283-301)

Graeme Bruce, J. (1970) *Steam to Silver* (London: London Transport Executive)

Great Western Railway (1939) *Track Topics*, composite ed (1987) (Newton Abbot: David & Charles)

Groves, G. L. (1934-35) 'Lambeth Bridge' (*Proceedings of the Institution of Civil Engineers* 239, 151)

Hall, Mr & Mrs S. C. (1884) *Book of the Thames* (London: Virtue)

Halsbury's Laws of England 4th ed re-issue

Harley, R. J. (2005) *London's Victoria Embankment* (Harrow: Capital Transport)

Harrison, D. (2004) *The Bridges of Medieval England* (Oxford: Oxford University Press)
(2004) 'Medieval Bridges' (*History Today* 54 (11) 22)

Hayden, M. (1976) *The Book of Bridges* (London: Marshall Cavendish)

Hayter, H. (1862-63) 'The Charing Cross Bridge' (*Proceedings of the Institution of Civil Engineers* 22 512-527)

Heap, C. & van Riemsdijk, J. (1972) *The Pre-Grouping Railways* 1 (London: Science Museum, HMSO)

Henry, D. & Jerome, J. A. (1965) *Modern British Bridges* (London: CR Books Ltd)

Herbert, A. P. (1966) *The Thames* (London: Weidenfeld & Nicolson)

Hopkins, H. J. (1970) *A Span of Bridges* (Newton Abbot: David & Charles)

Horne, M. (2003) *The Metropolitan Line* (Harrow Weald: Capital Transport)

Household, H. (1969) *The Thames & Severn Canal* (Newton Abbot: David & Charles)

Ireland, S. (1792) *Picturesque Views on the River Thames* 2 Vols (London: T. & I. Egerton)

Jackson, A. (1969) *London's Termini* (Newton Abbot: David & Charles)

Jackson, P. (1971) *London Bridge* (London: Cassell)

Jervoise, E. (1930) *The Ancient Bridges of the South of England* (London: Architectural Press)

'Kennington' (1977) *London County Council Tramways Handbook* (*Worthing*: Tramway & Light Railway Society)

Kidner, R. W. (1992) *The London Tramcar* (Oxford: Oakwood Press)

Knight, S. & Johnston, H. (eds) (1998) *Britain's Railways* 2nd ed (Peterborough: Apex Publications)

LCC (1950). *LCC Survey of London Vol XX* Chapter 17, 'Westminster Bridge', p66

Lee, C. E. (1972) *The Metropolitan Line* (London: London Transport)
(1968) *100 Years of the District* (London: London Transport)

Leyland, J. (1897) *The Thames Illustrated* (London: Newnes)

Macdermot, E. T. (1927) *History of the Great Western Railway* 2 Vols (London: GWR Co)

Maggs, C. G. (1967) *The Midland & South Western Junction Railway* (Newton Abbot: David & Charles)
(2004) Life before Preservation – 33: Swindon & Cricklade Railway (M&SWJR) (*Steam Days* No 179 July 390-399)

Maré, E. de (1954) *The Bridges of Britain* (London: B. T. Batsford)
(1975) *The Bridges of Britain* 2nd ed (London: B. T. Batsford)

Maw, W. H. & Dredge, J. (1872) *Modern Examples of Road and Railway Bridges* (London)

Mindell, R. & J. (1985) *Bridges over the Thames* (Poole, Dorset: Blandford Press)

Mitchell, V. & Smith, K. (1990) *Kingston and Hounslow Loops* (Midhurst: Middleton Press)
(1990) *Holborn Viaduct to Lewisham* (Midhurst: Middleton Press)
(1996) *West London Line – Clapham Junction to Willesden Junction* (Midhurst: Middleton Press)
(2002) *Branch Lines to Henley, Windsor and Marlow* (Midhurst: Middleton Press)
(1996) *Willesden Junction to Richmond* (Midhurst: Middleton Press)

Modern Railways Special (1997) *New Railways for London* (Addlestone: Ian Allan)

Murray, J. F. (1845) *Picturesque Tour of the River Thames* (London: H. G. Bohn)

National Rail (1997-2006) *London Connections: Rail Services Around London & the South East* (map)

Network SouthEast (1986-1994) *The London Connections* and other maps

Orleans House Gallery (1976) *Richmond Bridge* (London Borough of Richmond upon Thames)

Oxford Civic Society (1974) *Oxford's Waterways* (Oxford: Blackwell)

Palmer, J. & Cogswell, G. *Bridge Management 2* (Case Studies 2 & 3) (London: Thomas Telford)

Parker, J. S., Hardwick, G., Carroll, M., Nicholls, N. P. & Sandercock, D. (2003) 'Hungerford Bridge – millennium project – London' (*Proceedings of the Institution of Civil Engineers* 156, 70-77)

Partington, J. R. (1946) *General and Inorganic Chemistry for University Students* (London: Macmillan)

Pearson, A. (2002) 'Bridge on the River Thames' (*Building* 19 April 2002, 39-42)

Phillips, G. (1981) *Thames Crossings – Bridges, Tunnels and Ferries* (Newton Abbot: David & Charles)

Pierce, P. (2001) *Old London Bridge: the story of the oldest inhabited bridge in Europe* (London: Review)

Pocock, E. A. (1966) *Radcot and its Bridge* (Clanfield: author)

Potts, C. R. (2004) *Oxford to Princes Risborough* (Usk, Monmouth: Oakwood Press)

Prichard, M. & Carpenter, H. (1975) *A Thames Companion* (Headington: Oxford Illustrated Press)

Public Works Congress (1933) *British Bridges* (London)

Pudney, J. (1972) *Crossing London's River* (London: Dent)

Radcliffe, C. W. (1939) *Middlesex – The Jubilee of the County Council 1889-1939* (London: Evans Brothers)

Railway Magazine (March 2002) 'The Elizabethan Railway, Part 2' (*Railway Magazine* 148, 18-28) (August 2004) 'TOC Franchise Update' (*Railway Magazine* 150, 20-21)

Reyburn, W. (1972) *Bridge across the Atlantic – the Story of John Rennie* (London: Harrap)

Richards, J. M. (1984) *The National Trust Book of Bridges* (London: Jonathan Cape)

Roberts, C. (2005) *Cross River Traffic* (London: Granta)

Rodgers, J. (1947) *English Rivers* (London: Batsford)

Sands, T. B. (1959) (rev Jenkins, S. C., 1990) *The Midland & South Western Junction Railway* (Headington, Oxford: Oakwood Press)

Sharp, D. (2001) *National Trail Guides: The Thames Path* (London: Aurum Press)

Sherwood, T. (1991) *The Railways of Richmond upon Thames* (Wokingham: Forge Books)

Simmons, J. & Biddle, G. (eds) (1997) *The Oxford Companion to British Railway History* (Oxford: Oxford University Press)

Simmons, J. (ed) (1965) *A Visual History of Modern Britain* (Chaloner, W. H., & Musson A. E. *Industry & Technology*; Evans, R. H. *Government*; Simmons, J. *Transport*) (London: Readers Union (Studio Vista))

Smith, D. (2001) *Civil Engineering Heritage: London and the Thames Valley* (London: Thomas Telford)

Smith, M. (1994) *British Railway Bridges & Viaducts* (Shepperton: Ian Allan)

Smyth, W. J. R., Benaim, R. & Philpott, D. H. (1980) 'New Runnymede Bridge' (*Structural Engineer* 58A, 5-11)

Spearing, Nigel *How and why the half-tide Lock and Weir were built* (Port of London Authority)

Starkey, D. (2004) *The Monarchy of England, Vol 1: The Beginnings* (London: Chatto & Windus)

Stephens, J. H. (1976) *The Guinness Book of Structures* (Enfield: Guinness Superlatives Ltd)

Sudjic, D. (2001) *Blade of Light – the Story of London's Millennium Bridge* (London: Penguin)

Taunt, H. (1886/87) *A New Map of the River Thames* 5th ed, 1989 reprint (Gloucester: Alan Sutton)

Thacker, F. S. (1909) *The Stripling Thames* (London: author) (1914 & 1920, reprinted 1968) *The Thames Highway, Vol 1: General History* and *Vol 2: Locks and Weirs* (Newton Abbot: David & Charles)

Thomas, W. N. (1920) *The Development of Bridges* (Ealing: Parker & Gregg)

Tombleson (text by Fearnside, W. G.) (1865) *The Thames and Medway* (London: Thomas Holmes)

Uvarov, E. B., Chapman, D. R. & Isaacs, A. (1971) *A Dictionary of Science* (Harmondsworth: Penguin)

Villiers, E. de (1969) *Swinford Toll Bridge 1769-1969* (Eynsham: Eynsham History Group)

Wadsworth, H. J. & Waterhouse, A. (1967 & 1968) 'Modern Techniques and Problems in the restoration of Marlow suspension bridge' (*Proceedings of the Institution of Civil Engineers* 37, 297 and 39, 159)

Walker, R. J. B. (1979) *Old Westminster Bridge* (Newton Abbot: David & Charles)

Walters, D. (c1963) *British Railway Bridges* (London: Ian Allan)

Waters, L. (1986) *Rail Centres: Oxford* (London: Ian Allan) (1990) *Rail Centres: Reading* (London: Ian Allan) (2000) 'The Oxford, Thame & Princes Risborough Line' (*Steam Days* No 132 (August) 498)

Welch, C. (1896) *Modern History of the City of London* (London: Blades, East & Blade)

Williams, R. A. *The London & South Western Railway* (1968) *Vol 1 The Formative Years* and (1973) *Vol 2 Growth and Consolidation* (Newton Abbot: David & Charles)

Willoughby, D. W. & Oakley, E. R. (1972) *London Transport Tramways Handbook* (authors)

Wilson, D. G. (1977) *The Making of the Middle Thames* (Bourne End: Spurbooks) (1987) *The Thames – Record of a Working Waterway* (London: B. T. Batsford)

Wood, R. (1993) *British Rail Passenger Trains* (Harrow Weald: Capital Transport)

ACKNOWLEDGEMENTS

I have received much help from many individuals, authorities and institutions during the years I have worked on this book. Most of its information comes from the books and articles in the list of References, and I acknowledge my debt to all their authors. I thank the staff of the British Library, the Guildhall Library, the Library of the Institution of Structural Engineers, and the Library of the Institution of Civil Engineers, for making available to me the many works I do not own. In 1976 I was given an introduction to the ICE Library by Mr R. Horner, after he had given a talk on the Thames Barrier. Since then, I have enjoyed the privilege of using this library several times and have latterly received notable help from the librarian, Ms Debbie Francis. This help included scans of five illustrations in Dredge (1896-98) reproduced in this book. I am also indebted to the Local History room of the Kingston Museum and Heritage Service for a scan of Ireland's 1792 aquatint of old Kingston Bridge, also reproduced here.

The most valuable information in this book must surely be the hitherto unpublished material. For this I am indebted to the following authorities and officials:

ABC Bridges, Cirencester (Mr John Gibson, Managing Director); Babtie Group, Reading (Mr Marek Howes); Berkshire County Council (Mr G. H. Home); British Railways, Southern Region (Mr R. W. Richards); British Railways, Western Region (Mr D. Ewart); English Heritage; Environment Agency, Thames Region (Mr D. Vickers); Gloucestershire County Council (Mrs E. A. Kirkham); Highways Agency (Mr W. Marques); National Trails Office, Thames Path (Mr L. Eldred); Network Rail (Mr I. Frostick); Oxford City Council (Mr I. B. Howdill); Oxfordshire County Archive (Miss S. J. Barnes); Oxfordshire County Council (Mr J. W. Andrew and Mr M. Brain); Port of London Authority (Mr M. Garside); Royal Borough of Kingston upon Thames (Mr R. McFarlane); Summerleaze Limited (Mr M. A. Lowe); Surrey County Council (Mr L. Fish and Mr S. Coxon); Thames Water, Thames Conservancy Division (Mr C. J. Lucas); Transport for London (Mr D. Yell); Wiltshire County Council (Mr C. R. Henson and Mr D. Weston); and the unitary authority of Windsor & Maidenhead (Mrs V. Lewis).

I thank for excellent and varied help: Paul and Tricia Baron – Paul for getting me into, then guiding me within, word processing; Brian Coe – for inspiring me to write books, and lending me Thames books and photographs when he was curator of the Kodak Museum at Wealdstone; Arna Davis – for her company on visits to the Thames and more help with word processing; and Chris and Ann Roberts – who took me to photograph Thames bridges since the early days of my interest and provided yet more help with word processing. Others who have contributed are Mr D. W. Freeth – owner of Brook and Manor Farms, near Cricklade, for allowing me to photograph Thames bridges on his land; Elizabeth Gooch – for help with history; Bernard Howarth Loomes – friend of Brian Coe, for lending me early Thames photographs, some of them book illustrations; Anne Jakeman – for providing Internet material; David Lush – for lending me his copy of Dalton's *New and Complete English Traveller* (1794); John Pepper – for lending me his schooldays copy of Radcliffe's *Middlesex* (1939); and Phyllis West – for lending me *The Thames Book, 1966*, which contains Chaplin's article, 'Thames Bridges'.

Two people deserve my concluding thanks. The first is my sister Jean, who accompanied me on numerous Thames holidays, typed the first, uncompleted, text of the book, and gave me the great amount of time I have expended on it. The second is Will Adams, Editor for Silver Link Publishing, who recommended the work to the publisher and, after its acceptance, was, with Production Manager Mick Sanders, responsible for the volume you see.

INDEX

Bridges

Authorities

Railway companies that built Thames bridges

For railway companies using them, see Appendix 2